HAESE MATHEMATICS

Specialists in mathem

Mathematics

Core Topics SL

for use with
Mathematics: Analysis and Approaches SL
Mathematics: Applications and Interpretation SL

1

Michael Haese

Mark Humphries

Chris Sangwin

Ngoc Vo

for use with
IB Diploma
Programme

MATHEMATICS: CORE TOPICS SL

Michael Haese   B.Sc.(Hons.), Ph.D.
Mark Humphries   B.Sc.(Hons.)
Chris Sangwin   M.A., M.Sc., Ph.D.
Ngoc Vo   B.Ma.Sc.

Published by Haese Mathematics
152 Richmond Road, Marleston, SA 5033, AUSTRALIA
Telephone: +61 8 8210 4666, Fax: +61 8 8354 1238
Email: info@haesemathematics.com
Web: www.haesemathematics.com

National Library of Australia Card Number & ISBN 978-1-925489-55-2

© Haese & Harris Publications 2019

First Edition   2019

Editorial review by Denes Tilistyak (Western International School of Shanghai).

Cartoon artwork by John Martin.

Artwork by Brian Houston, Charlotte Frost, Yi-Tung Huang, and Nicholas Kellett-Southby.

Typeset by Deanne Gallasch and Charlotte Frost. Typeset in Times Roman 10.

Computer software by Yi-Tung Huang, Huda Kharrufa, Brett Laishley, Bronson Mathews, Linden May, Joshua Douglass-Molloy, Jonathan Petrinolis, and Nicole Szymanczyk.

Production work by Sandra Haese, Bradley Steventon, Nicholas Kellett-Southby, Cashmere Collins-McBride, and Joseph Small.

We acknowledge the contribution of Marjut Mäenpää, Mal Coad, and Glen Whiffen, for material from previous courses which now appears in this book. The publishers wish to make it clear that acknowledging these individuals does not imply any endorsement of this book by any of them, and all responsibility for the content rests with the authors and publishers.

Printed in China by Prolong Press Limited.

4012300028647

FOREWORD

Mathematics: Core Topics SL has been written for the International Baccalaureate Diploma Programme courses *Mathematics: Analysis and Approaches SL*, and *Mathematics: Applications and Interpretation SL*, for first teaching in August 2019, and first assessment in May 2021.

This is the first of two books students will require for the completion of their SL Mathematics course, and it contains the content that is common to both courses. Upon the completion of this book, students progress to the particular SL textbook for their course. This is expected to occur approximately 6-7 months into the two year course.

SL Mathematics

We have chosen to write in this way so that:
- The courses can be thoroughly covered while keeping the books reasonably sized.
- All SL students can start together, and potentially delay making a final choice of course.

There is some material in this book that is only relevant for students studying *Mathematics: Analysis and Approaches SL*. This material is indicated in the table of contents. This material is included in Mathematics: Core Topics SL because:
- It is more sensible to include the material under the appropriate chapter headings here, rather than making smaller stand-alone sections in the Mathematics: Analysis and Approaches SL textbook.
- The material may be useful in directing students who have not yet decided which SL course they will choose.
- The *Mathematics: Analysis and Approaches SL* course is significantly larger than the *Mathematics: Applications and Interpretation SL* course, so it is useful to cover some material exclusive to *Mathematics: Analysis and Approaches SL* while the two groups are still working as one class.

A set of background knowledge chapters is included online (see page 9). These cover a fairly robust list of skills, including short summaries of theory, worked examples, and practice questions. However, we do not anticipate there will be sufficient class time for teaching this material, so if students require revision of these topics, this should occur before the start of the school year.

When students complete this book and move on to the second book, it is important that they retain this book, as it will be essential for exam revision.

Each chapter begins with an Opening Problem, offering an insight into the application of the mathematics that will be studied in the chapter. Important information and key notes are highlighted, while worked examples provide step-by-step instructions with concise and relevant explanations. Discussions, Activities, Investigations, and Research exercises are used throughout the chapters to develop understanding, problem solving, and reasoning.

In this changing world of mathematics education, we believe that the contextual approach shown in this book, with the associated use of technology, will enhance the students' understanding, knowledge and appreciation of mathematics, and its universal application.

We welcome your feedback.

Email: info@haesemathematics.com   Web: www.haesemathematics.com

PMH, MAH, CS, NV

ACKNOWLEDGEMENTS

The photo of Kenenisa Bekele on page 35 was taken by Katie Chan. This photo is licensed under the Creative Commons Attribution-ShareAlike 4.0 Generic License. To view a copy of this license, visit https://creativecommons.org/licenses/by-sa/4.0/ or send a letter to Creative Commons, PO Box 1866, Mountain View, CA 94042, USA.

ABOUT THE AUTHORS

Michael Haese completed a BSc at the University of Adelaide, majoring in Infection and Immunity, and Applied Mathematics. He completed Honours in Applied Mathematics, and a PhD in high speed fluid flows. Michael has a keen interest in education and a desire to see mathematics come alive in the classroom through its history and relationship with other subject areas. He is passionate about girls' education and ensuring they have the same access and opportunities that boys do. His other interests are wide-ranging, including show jumping, cycling, and agriculture. He has been the principal editor for Haese Mathematics since 2008.

Mark Humphries completed a degree in Mathematical and Computer Science, and an Economics degree at the University of Adelaide. He then completed an Honours degree in Pure Mathematics. His mathematical interests include public key cryptography, elliptic curves, and number theory. Mark enjoys the challenge of piquing students' curiosity in mathematics, and encouraging students to think about mathematics in different ways. He has been working at Haese Mathematics since 2006, and is currently the writing manager.

Chris Sangwin completed a BA in Mathematics at the University of Oxford, and an MSc and PhD in Mathematics at the University of Bath. He spent thirteen years in the Mathematics Department at the University of Birmingham, and from 2000 - 2011 was seconded half time to the UK Higher Education Academy "Maths Stats and OR Network" to promote learning and teaching of university mathematics. He was awarded a National Teaching Fellowship in 2006, and is now Professor of Technology Enhanced Science Education at the University of Edinburgh.

His research interests focus on technology and mathematics education and include automatic assessment of mathematics using computer algebra, and problem solving using the Moore method and similar student-centred approaches.

Ngoc Vo completed a BMaSc at the University of Adelaide, majoring in Statistics and Applied Mathematics. Her mathematical interests include regression analysis, Bayesian statistics, and statistical computing. Ngoc has been working at Haese Mathematics as a proof reader and writer since 2016.

Dedicated to Kenneth Capp, Dennis Marples, and Zachary Rau, who opened my eyes.
Never have I seen more devotion or selfless love for students than yours.
Thank you.

Michael

ONLINE FEATURES

With the purchase of a new textbook you will gain 24 months subscription to our online product. This subscription can be renewed for a small fee.

Access is granted through **SNOWFLAKE**, our book viewing software that can be used in your web browser or may be installed to your tablet or computer.

Students can revisit concepts taught in class and undertake their own revision and practice online.

COMPATIBILITY

For iPads, tablets, and other mobile devices, some of the interactive features may not work. However, the digital version of the textbook can be viewed online using any of these devices.

REGISTERING

You will need to register to access the online features of this textbook.

Visit www.haesemathematics.com/register and follow the instructions. Once registered, you can:
- activate your digital textbook
- use your account to make additional purchases.

To activate your digital textbook, contact Haese Mathematics. On providing proof of purchase, your digital textbook will be activated. **It is important that you keep your receipt as proof of purchase.**

For general queries about registering and subscriptions:
- Visit our **SNOWFLAKE** help page: https://snowflake.haesemathematics.com.au/help
- Contact Haese Mathematics: info@haesemathematics.com

SELF TUTOR

Simply 'click' on the ◀) **Self Tutor** (or anywhere in the example box) to access the worked example, with a teacher's voice explaining each step necessary to reach the answer.

Play any line as often as you like. See how the basic processes come alive using movement and colour on the screen.

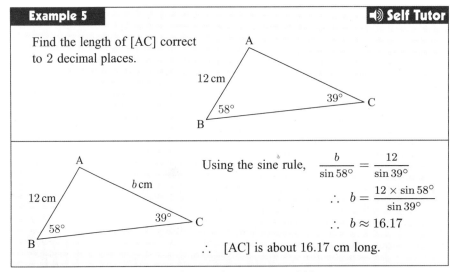

Example 5   ◀) **Self Tutor**

Find the length of [AC] correct to 2 decimal places.

Using the sine rule, $\dfrac{b}{\sin 58^\circ} = \dfrac{12}{\sin 39^\circ}$

$\therefore b = \dfrac{12 \times \sin 58^\circ}{\sin 39^\circ}$

$\therefore b \approx 16.17$

$\therefore$ [AC] is about 16.17 cm long.

See **Chapter 8, Non-right angled triangle trigonometry**, p. 213

INTERACTIVE LINKS

Interactive links to in-browser tools which complement the text are included to assist teaching and learning.

Icons like this will direct you to:

- interactive demonstrations to illustrate and animate concepts
- games and other tools for practising your skills
- graphing and statistics packages which are fast, powerful alternatives to using a graphics calculator
- printable pages to save class time.

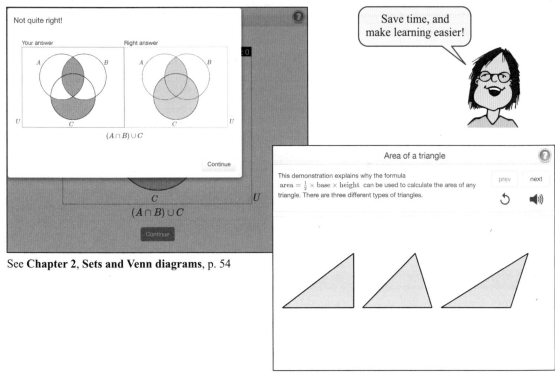

See **Chapter 2, Sets and Venn diagrams**, p. 54

See **Chapter 8, Non-right angled triangle trigonometry**, p. 204

GRAPHICS CALCULATOR INSTRUCTIONS

Graphics calculator instruction booklets are available for the **Casio fx-CG50, TI-84 Plus CE, TI-$n$spire**, and the **HP Prime**. Click on the relevant icon below.

CASIO fx-CG50

TI-84 Plus CE

TI-$n$spire

HP Prime

When additional calculator help may be needed, specific instructions are available from icons within the text.

GRAPHICS CALCULATOR INSTRUCTIONS

THEORY OF KNOWLEDGE

Theory of Knowledge is a Core requirement in the International Baccalaureate Diploma Programme.

Students are encouraged to think critically and challenge the assumptions of knowledge. Students should be able to analyse different ways of knowing and areas of knowledge, while considering different cultural and emotional perceptions, fostering an international understanding.

The activities and discussion topics in the below table aim to help students discover and express their views on knowledge issues.

Chapter 2: Sets and Venn diagrams p. 46	MATHEMATICAL PROOF
Chapter 5: Sequences and series p. 131	HOW MANY TERMS DO WE NEED TO CONSIDER BEFORE A RESULT IS PROVEN?
Chapter 5: Sequences and series p. 139	THE NATURE OF INFINITY
Chapter 7: Right angled triangle trigonometry p. 172	OBSERVATION AND BELIEF
Chapter 8: Non-right angled triangle trigonometry p. 221	MATHEMATICS IN SOCIETY
Chapter 9: Points in space p. 234	EUCLID'S POSTULATES
Chapter 10: Probability p. 276	APPLICATIONS OF PROBABILITY
Chapter 11: Sampling and data p. 290	CLINICAL TRIALS
Chapter 12: Statistics p. 312	MEASURES OF CENTRE

THEORY OF KNOWLEDGE

The study of celestial objects such as the sun, moon, stars, and planets is called **astronomy**. It has been important to civilisations all over the world for thousands of years, not only because it allowed them to navigate at night, but because the celestial objects feature in so many of their myths and beliefs.

To create an accurate star map, astronomers measure the angles between objects in the sky. The oldest known star map was found in the Silk Road town of Dunhuang in 1907. It was made in the 7th century AD, presumably from the Imperial Observatory in either Chang'an (present day Xi'an) or Luoyang. A possible author of the map was the mathematician and astronomer **Li Chunfeng** (602 - 670). The map shows 1339 stars in 257 star groups recorded with great precision on 12 charts, each covering approximately 30 degree sections of the night sky.[1]

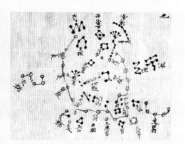

1 How much of what we *believe* comes from what we *observe*? Is it necessary to *understand* something, in order to *believe* it? How much of what we *study* is a quest to *understand* what we *observe*, and *prove* what we *believe*?

2 How much of what we want to know is a common desire of people and cultures all over the world?

3 How did ancient people calculate with such accuracy before computer technology?

[1] "The Dunhuang Chinese Sky: A comprehensive study of the oldest known star atlas", J-M Bonnet-Bidaud, F. Praderie, S. Whitfield, *J. Astronomical History and Heritage*, 12(1), 39-59 (2009).

See **Chapter 7, Right angled triangle trigonometry**, p. 172

BACKGROUND KNOWLEDGE

These chapters can be accessed through your online subscription. They are provided to help address areas of weakness, particularly for students lacking preparation arriving at a new school. It is important to note that there will **not** be time to teach the material in class.

Click on the icon to view the Background Knowledge chapters.

BACKGROUND KNOWLEDGE

1 NUMBER
A   Operations with numbers
B   Exponent notation
C   Factors
D   Primes and composites
E   Highest common factor
F   Multiples
G   Square roots and cube roots
H   Order of operations
I   Modulus or absolute value
J   Rounding numbers
K   Approximations

2 ALGEBRA
A   Algebraic notation
B   Collecting like terms
C   Expansion and simplification
D   Adding and subtracting algebraic fractions
E   Multiplying and dividing algebraic fractions
F   Factorisation
G   Substitution
H   Linear equations
I   Linear inequalities
J   Rational equations
K   Power equations
L   Formulae
M   Formula rearrangement

3 MEASUREMENT
A   International system (SI) units
B   Perimeter
C   Area
D   Speed

4 PYTHAGORAS' THEOREM
A   Pythagoras' theorem
B   The converse of Pythagoras' theorem
C   Right angles in geometric figures
D   Problem solving

5 COORDINATE GEOMETRY
A   The distance between two points
B   Midpoints
C   Gradient
D   Parallel and perpendicular lines

6 TRANSFORMATION GEOMETRY
A   Translations
B   Reflections
C   Rotations
D   Dilations (enlargements, reductions, and stretches)

7 SIMILARITY
A   Similar figures
B   Similar triangles
C   Problem solving
D   Areas and volumes of similar objects

TABLE OF CONTENTS

Sections which are shaded are only required for *Mathematics: Analysis and Approaches SL* students. Headings for these sections and their related exercise and review set questions are also shaded green.

SYMBOLS AND NOTATION USED IN THIS COURSE

$\mathbb{N}$ the set of positive integers and zero, $\{0, 1, 2, 3, ...\}$

$\mathbb{Z}$ the set of integers, $\{0, \pm 1, \pm 2, \pm 3, ...\}$

$\mathbb{Z}^+$ the set of positive integers, $\{1, 2, 3, ...\}$

$\mathbb{Q}$ the set of rational numbers

$\mathbb{Q}'$ the set of irrational numbers

$\mathbb{R}$ the set of real numbers

$\{x_1, x_2, ...\}$ the set with elements $x_1, x_2, ...$

$n(A)$ the number of elements in set A

$\{x \mid ....\}$ the set of all x such that

$\in$ is an element of

$\notin$ is not an element of

$\varnothing$ or $\{\ \}$ the empty (null) set

U the universal set

$\cup$ union

$\cap$ intersection

$\subset$ is a proper subset of

$\subseteq$ is a subset of

A' the complement of the set A

$a^{\frac{1}{n}}, \sqrt[n]{a}$ a to the power of $\dfrac{1}{n}$, nth root of a (if $a \geqslant 0$ then $\sqrt[n]{a} \geqslant 0$)

$a^{\frac{1}{2}}, \sqrt{a}$ a to the power $\frac{1}{2}$, square root of a (if $a \geqslant 0$ then $\sqrt{a} \geqslant 0$)

$|x|$ the modulus or absolute value of x

$|x| = \begin{cases} x & \text{for } x \geqslant 0 \quad x \in \mathbb{R} \\ -x & \text{for } x < 0 \quad x \in \mathbb{R} \end{cases}$

$\equiv$ identity or is equivalent to

$\approx$ is approximately equal to

$>$ is greater than

$\geq$ or $\geqslant$ is greater than or equal to

$<$ is less than

$\leq$ or $\leqslant$ is less than or equal to

$\ngtr$ is not greater than

$\nless$ is not less than

u_n the nth term of a sequence or series

d the common difference of an arithmetic sequence

r the common ratio of a geometric sequence

S_n the sum of the first n terms of a sequence, $u_1 + u_2 + ... + u_n$

S_∞ or S the sum to infinity of a sequence, $u_1 + u_2 + ...$

$\displaystyle\sum_{i=1}^{n} u_i$ $u_1 + u_2 + ... + u_n$

$n!$ $n \times (n-1) \times (n-2) \times .... \times 3 \times 2 \times 1$

$\binom{n}{r}$ or ^nC_r the rth binomial coefficient, $r = 0, 1, 2, ...$ in the expansion of $(a+b)^n$

$f : x \mapsto y$ f is a function which maps x onto y

$f(x)$ the image of x under the function f

f^{-1} the inverse function of the function f

$f \circ g$ the composite function of f and g

$\displaystyle\lim_{x \to a} f(x)$ the limit of $f(x)$ as x tends to a

$\dfrac{dy}{dx}$ the derivative of y with respect to x

$f'(x)$ the derivative of $f(x)$ with respect to x

$\dfrac{d^2y}{dx^2}$ the second derivative of y with respect to x

$f''(x)$ the second derivative of $f(x)$ with respect to x

$\int y\, dx$ the indefinite integral of y with respect to x

$\displaystyle\int_a^b y\, dx$ the definite integral of y with respect to x between the limits $x = a$ and $x = b$

e^x exponential function of x

$\log_a x$ the logarithm in base a of x

$\ln x$ the natural logarithm of x, $\log_e x$

$\sin, \cos, \tan$ the circular functions

$\sin^{-1}, \cos^{-1}, \tan^{-1}$ the inverse circular functions

$A(x, y)$	the point A in the plane with Cartesian coordinates x and y	μ	population mean
$[AB]$	the line segment with end points A and B	σ	population standard deviation
AB	the length of $[AB]$	σ^2	population variance
(AB)	the line containing points A and B	$\overline{x}$	sample mean
$PB(A, B)$	the perpendicular bisector of $[AB]$	s^2	sample variance
$\widehat{A}$	the angle at A	s	standard deviation of the sample
$C\widehat{A}B$	the angle between $[CA]$ and $[AB]$	$B(n, p)$	binomial distribution with parameters n and p
$\triangle ABC$	the triangle whose vertices are A, B, and C	$N(\mu, \sigma^2)$	normal distribution with mean μ and variance σ^2
$\parallel$	is parallel to	$\sim$	is distributed as
$\perp$	is perpendicular to	z	standardised normal z-score, $z = \dfrac{x - \mu}{\sigma}$
$P(A)$	probability of event A		
$P(A')$	probability of the event 'not A'	r	Pearson's product-moment correlation coefficient
$P(A \mid B)$	probability of the event A given B	H_0	the null hypothesis
$x_1, x_2, ...$	observations of a variable	H_1	the alternative hypothesis
$f_1, f_2, ...$	frequencies with which the observations $x_1, x_2, x_3, ...$ occur	$T \sim t_{n-1}$	the random variable T has the Student's t distribution with $n - 1$ degrees of freedom
$p_1, p_2, ...$	probabilities with which the observations $x_1, x_2, x_3, ...$ occur	χ^2	chi-squared
$P(X = x)$	the probability distribution function of the discrete random variable X	χ^2_{calc}	calculated chi-squared value
$P(x)$	the probability mass function of a discrete random variable X	χ^2_{crit}	critical value of the chi-squared distribution
$E(X)$	the expected value of the random variable X	f_{obs}	observed frequency
		f_{exp}	expected frequency

GEOMETRIC FACTS

TRIANGLE FACTS

- The sum of the interior angles of a triangle is $180°$.

- In any isosceles triangle:
  - ▸ the base angles are equal
  - ▸ the line joining the apex to the midpoint of the base bisects the vertical angle and meets the base at right angles.

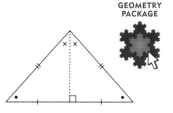

GEOMETRY PACKAGE

QUADRILATERAL FACTS

- The sum of the interior angles of a quadrilateral is $360°$.
- A **parallelogram** is a quadrilateral which has opposite sides parallel.

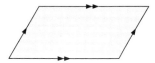

Properties:
- ▸ opposite sides are equal in length
- ▸ opposite angles are equal in size
- ▸ diagonals bisect each other.

GEOMETRY PACKAGE

- A **rectangle** is a parallelogram with four equal angles of $90°$.

Properties:
- ▸ opposite sides are parallel and equal
- ▸ diagonals bisect each other
- ▸ diagonals are equal in length.

GEOMETRY PACKAGE

- A **rhombus** is a parallelogram in which all sides are equal in length.

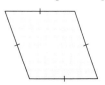

Properties:
- ▸ opposite sides are parallel
- ▸ opposite angles are equal in size
- ▸ diagonals bisect each other at right angles
- ▸ diagonals bisect the angles at each vertex.

GEOMETRY PACKAGE

- A **square** is a rhombus with four equal angles of $90°$.

Properties:
- ▸ opposite sides are parallel
- ▸ diagonals bisect each other at right angles
- ▸ diagonals bisect the angles at each vertex
- ▸ diagonals are equal in length.

GEOMETRY PACKAGE

- A **trapezium** is a quadrilateral which has a pair of parallel opposite sides.

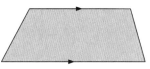

- A **kite** is a quadrilateral which has two pairs of adjacent sides equal in length.

Properties:
- ▸ one diagonal is a line of symmetry
- ▸ one pair of opposite angles are equal
- ▸ diagonals cut each other at right angles
- ▸ **one** diagonal bisects **one** pair of angles at the vertices
- ▸ one of the diagonals bisects the other.

CIRCLE FACTS

Name of theorem	Statement	Diagram
Angle in a semi-circle	The angle in a semi-circle is a right angle.	$\widehat{ABC} = 90°$ GEOMETRY PACKAGE
Chords of a circle	The perpendicular from the centre of a circle to a chord bisects the chord.	$AM = BM$ GEOMETRY PACKAGE
Radius-tangent	The tangent to a circle is perpendicular to the radius at the point of contact.	$O\widehat{A}T = 90°$ GEOMETRY PACKAGE
Tangents from an external point	Tangents from an external point are equal in length.	$AP = BP$ GEOMETRY PACKAGE
Angle at the centre	The angle at the centre of a circle is twice the angle on the circle subtended by the same arc.	$A\widehat{O}B = 2 \times A\widehat{C}B$ GEOMETRY PACKAGE
Angles subtended by the same arc	Angles subtended by an arc on the circle are equal in size.	$A\widehat{D}B = A\widehat{C}B$ GEOMETRY PACKAGE
Angle between a tangent and a chord	The angle between a tangent and a chord at the point of contact is equal to the angle subtended by the chord in the alternate segment.	$B\widehat{A}S = A\widehat{C}B$ GEOMETRY PACKAGE

USEFUL FORMULAE

PERIMETER FORMULAE

 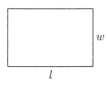

square	rectangle	triangle	circle	arc
$P = 4l$	$P = 2(l + w)$	$P = a + b + c$	$C = 2\pi r$ or $C = \pi d$	$l = \left(\frac{\theta}{360}\right) 2\pi r$

AREA FORMULAE

Shape	Diagram	Formula
Rectangle		$A = \text{length} \times \text{width}$
Triangle		$A = \frac{1}{2} \times \text{base} \times \text{height}$
Parallelogram		$A = \text{base} \times \text{height}$
Trapezium or **Trapezoid**		$A = \left(\frac{a + b}{2}\right) \times h$
Circle		$A = \pi r^2$
Sector		$A = \left(\frac{\theta}{360}\right) \times \pi r^2$

SURFACE AREA FORMULAE

RECTANGULAR PRISM

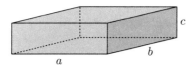

$$A = 2(ab + bc + ac)$$

CYLINDER

Object	Outer surface area
Hollow cylinder	$A = 2\pi rh$ (no ends)
Open cylinder	$A = 2\pi rh + \pi r^2$ (one end)
Solid cylinder	$A = 2\pi rh + 2\pi r^2$ (two ends)

CONE

Object	Outer surface area
Open cone	$A = \pi rs$ (no base)
Solid cone	$A = \pi rs + \pi r^2$ (solid)

SPHERE

$$A = 4\pi r^2$$

VOLUME FORMULAE

Object	Diagram	Volume
Solids of uniform cross-section	height, end, height, end	$V = $ **area of end $\times$ length**
Pyramids and cones	height, height, h, base, base	$V = \frac{1}{3}($**area of base $\times$ height**$)$
Spheres	r	$V = \frac{4}{3}\pi r^3$

WRITING A MATHEMATICAL EXPLORATION

In addition to sitting examination papers, students are also required to complete a **mathematical exploration**. This is a short report written by the student, based on a topic of his or her choice, and should focus on the mathematics of that topic. The mathematical exploration comprises 20% of the final mark.

The exploration should be approximately 12-20 pages long, and should be written at a level which is accessible to an audience of your peers. The exploration should also include a bibliography.

Group work should not be used for explorations. Each student's exploration is an individual piece of work.

When deciding how to structure your exploration, you may wish to include the following sections:

Introduction: This section can be used to explain why the topic has been chosen, and to include any relevant background information.

Aim: A clear statement of intent should be given to provide perspective and direction to your exploration. This should be a short paragraph which outlines the problem or scenario under investigation.

Method and Results: This section can be used to describe the process which was followed to investigate the problem, as well as recording the unprocessed results of your investigations, in the form of a table, for example.

Analysis of Results: In this section, you should use graphs, diagrams, and calculations to analyse your results. Any graphs and diagrams should be included in the appropriate place in the report, and not attached as appendices at the end. You should also form some conjectures based on your analysis.

Conclusion: You should summarise your investigation, giving a clear response to your aim. You should also reflect on your exploration. Limitations and sources of error could be discussed, as well as potential for further exploration.

Click on the icon to view some examples of mathematical explorations from previous IB students. Our sincere thanks goes to these students for allowing us to reproduce their work.

MATHEMATICAL
EXPLORATIONS

Chapter 1

Straight lines

Contents:

OPENING PROBLEM

The cycle department of a toy store sells bicycles and tricycles.

George observes that there are 13 cycles in total. His brother James counts 31 wheels in total.

Things to think about:

a Is it possible to determine the numbers of bicycles and tricycles using only:

    i George's observation   **ii** James' observation?

b What combination(s) of bicycles and tricycles satisfy:

    i George's observation   **ii** James' observation   **iii** both boys' observations?

c How can we solve problems like this without listing all of the possible combinations?

In this Chapter we study the equations and graphs of straight lines. We will discover how to solve problems like the **Opening Problem** by solving **simultaneous linear equations**. The solutions to simultaneous linear equations correspond to the intersection of lines.

A   THE EQUATION OF A LINE

In previous years we have represented linear relationships using:

- a table of values
- a graph
- an equation.

For example, suppose a theme park charges a $10 entrance fee, and $6 for each ride.

We can construct a table of values to show how the total cost (y) is related to the number of rides x:

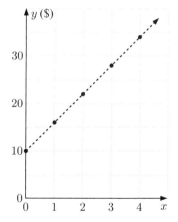

Number of rides (x)	0	1	2	3	4
Total cost (y)	10	16	22	28	34

$+6$ $+6$ $+6$ $+6$

When we plot these points (x, y) on a Cartesian plane, we see that they lie on a straight line. We say that the relationship between the variables is **linear**.

PROPERTIES OF LINES

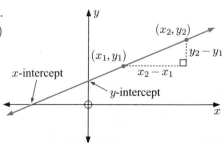

- The **gradient** of a line is a measure of its steepness.
  The gradient of the line passing through (x_1, y_1)
  and (x_2, y_2) is $\dfrac{y\text{-step}}{x\text{-step}} = \dfrac{y_2 - y_1}{x_2 - x_1}$.

- The **y-intercept** of a line is the value of y where the line cuts the y-axis.

- The **x-intercept** of a line is the value of x where the line cuts the x-axis.

For the theme park graph on the previous page:

- The line passes through $(0, 10)$ and $(1, 16)$, so the gradient is $\dfrac{16 - 10}{1 - 0} = 6$. We observe this because each ride adds an extra \$6 to the total cost.

- The y-intercept is 10. This represents the initial entrance fee of \$10.

PARALLEL AND PERPENDICULAR LINES

Two lines are **parallel** if they have the same gradient.

Two lines are **perpendicular** if their gradients are negative reciprocals of one another.

$$m_2 = -\frac{1}{m_1}$$

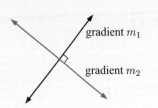

THE EQUATION OF A LINE

The **equation of a line** is an equation which connects the x and y values for every point on the line.

Using the gradient formula, the position of a general point (x, y) on a line with gradient m passing through (x_1, y_1), is given by $\dfrac{y - y_1}{x - x_1} = m$.

Rearranging, we find the **equation of the line** is $y - y_1 = m(x - x_1)$.

We call this **point-gradient** form. It allows us to quickly write down the equation of a line given its gradient and any point on it.

We can then rearrange the equation into other forms:

- In **gradient-intercept form**, the equation of the line with gradient m and y-intercept c is $y = mx + c$.

  The equation connecting the number of rides x and the total cost \$$y$ is $y = 6x + 10$.
  If we are given the value of one variable, we can substitute it into the equation to find the value of the other variable.
  For the theme park example, when $x = 5$, $y = 6(5) + 10 = 40$. This tells us that if a visitor goes on 5 rides, the total cost for the visit to the theme park is \$40.

- In **general form**, the equation of a line is $ax + by = d$ where a, b, d are constants.

  The general form allows us to write the equations of vertical lines, for which the gradient is undefined.
  For the line $x = 1$ we let $a = 1$, $b = 0$, and $d = 1$.

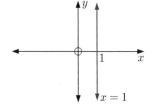

In examinations, you may also be asked to write the equation of a line in the form $ax + by + d = 0$.

Example 1   ◀)) **Self Tutor**

Find, in gradient-intercept form, the equation of the line with gradient -3 that passes through $(4, -5)$.

The equation of the line is $y - (-5) = -3(x - 4)$

$\therefore \quad y + 5 = -3x + 12$

$\therefore \quad y = -3x + 7$

We can find the equation of a line if we are given the gradient and a point which lies on the line.

EXERCISE 1A

1 State the gradient and y-intercept of the line with equation:

    a $y = 3x + 7$ **b** $y = -2x - 5$ **c** $y = \frac{2}{3}x - \frac{1}{3}$

    d $y = 11 - 4x$ **e** $y = -6 - x$ **f** $y = \frac{9}{5} - \frac{6}{5}x$

    g $y = \dfrac{7x + 2}{9}$ **h** $y = \dfrac{2x - 3}{6}$ **i** $y = \dfrac{3 - 5x}{8}$

2 Find, in gradient-intercept form, the equation of the line which has:

    a gradient 3 and passes through $(4, 1)$ **b** gradient -2 and passes through $(-3, 5)$

    c gradient $\frac{1}{4}$ and passes through $(4, -3)$ **d** gradient $-\frac{2}{3}$ and passes through $(-2, -7)$

    e gradient 2 and y-intercept -9 **f** gradient $-\frac{3}{4}$ and y-intercept 4.

3 Consider the table of values alongside.

    a Draw a graph of y against x.

    b Are the variables linearly related? Explain your answer.

    c Find the gradient and y-intercept of the graph.

    d Find the equation connecting x and y.

    e Find the value of y when $x = 10$.

x	0	1	2	3	4
y	5	8	11	14	17

4 Calculate the gradient of the illustrated road. Write your answer as a percentage.

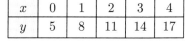

5 Two ponds in a garden are being filled with water from separate hoses. The amount of water in each pond after t minutes is shown below.

Pond P:

Time (t minutes)	0	1	2	3	4
Amount of water (A L)	10	20	30	45	60

Pond Q:

Time (t minutes)	0	1	2	3	4
Amount of water (A L)	5	20	35	50	65

    a Plot A against t for each pond.

    b Which pond is being filled at a constant rate? Explain your answer.

    c For the pond which is being filled at a constant rate:

       i Find the gradient and A-intercept of the line, and explain what these values mean.

       ii Find the equation connecting A and t.

       iii Find the amount of water in the pond after 8 minutes.

6 An unused bank account is charged a yearly fee. The graph alongside shows the balance of the account after x years.

    a Find the gradient and y-intercept of the line, and interpret your answers.

    b Find the equation of the line.

    c How long will it take for the account to run out of money?

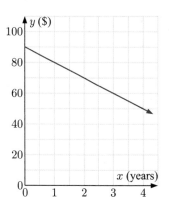

7 The graph alongside shows the descent of a train down a hill. The units are metres.

    a Calculate the gradient of the train's descent.

    b Find the equation of the train line.

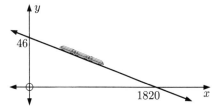

8 The height of a helicopter above sea level t minutes after taking off is $H = 150 + 120t$ metres.

    a What height above sea level did the helicopter take off from?

    b Interpret the value 120 in the equation.

    c Find the height of the helicopter above sea level after 2 minutes.

    d How long will it take for the helicopter to be 650 m above sea level?

Example 2 ◀)) **Self Tutor**

Write the equation:

    a $y = -\frac{2}{3}x + 2$ in general form

    b $3x - 4y = 2$ in gradient-intercept form.

    a $\qquad y = -\frac{2}{3}x + 2$

    $\therefore \quad 3y = -2x + 6 \qquad$ {multiplying both sides by 3}

    $\therefore \quad 2x + 3y = 6 \qquad$ {adding $2x$ to both sides}

    b $3x - 4y = 2$

    $\therefore \quad -4y = -3x - 2 \qquad$ {subtracting $3x$ from both sides}

    $\therefore \quad y = \frac{3}{4}x + \frac{1}{2} \qquad$ {dividing both sides by -4}

---

9 Write in general form:

    a $y = -4x + 6$ **b** $y = 5x - 3$ **c** $y = -\frac{3}{4}x + \frac{5}{4}$

    d $y = -\frac{2}{9}x + \frac{8}{9}$ **e** $y = \frac{3}{5}x - \frac{1}{5}$ **f** $y = \frac{5}{6}x + 3$

10 Write in gradient-intercept form:

    a $5x + y = 2$ **b** $3x + 7y = 2$ **c** $4x + 3y = -1$

    d $2x - y = 6$ **e** $3x - 13y = -4$ **f** $10x - 3y = 7$

11 Explain why the gradient of the line with general form $ax + by = d$ is $-\dfrac{a}{b}$.

12 Match pairs of lines which are parallel:

A $y = -x + 3$ **B** $y + 2 = 3(x - 1)$

C $3x - y = -2$ **D** $x + y = 4$

13 Match pairs of lines which are perpendicular:

A $x + 2y = 1$ **B** $2x + y = -3$

C $y - 7 = 2(x + 4)$ **D** $y = 2x - 7$

Parallel lines have equal gradients. Perpendicular lines have gradients which are negative reciprocals.

Example 3   🔊 **Self Tutor**

Find, in general form, the equation of the line with gradient $\frac{2}{3}$ that passes through $(-2, -1)$.

Since the line has gradient $\frac{2}{3}$, the general form of its equation is $2x - 3y = d$

Using the point $(-2, -1)$, the equation is $2x - 3y = 2(-2) - 3(-1)$

which is $2x - 3y = -1$.

---

14 Find, in general form, the equation of the line which has:

   a gradient -4 and passes through $(1, 2)$ **b** gradient $\frac{1}{2}$ and passes through $(3, -5)$

   c gradient $-\frac{5}{3}$ and passes through $(-2, 6)$ **d** gradient $\frac{7}{6}$ and passes through $(-1, -4)$.

Example 4   🔊 **Self Tutor**

Find, in gradient-intercept form, the equation of the line which passes through A$(3, 2)$ and B$(5, -1)$.

The line has gradient $= \dfrac{-1 - 2}{5 - 3} = \dfrac{-3}{2} = -\dfrac{3}{2}$,

and passes through the point A$(3, 2)$.

We could use *either* A or B as the point which lies on the line.

$\therefore$ the equation of the line is $y - 2 = -\frac{3}{2}(x - 3)$

$\therefore \ y - 2 = -\frac{3}{2}x + \frac{9}{2}$

$\therefore \ y = -\frac{3}{2}x + \frac{13}{2}$

---

15 Find, in gradient-intercept form, the equation of the line which passes through:

   a A$(-2, 1)$ and B$(3, 11)$ **b** A$(7, 2)$ and B$(4, 5)$ **c** A$(-5, 13)$ and B$(1, -17)$

   d P$(6, -4)$ and Q$(-3, -10)$ **e** M$(-2, -5)$ and N$(3, 2)$ **f** R$(5, -1)$ and S$(-7, 9)$.

16 Find, in general form, the equation of each line:

   a

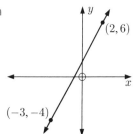

   b

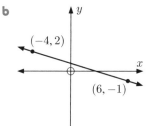

   c

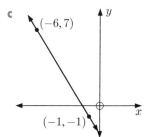

17   **a**   Find, in gradient-intercept form, the equation of *line 2*.
   b   Hence find the y-intercept of *line 2*.

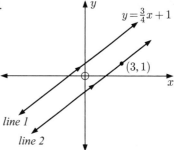

18   Find the equation of the line which is:
   a   parallel to $y = 3x - 2$ and passes through $(1, 4)$
   b   parallel to $2x - y = -3$ and passes through $(3, -1)$
   c   perpendicular to $y = -2x + 1$ and passes through $(-1, 5)$
   d   perpendicular to $x + 2y = 6$ and passes through $(-2, -1)$.

Example 5   ◀⸝ **Self Tutor**

Determine whether:
   a $(2, -2)$ lies on the line with equation $y = -x + 1$
   b $(3, -1)$ lies on the line with equation $3x - 2y = 11$.

a When $x = 2$, we have $\qquad y = -(2) + 1$ $\qquad\quad = -1$ ✘ So, $(2, -2)$ does *not* lie on the line.	**b** Substituting $x = 3$ and $y = -1$ into the LHS gives $\quad 3(3) - 2(-1)$ $\qquad\qquad\qquad = 9 + 2$ $\qquad\qquad\qquad = 11$ ✓ So, $(3, -1)$ does lie on the line.

---

19   Determine whether:
   a $(3, 11)$ lies on the line with equation $y = 4x - 1$
   b $(-6, -2)$ lies on the line with equation $y = \frac{2}{3}x - 6$
   c $(-4, -8)$ lies on the line with equation $7x - 3y = -4$
   d $(-\frac{1}{2}, 2)$ lies on the line with equation $6x + 10y = 17$.

Example 6   ◀⸝ **Self Tutor**

   a   Find m given that $(-2, 3)$ lies on the line with equation $y = mx + 7$.
   b   Find k given that $(3, k)$ lies on the line with equation $x + 4y = -9$.

a Substituting $x = -2$ and $y = 3$ into the equation gives $\qquad\qquad 3 = m(-2) + 7$ $\quad \therefore\ 2m = 4$ $\quad \therefore\ \ m = 2$	**b** Substituting $x = 3$ and $y = k$ into the equation gives $\qquad\qquad 3 + 4k = -9$ $\quad \therefore\ 4k = -12$ $\quad \therefore\ \ k = -3$

20 **a** Find c given that $(2, 15)$ lies on the line with equation $y = 4x + c$.

  b Find m given that $(\frac{1}{2}, 3)$ lies on the line with equation $y = mx - \frac{5}{2}$.

  c Find t given that $(t, 4)$ lies on the line with equation $y = \frac{2}{3}x - \frac{4}{3}$.

21 Find k given that:

  a $(6, -3)$ lies on the line with equation $2x + 5y = k$

  b $(-8, -5)$ lies on the line with equation $7x - y = k$

  c $(k, 0)$ lies on the line with equation $3x - 4y + 36 = 0$.

22 **a** Find the equation of *line 2*. Write your answer in the form $ax + by + d = 0$.

  b Find the x-intercept of *line 2*.

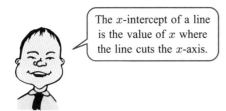

The x-intercept of a line is the value of x where the line cuts the x-axis.

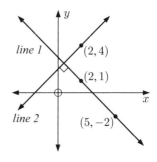

B GRAPHING A STRAIGHT LINE

LINES IN GRADIENT-INTERCEPT FORM

To draw the graph of $y = mx + c$ we:

- Use the y-intercept c to plot the point $(0, c)$.
- Use x and y-steps from the gradient m to locate another point on the line.
- Join the two points and extend the line in either direction.

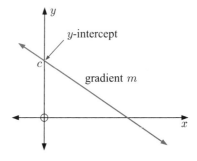

LINES IN GENERAL FORM

To draw the graph of $ax + by = d$ we:

- Find the y-intercept by letting $x = 0$.
- Find the x-intercept by letting $y = 0$.
- Join the points where the line cuts the axes and extend the line in either direction.

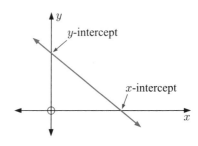

If $d = 0$ then the graph passes through the origin. In this case we plot $y = -\dfrac{a}{b}x$ using its gradient.

Example 7

◀》 Self Tutor

Draw the graph of: **a** $y = -\frac{1}{3}x + 2$ **b** $2x - 4y = 12$

a For $y = -\frac{1}{3}x + 2$:

- the y-intercept is $c = 2$
- the gradient is
$$m = \frac{-1}{3} \xleftarrow{} \text{y-step} \atop \xleftarrow{} \text{x-step}$$

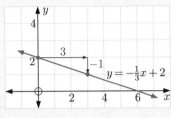

In part **a**, we choose a positive x-step.

b When $x = 0$, $-4y = 12$

$\therefore\ y = -3$

So, the y-intercept is -3.

When $y = 0$, $2x = 12$

$\therefore\ x = 6$

So, the x-intercept is 6.

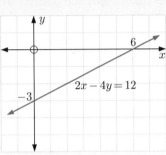

EXERCISE 1B

1 Draw the graph of:

a $y = \frac{1}{2}x + 1$ **b** $y = 3x - 2$ **c** $y = -\frac{3}{2}x + 4$

d $y = -2x + 5$ **e** $y = \frac{3}{4}x - 1$ **f** $y = -4x$

g $y = -x + 4$ **h** $y = \frac{6}{5}x - 3$ **i** $y = -\frac{5}{3}x - 1$

Check your answers using technology.

GRAPHICS CALCULATOR INSTRUCTIONS

GRAPHING PACKAGE

2 Draw the graph of:

a $3x + 2y = 12$ **b** $x + 3y = 6$ **c** $2x - 5y = 10$

d $4x - y = 8$ **e** $5x + 8y = 40$ **f** $3x - 4y = -24$

g $2x + 5y = 15$ **h** $6x + 4y = -36$ **i** $7x + 4y = 42$

3 Consider the line with equation $y = -\frac{3}{4}x + 2$.

a Find the gradient and y-intercept of the line.

b Determine whether the following points lie on the line:

i $(8, -4)$ **ii** $(1, 3)$ **iii** $(-2, \frac{7}{2})$

c Draw the graph of the line, showing your results from **a** and **b**.

4 Consider the line with equation $2x - 3y = 18$.

a Find the axes intercepts of the line.

b Determine whether the following points lie on the line: **i** $(3, -4)$ **ii** $(7, -2)$

c Find c such that $(-3, c)$ lies on the line.

d Draw the graph of the line, showing your results from **a**, **b**, and **c**.

5 The cost of hiring a trailer for t hours is $C = 5t + 10$ dollars.

    a Find the cost of hiring a trailer for 4 hours.

    b Draw the graph of C against t. Mark a point on your graph to indicate your answer to **a**.

6 At a sushi restaurant, *nigiri* costs \$4.50 per serve and *sashimi* costs \$9.00 per serve. Hiroko spent a total of \$45 buying x serves of *nigiri* and y serves of *sashimi*.

    a Explain why $4.5x + 9y = 45$.

    b If Hiroko bought 4 serves of *nigiri*, how much *sashimi* did she buy?

    c If Hiroko bought 1 serve of *sashimi*, how much *nigiri* did she buy?

    d Draw the graph of $4.5x + 9y = 45$. Mark two points on your graph to indicate your answers to **b** and **c**.

C   PERPENDICULAR BISECTORS

The **perpendicular bisector** of a line segment [AB] is the line perpendicular to [AB] which passes through its midpoint.

Notice that:

* Points on the perpendicular bisector are equidistant from A and B.

* The perpendicular bisector divides the number plane into two regions. On one side of the line are points that are closer to A than to B, and on the other side are points that are closer to B than to A.

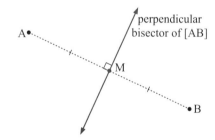

perpendicular bisector of [AB]

Example 8   ◀)) **Self Tutor**

Given A(4, −3) and B(−2, 7), find the equation of the perpendicular bisector of [AB].

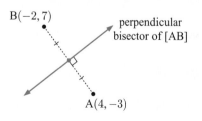

perpendicular bisector of [AB]

The midpoint M of [AB] is $\left(\dfrac{4 + -2}{2}, \dfrac{-3 + 7}{2} \right)$ or $(1, 2)$.

The gradient of [AB] is $\dfrac{7 - -3}{-2 - 4} = \dfrac{10}{-6} = -\dfrac{5}{3}$

∴ the gradient of the perpendicular bisector is $\tfrac{3}{5}$.

∴ the equation of the perpendicular bisector is $3x - 5y = 3(1) - 5(2)$ which is $3x - 5y = -7$.

EXERCISE 1C

1 Consider the points A(3, 1) and B(5, 7).

    a Find the midpoint of [AB].   **b** Find the gradient of [AB].

    c Hence state the gradient of the perpendicular bisector.

    d Find the equation of the perpendicular bisector.

2 Find the equation of the perpendicular bisector of:

    a A(5, 2) and B(1, 4)   **b** A(−1, 5) and B(5, 3)   **c** M(6, −3) and N(2, 1)

    d M(7, 2) and N(−1, 6)   **e** O(0, 0) and P(9, 0)   **f** A(3, 6) and B(−1, 3).

3 Suppose P is (6, −1) and Q is (2, 5).

    a Find the equation of the perpendicular bisector of [PQ].

    b Show that R(1, 0) lies on the perpendicular bisector.

    c Show that R is equidistant from P and Q.

4 Consider the quadrilateral ABCD.

    a Use side lengths to show that ABCD is a rhombus.

    b Find the equation of the perpendicular bisector of [AC].

    c Show that B and D both lie on this perpendicular bisector.

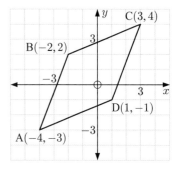

5 A line segment has equation $3x - 2y + 1 = 0$. Its midpoint is (3, 5).

    a State the gradient of: **i** the line segment   **ii** its perpendicular bisector.

    b State the equation of the perpendicular bisector. Write your answer in the form $ax + by + d = 0$.

6 Consider the points A(x_1, y_1) and B(x_2, y_2).

    a Show that the equation of the perpendicular bisector of [AB] is

$$(x_2 - x_1)x + (y_2 - y_1)y = \frac{(x_2^{\,2} + y_2^{\,2}) - (x_1^{\,2} + y_1^{\,2})}{2}.$$

    b Suggest one advantage of writing the equation in this form.

7 Consider three points A(1, 2), B(4, 5), and C(2, −1).

    a Find the equation of the perpendicular bisector of:

        i [AB]   **ii** [AC]   **iii** [BC].

    b Graph the three perpendicular bisectors on the same set of axes. Discuss your observations.

    c Describe how you can find the centre of the circle which passes through three non-collinear points.

8 Three post offices are located in a small city at P(−8, −6), Q(1, 5), and R(4, −2).

    a Find the equation of the perpendicular bisector of:

        i [PQ]   **ii** [PR]   **iii** [QR].

    b Graph the three post offices and the three perpendicular bisectors on the same set of axes. Use these lines to locate the point that is equidistant from all three post offices. Shade regions of your graph in different colours according to their closest post office.

SIMULTANEOUS EQUATIONS

The **Opening Problem** on page **20** can be represented using two linear equations, one for George's observation that there are 13 cycles in total, and one for James' observation that there are 31 wheels in total.

Suppose there are x bicycles and y tricycles.

Since there are 13 cycles in total, $x + y = 13$

Since there are 31 wheels in total, $2x + 3y = 31$

> We need to find values for x and y which satisfy both equations *at the same time.*

We say that $\begin{cases} x + y = 13 \\ 2x + 3y = 31 \end{cases}$ is a system of **simultaneous equations**.

In this Section we consider three methods of solution for simultaneous linear equations:

- graphical solutions
- algebraic substitution
- algebraic elimination.

GRAPHICAL SOLUTION

One of the simplest methods for solving simultaneous linear equations is to graph the lines on the same set of axes. The point of intersection gives us the solution to the simultaneous equations.

Example 9   ◀» **Self Tutor**

Solve the following simultaneous equations graphically: $\begin{cases} y = 3x - 1 \\ x + y = 3 \end{cases}$

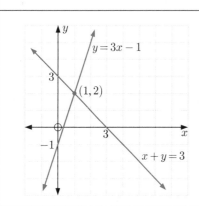

We draw the graphs of $y = 3x - 1$ and $x + y = 3$ on the same set of axes.

The graphs meet at the point $(1, 2)$.

$\therefore$ the solution is $x = 1$, $y = 2$.

Check:

Substituting these values into:

- $y = 3x - 1$ gives $2 = 3(1) - 1$ ✓
- $x + y = 3$ gives $1 + 2 = 3$ ✓

EXERCISE 1D.1

1 Solve the following simultaneous equations graphically:

a $\begin{cases} y = 3x + 2 \\ y = x - 2 \end{cases}$
b $\begin{cases} y = -4x + 1 \\ y = 3x - 6 \end{cases}$
c $\begin{cases} y = 2x - 5 \\ y = \frac{1}{2}x + 4 \end{cases}$

2 Solve the following simultaneous equations graphically:

a $\begin{cases} y = x - 1 \\ 2x + 3y = 12 \end{cases}$
b $\begin{cases} x + 3y = 9 \\ x - 2y = 4 \end{cases}$
c $\begin{cases} 3x - 2y = 30 \\ 4x + y = -4 \end{cases}$

3 Try to solve the following simultaneous equations graphically. State the number of solutions in each case.

a $\begin{cases} y = -2x + 5 \\ y = -2x - 1 \end{cases}$

b $\begin{cases} x - \frac{1}{4}y = -2 \\ y = 4x + 8 \end{cases}$

c $\begin{cases} 3x + 4y = -24 \\ 3x + 4y = -12 \end{cases}$

SOLUTION BY SUBSTITUTION

The method of **solution by substitution** is used most easily when at least one equation is given with either x or y as the **subject** of the formula. We **substitute** an expression for this variable into the other equation.

Example 10	◀)) **Self Tutor**

Solve simultaneously by substitution: $\begin{cases} y = x - 3 \\ 2x + 3y = 16 \end{cases}$

$y = x - 3$ .... (1)
$2x + 3y = 16$ .... (2)

Substituting (1) into (2) gives $2x + 3(x - 3) = 16$
$$\therefore\ 2x + 3x - 9 = 16$$
$$\therefore\ 5x = 25$$
$$\therefore\ x = 5$$

Substituting $x = 5$ into (1) gives $y = 5 - 3$
$$\therefore\ y = 2$$

The solution is $x = 5,\ y = 2$.

Check: Substituting into (2), $2(5) + 3(2) = 10 + 6 = 16$ ✓

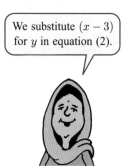

We substitute $(x - 3)$ for y in equation (2).

EXERCISE 1D.2

1 Solve the following sets of simultaneous equations:

a $\begin{cases} y = x + 2 \\ 2x + 3y = 21 \end{cases}$

b $\begin{cases} y = 2x - 3 \\ 4x - 3y = 7 \end{cases}$

c $\begin{cases} 5x + 3y = 19 \\ y = 6 - 2x \end{cases}$

d $\begin{cases} y = 3x + 1 \\ y = 7x - 1 \end{cases}$

e $\begin{cases} y = 6x - 8 \\ 3x + 2y = -6 \end{cases}$

f $\begin{cases} 4x - 7y = 1 \\ y = 11 - 3x \end{cases}$

2 Solve the following sets of simultaneous equations:

a $\begin{cases} x = y - 3 \\ 5x - 2y = 9 \end{cases}$

b $\begin{cases} 2x - 3y = -8 \\ x = 3y - 1 \end{cases}$

c $\begin{cases} x = 4y + 3 \\ x = 9 + 7y \end{cases}$

d $\begin{cases} y = 5x - 3 \\ x = 2y + 3 \end{cases}$

e $\begin{cases} 3x + 4y = -13 \\ x = 8y - 2 \end{cases}$

f $\begin{cases} x = -5y - 2 \\ 7x + 4y = -10 \end{cases}$

3 Solve the following sets of simultaneous equations:

a $\begin{cases} y = \frac{1}{2}x + 5 \\ 3x + 4y = 5 \end{cases}$

b $\begin{cases} x = -\frac{3}{4}y \\ 4x - 5y = -24 \end{cases}$

c $\begin{cases} x + 6y = -6 \\ y = \frac{1}{3}x - 5 \end{cases}$

d $\begin{cases} y = -\frac{1}{2}x + 3 \\ 5x + 4y = 14 \end{cases}$

e $\begin{cases} 3x + 7y = 6 \\ x = \frac{5}{3}y - 1 \end{cases}$

f $\begin{cases} 3x + 4y = 10 \\ y = \frac{3}{4}x + 2 \end{cases}$

SOLUTION BY ELIMINATION

If both equations are presented in the form $ax + by = d$,   then solution by substitution is tedious. We instead use the method of **elimination**.

In this method, we make the coefficients of x (or y) the **same size** but **opposite in sign**, and then **add** the equations. This has the effect of **eliminating** one of the variables.

Example 11   ◀》 **Self Tutor**

Solve by elimination: $\begin{cases} 5x - 2y = 7 \\ 3x + 2y = 17 \end{cases}$

The coefficients of y are the same size but opposite in sign.

We *add* the LHSs and the RHSs to get an equation which contains x only.

$$5x - 2y = 7 \quad \text{.... (1)}$$
$$3x + 2y = 17 \quad \text{.... (2)}$$

Adding, $8x \qquad = 24$

$\qquad\qquad \therefore \quad x = 3$

By adding the equations, we **eliminate** the y variable.

Substituting $x = 3$ into (1) gives $5(3) - 2y = 7$

$\qquad\qquad\qquad\qquad\qquad \therefore \quad 15 - 2y = 7$

$\qquad\qquad\qquad\qquad\qquad \therefore \quad -2y = -8$

$\qquad\qquad\qquad\qquad\qquad \therefore \quad y = 4$

The solution is $x = 3$, $y = 4$.

Check: In (2): $3(3) + 2(4) = 9 + 8 = 17$ ✓

In problems where the coefficients of x (or y) are **not** the **same size** or **opposite in sign**, we must first **multiply** one or both equations by a constant.

Example 12   ◀》 **Self Tutor**

Solve by elimination: $\begin{cases} 3x + 4y = 2 \\ 2x - 3y = 7 \end{cases}$

$3x + 4y = 2$ .... (1)
$2x - 3y = 7$ .... (2)

To make the coefficients of y the same size but opposite in sign, we multiply (1) by 3 and (2) by 4.

$\qquad \therefore \quad 9x + 12y = 6 \quad \{(1) \times 3\}$
$\qquad\qquad\ \ 8x - 12y = 28 \quad \{(2) \times 4\}$

Adding, $17x \qquad = 34$

$\qquad\qquad \therefore \quad x = 2$

We can choose to eliminate either x or y.

Substituting $x = 2$ into (1) gives $3(2) + 4y = 2$

$$\therefore \quad 6 + 4y = 2$$
$$\therefore \quad 4y = -4$$
$$\therefore \quad y = -1$$

The solution is $x = 2$, $y = -1$.

Check: In (2): $2(2) - 3(-1) = 4 + 3 = 7$ ✓

EXERCISE 1D.3

1 Solve using the method of elimination:

a $\begin{cases} 3x - y = 5 \\ 4x + y = 9 \end{cases}$
 b $\begin{cases} 5x - 2y = 17 \\ 3x + 2y = 7 \end{cases}$
 c $\begin{cases} -4x + 3y = 31 \\ 4x - y = -21 \end{cases}$

d $\begin{cases} 6x + 5y = 9 \\ -6x + 7y = -45 \end{cases}$
 e $\begin{cases} 2x - 3y = 18 \\ 5x + 3y = 24 \end{cases}$
 f $\begin{cases} -4x + 6y = -21 \\ 4x - 2y = 11 \end{cases}$

2 Solve using the method of elimination:

a $\begin{cases} 3x + y = 16 \\ 7x - 2y = 7 \end{cases}$
 b $\begin{cases} 4x + 3y = -14 \\ -x + 5y = 15 \end{cases}$
 c $\begin{cases} 5x - 2y = 7 \\ 2x - y - 4 = 0 \end{cases}$

d $\begin{cases} 3x - 7y = -27 \\ -6x + 5y = 18 \end{cases}$
 e $\begin{cases} 9x + 2y = -24 \\ -7x + 4y = 27 \end{cases}$
 f $\begin{cases} 3x - 7y = -8 \\ 9x + 11y = 16 \end{cases}$

3 Solve using the method of elimination:

a $\begin{cases} 4x + 3y = 14 \\ 3x - 4y = 23 \end{cases}$
 b $\begin{cases} 2x - 3y = 6 \\ 5x - 4y = 1 \end{cases}$
 c $\begin{cases} 5x + 6y = 17 \\ 3x - 7y = 42 \end{cases}$

d $\begin{cases} 2x + 10y = -5 \\ 3x - 7y = 9 \end{cases}$
 e $\begin{cases} 4x + 2y = -23 \\ 5x - 7y = -5 \end{cases}$
 f $\begin{cases} 4x - 7y = 9 \\ 5x - 8y = -2 \end{cases}$

ACTIVITY 1   PARALLEL AND COINCIDENT LINES

What to do:

1 Consider the simultaneous equations $\begin{cases} y = 4x + 7 \\ 2y - 8x = 1. \end{cases}$

  a Graph each line on the same set of axes. What do you notice?

  b Try to solve the simultaneous equations using:

   i substitution   **ii** elimination.

  c How many solutions does this system of simultaneous equations have?

2 Consider the simultaneous equations $\begin{cases} y = -2x + 5 \\ 4x + 2y = 10. \end{cases}$

  a Graph each line on the same set of axes. What do you notice?

  b Try to solve the simultaneous equations using:

   i substitution   **ii** elimination.

  c How many solutions does this system of simultaneous equations have?

ACTIVITY 2   SIMULTANEOUS EQUATIONS USING TECHNOLOGY

Click on the icon for this Activity which explains how to solve simultaneous   SIMULTANEOUS
EQUATIONS
equations using:

- graphs   • the solver function.

E   PROBLEM SOLVING WITH SIMULTANEOUS EQUATIONS

Many problems can be described using a pair of linear equations. You should follow these steps:

Step 1:   Decide on the two unknowns, for example x and y. Do not forget the units.

Step 2:   Write down **two** equations connecting x and y.

Step 3:   Solve the equations simultaneously.

Step 4:   Check your solutions with the original data given.

Step 5:   Write your answer in sentence form.

Example 13   ◀) **Self Tutor**

Two adults' tickets and three children's tickets to a cricket match cost £45. Three adults' and four children's tickets cost £64. Find the cost of each type of ticket.

Let £x be the cost of an adult's ticket and £y be the cost of a child's ticket.

$\therefore$ $2x + 3y = 45$ .... (1)

$3x + 4y = 64$ .... (2)

$\therefore$ $6x + 9y = 135$ $\{3 \times (1)\}$

$\underline{-6x - 8y = -128}$ $\{-2 \times (2)\}$

Adding, $y = 7$

Substituting $y = 7$ into (1) gives $2x + 3(7) = 45$

$\therefore$ $2x + 21 = 45$

$\therefore$ $2x = 24$

$\therefore$ $x = 12$

So, an adult's ticket costs £12 and a child's ticket costs £7.

Check: In (2): $3(12) + 4(7) = 36 + 28 = 64$ $\checkmark$

EXERCISE 1E

1   Five plates and two bowls cost £53. Three plates and eight bowls cost £93. Find the cost of each item.

2   A violinist is learning a waltz and a sonatina. One day she practises for 33 minutes by playing the waltz 4 times and the sonatina 3 times. The next day she plays the waltz 6 times and the sonatina only once, for a total of 25 minutes. Determine the length of each piece.

3 A shop sells two lengths of extension cable. Tomasz buys 2 short cables and 5 long cables with total length 26 m. Alicja buys 3 short cables and 4 long cables with total length 24.3 m. Find the two different lengths of the extension cables.

4 In an archery competition, competitors fire 8 arrows at a target. They are awarded points based on which region of the target is hit. The results for two of the competitors are shown opposite.

How many points are awarded for hitting the:

  a red   **b** blue region?

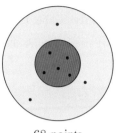 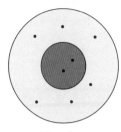

68 points   56 points

5 A hardware store sells 3 litre cans of paint for €36 and 5 litre cans of paint for €48. In one day the store sells 71 litres of paint worth a total of €768. How many cans of paint did the store sell?

6 Lidia is paid at a standard rate per hour before 5 pm, and then at a higher rate per hour after 5 pm. On Monday she worked from 2 pm to 7 pm, and earned \$110. On Tuesday she worked from 11 am to 8 pm, and earned \$195. On Wednesday Lidia worked from noon to 6 pm. How much did she earn on Wednesday?

7 The current world record holder in both the 5000 m and 10 000 m is the Ethiopian runner Kenenisa Bekele. In his career he won 3 Olympic gold medals and 5 world championships.

His world record times are:
  • 12 min 37.35 s for 5000 m
  • 26 min 17.53 s for 10 000 m.

  a Kenenisa's tactic in the 5000 m was to run at a constant speed of 6.5 m s^{-1} for most of the race, then sprint the last section at 7.7 m s^{-1}. How far did Kenenisa sprint at the end?

  b In the 10 000 m, Kenenisa was not able to run quite as fast. He ran at 6.3 m s^{-1} for most of the race, then sprinted at 7.5 m s^{-1} at the end. At what point did Kenenisa sprint in this race?

8 Find the area of the triangle defined by:
  a $y = x + 2$, $x + y = 9$, and $y = 2$
  b $5x - 2y = 18$, $2x + 5y = 13$, and $8x - 9y = 11.4$

DISCUSSION

Whenever we solve problems in a real-world context, it is important to consider whether the solution is *reasonable*. This includes:

  • Is the solution physically possible?   • Is the solution within the range we might expect?

Consider the simultaneous equations: $\begin{cases} 2x + y = 6 \\ 4x - y = 15 \end{cases}$

The solution is $x = 3.5$, $y = -1$.

  1 Discuss whether this solution might be reasonable if x represents:
    a an amount of money   **b** the number of cups of flour in a recipe
    c the number of people in a class.

2 Discuss whether this solution might be reasonable if y represents:

  a an amount of money   **b** the number of cups of flour in a recipe

  c the number of people in a class.

3 How do we know what a reasonable range for a solution is?

4 What other factors do we need to think about when considering the reasonableness of a solution?

REVIEW SET 1A

1 Consider the table of values alongside.

  a Draw a graph of y against x.

  b Are the variables linearly related? Explain your answer.

  c Find the gradient and y-intercept of the graph.

  d Find the equation connecting x and y.

  e Find the value of y when $x = 7$.

x	0	1	2	3	4
y	20	17	14	11	8

2 The weekly income £I of a salesperson varies depending on their total weekly sales £S. The chart alongside shows the relationship between I and S.

  a Find the gradient and I-intercept of the line, and explain what these values mean.

  b Find the equation of the line.

  c Find the salesperson's weekly income if £3400 in sales are made.

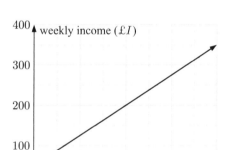

3 **a** Find, in gradient-intercept form, the equation of the line which has gradient $-\frac{1}{3}$ and passes through $(6, 2)$.

  b Write the equation of the line in the form $ax + by + d = 0$.

4 **a** Find, in general form, the equation of *line 2*.

  b Hence find the x-intercept of *line 2*.

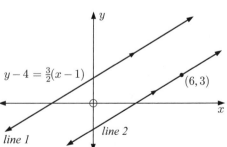

5 Determine whether:

  a $(5, -2)$ lies on the line with equation $y = -x + 3$

  b $(-3, \frac{1}{2})$ lies on the line with equation $3x + 8y = -5$.

6 Draw the graph of:

    a $y = 2x - 3$ **b** $y = -\frac{3}{4}x + 1$ **c** $5x + 3y = 30$

    d $y = \frac{2}{3}x + 1$ **e** $3x - 4y = 72$ **f** $2x + 5y = -20$

7 Find the equation of the perpendicular bisector of:

    a A(5, 2) and B(5, −4)   **b** A(8, 1) and B(2, 5).

8 Solve graphically: **a** $\begin{cases} y = x + 1 \\ y = -2x + 10 \end{cases}$ **b** $\begin{cases} x + 3y = 6 \\ x - y = -6 \end{cases}$

9 Solve by substitution: **a** $\begin{cases} y = 3x + 4 \\ 2x - y = -5 \end{cases}$ **b** $\begin{cases} x = 2y - 5 \\ 3x + 4y = 5 \end{cases}$

10 Solve by elimination: **a** $\begin{cases} 3x + 2y = 7 \\ 5x - 2y = 17 \end{cases}$ **b** $\begin{cases} 2x + 7y = 13 \\ -4x + 3y = 25 \end{cases}$

11 Consider the line with equation $y = -\frac{1}{2}x + 4$.

    a Write down the gradient and y-intercept of the line.

    b Determine whether (6, 1) lies on the line.

    c Find k such that $(k, 5)$ lies on the line.

    d Draw the graph of the line, showing your results from **a**, **b**, and **c**.

12 A furniture store sells tables and chairs.
Two possible arrangements and their costs
are shown alongside.
Find the cost of:

    a each table   **b** each chair.

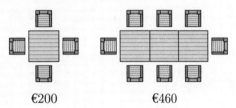

€200   €460

13 A machine tests solar batteries for faults. A working battery takes 2 minutes to test, but a faulty
battery requires 5 minutes to detect and repair. In an 83 minute session, 37 batteries were tested.
How many were faulty?

14 Quadrilateral ABCD has vertices A(3, 2), B(2, −4), C(−4, −3), and D(−3, 3).

    a Find the equation of the perpendicular bisector of: **i** [AC]   **ii** [BD].

    b Classify quadrilateral ABCD.

REVIEW SET 1B

1 The speed of a pebble thrown from the top of a cliff
is shown alongside.

    a Find the gradient and y-intercept of the line, and
explain what these values mean.

    b Find the equation of the line.

    c Find the speed of the pebble after 8 seconds.

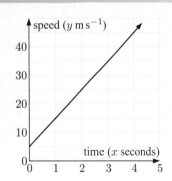

2 Find, in general form, the equation of the line which has:

    a gradient 5 and passes through $(2, -1)$ **b** gradient $-\frac{1}{4}$ and passes through $(-3, -4)$.

3 Find the equation of the line which is:

    a parallel to $y = 3x - 8$ and passes through $(2, 7)$

    b perpendicular to $2x + 5y = 7$ and passes through $(-1, -1)$.

4 Find k given that:

    a $(2, k)$ lies on the line with equation $y = 5x - 3$

    b $(\frac{1}{2}, -\frac{3}{2})$ lies on the line with equation $5x + 9y = k$.

5 Draw the graph of:

    a $2x - 3y = 18$ **b** $y = \frac{5}{2}x - 3$ **c** $3x + 2y = 30$

    d $y = -2x + 5$ **e** $y = -\frac{1}{3}x + \frac{4}{3}$ **f** $5x + 2y = -30$

6 Find the equation of the perpendicular bisector of $P(-3, 2)$ and $Q(5, -6)$.

7 A line segment has equation $x - 5y + 6 = 0$. Its midpoint is $(4, 2)$.

    a State the gradient of: **i** the line segment   **ii** its perpendicular bisector.

    b State the equation of the perpendicular bisector.

8 Solve the following simultaneous equations graphically:

    a $\begin{cases} y = 3x + 1 \\ x - y = 3 \end{cases}$ **b** $\begin{cases} 2x + y = 6 \\ x - 2y = 8 \end{cases}$

9 Solve by substitution:

    a $\begin{cases} y = 6x + 2 \\ 3x - 2y = -7 \end{cases}$ **b** $\begin{cases} y = \frac{1}{2}x + 5 \\ 4x + 3y = 4 \end{cases}$

10 Solve by elimination:

    a $\begin{cases} 3x + 2y = 8 \\ 5x - 4y = 17 \end{cases}$ **b** $\begin{cases} 4x + 6y = -15 \\ 3x - 5y = 22 \end{cases}$

11 Consider the line with equation $y = \frac{2}{3}x - \frac{8}{3}$.

    a Find the gradient of the line.

    b Determine whether: **i** $(-2, -4)$ **ii** $(4, 5)$ lie on the line.

    c Draw the graph of the line, showing your results from **a** and **b**.

12 There are 500 tickets for sale in a raffle. Tickets cost $3 each, or $20 for a book of 10. All 500 tickets were sold, and $1350 was raised. How many books of 10 tickets were sold?

13 A piano teacher charges $30 for a one hour lesson, and $50 for a two hour lesson. She works for 25 hours in one week, and earns $690. How many two hour lessons did she give?

14 Triangle ABC has vertices $A(3, 6)$, $B(-1, 4)$, and $C(1, 0)$.

    a Find the equation of the perpendicular bisector of:

        i [AB]   **ii** [AC]   **iii** [BC].

    b Graph the three perpendicular bisectors on the same set of axes. Discuss your observations.

Chapter 2

Sets and Venn diagrams

OPENING PROBLEM

The Human Development Index (HDI) is a composite statistic of life expectancy, education, and per capita income indicators used to rank nations on their levels of human development.

Suppose L represents the nations which have a life expectancy of more than 75 years, S represents the nations where the mean years of schooling is greater than 10, and I represents the nations where the gross national income (GNI) is more than $18\,000$ USD per capita.

In 2016, of the 100 nations with the highest HDI:

- 69 were in L
- 50 were in L and I
- 37 were in L, S, and I
- 58 were in S
- 44 were in S and I
- 61 were in I
- 43 were in L and S

Things to think about:

a How can we display this information on a diagram?

b Can we find how many nations out of the 100 with the highest HDI were not in any of L, S, or I?

c How many nations were in:
  i S only   **ii** L or I but not S **iii** S and I but not L?

d Do you think that life expectancy, mean years of schooling, and gross national income are linked in any way? You may wish to visit the link alongside to consider data for nations ranked outside of the top 100 for HDI.

LINK

A   SETS

A **set** is a collection of numbers or objects.

Each object is called an **element** or **member** of the set.

When we record a set, we write its members within curly brackets, with commas between them.

We often use a capital letter to represent a set so that we can refer to it easily.

For example:

> The curly brackets are read as "the set of".

- If D is the set of digits we use to write numbers, then $D = \{0, 1, 2, 3, 4, 5, 6, 7, 8, 9\}$.

- If C is the set of countries with coastlines on the Caspian Sea, then $C = \{$Azerbaijan, Iran, Kazakhstan, Russia, Turkmenistan$\}$.

SET NOTATION

$\in$ means   "is an element of" or "is in"

$\notin$ means   "is not an element of" or "is not in"

$n(A)$ means   "the number of elements in set A".

For example, if $P = \{$prime numbers less than $20\} = \{2, 3, 5, 7, 11, 13, 17, 19\}$ then $11 \in P$, $15 \notin P$, and $n(P) = 8$.

FINITE AND INFINITE SETS

Set A is a **finite set** if $n(A)$ has a particular defined value.

If A has an endless number of elements, we say it is an **infinite set**.

EQUAL SETS

Two sets are **equal** if they contain exactly the same elements.

For example, $\{4, 1, 8\} = \{8, 4, 1\}$.

SUBSETS

Set A is a **subset** of set B if every element of A is also an element of B. We write $A \subseteq B$.

For example, if $A = \{2, 4, 6\}$ and $B = \{\text{even numbers}\}$, then every element of A is also an element of B. A is a subset of B, and we write $A \subseteq B$.

A is a **proper subset** of B if every element of A is also an element of B, but $A \neq B$. We write $A \subset B$.

EMPTY SET

The **empty set** $\varnothing$ or $\{\ \}$ is a set which contains no elements.

For example, the set of perfect squares between 150 and 160 is the empty set.

The empty set is a subset of all other sets.

Example 1
◀》 **Self Tutor**

Let P be the set of letters in the word AMATEUR
and Q be the set of letters in the word TEAM.

   a List the elements of P and Q.

   b Find $n(P)$ and $n(Q)$.

   c Decide whether the statement is true or false:

       i $U \in Q$ **ii** $R \notin Q$ **iii** $P \subseteq Q$ **iv** $Q \subset P$

---

a $P = \{A, M, T, E, U, R\}, \quad Q = \{T, E, A, M\}$

b $n(P) = 6, \quad n(Q) = 4$

c   **i** U is not in the word TEAM, so $U \in Q$ is false.

     ii R is not in the word TEAM, so $R \notin Q$ is true.

    iii $U \in P$ but $U \notin Q$, so $P \subseteq Q$ is false.

    iv Every element in Q is also an element of P, so $Q \subseteq P$.

        However, $U \in P$ but $U \notin Q$, so $Q \neq P$.

        $\therefore \quad Q \subset P$ is true.

> We do not include duplicates when listing elements of a set. So, A appears only once in P.

EXERCISE 2A

1 Write using set notation:

   a 5 is an element of set D **b** 6 is not an element of set G

   c d is not an element of the set of all English vowels

   d $\{2, 5\}$ is a subset of $\{1, 2, 3, 4, 5, 6\}$

   e $\{3, 8, 6\}$ is not a subset of $\{1, 2, 3, 4, 5, 6\}$.

2 Decide whether each set is finite or infinite:

   a {factors of 10}   **b** {multiples of 10}   **c** {perfect squares}

3 For each set A, list the elements of A and hence state $n(A)$:

   a {factors of 8}   **b** {composite numbers less than 20}

   c {letters in the word AARDVARK}   **d** {months of the year}

   e {prime numbers between 40 and 50}

4 Let $S = \{1, 2, 4, 5, 9, 12\}$ and $T = \{2, 5, 9\}$.

   a Find: **i** $n(S)$ **ii** $n(T)$.

   b Decide whether the statement is true or false:

      i $4 \in S$ **ii** $4 \in T$ **iii** $1 \notin T$ **iv** $T \subseteq S$ **v** $T \subset S$

5 Let $S = \{1, 2\}$ and $T = \{1, 2, 3\}$.

   a List *all* the subsets of S and T.

   b Is every subset of S a subset of T?

   c What fraction of the subsets of T are also subsets of S?

6 State the number of subsets of $\{p, q, r, s\}$. Explain your answer.

7 Suppose $A = \{$prime numbers between 30 and 40$\}$, $B = \{$even numbers between 30 and 40$\}$, $C = \{$composite numbers between 30 and 40$\}$, and $D = \{$multiples of 21 between 30 and 40$\}$.

   a List the elements of each set.

   b Find: **i** $n(A)$ **ii** $n(D)$.

   c Which of the sets listed are:

      i subsets of A **ii** proper subsets of C?

   d True or false?   **i** $33 \in C$ **ii** $37 \notin A$ **iii** $35 \in B$

8 Consider two sets A and B such that $A \subseteq B$. Find the possible values of x if $A = \{2, 4, 6, x\}$ and $B = \{2, 3, 5, 6, \ x+1\}$.

B   INTERSECTION AND UNION

INTERSECTION

The **intersection** of two sets A and B is the set of elements that are in **both** set A **and** set B.

The intersection of sets A and B is written $\boldsymbol{A \cap B}$.

For example, if $A = \{1, 3, 4\}$ and $B = \{2, 3, 5\}$, then $A \cap B = \{3\}$.

Two sets A and B are **disjoint** or **mutually exclusive** if they have no elements in common. In this case $A \cap B = \varnothing$.

UNION

The **union** of two sets A and B is the set of elements that are in **either** set A **or** set B.

The union of sets A and B is written $\boldsymbol{A \cup B}$.

> Elements in both A and B **are included** in the union of A and B.

For example, if $A = \{1, 3, 4\}$ and $B = \{2, 3, 5\}$, then $A \cup B = \{1, 2, 3, 4, 5\}$.

Example 2	◀)) Self Tutor

$M = \{2, 3, 5, 7, 8, 9\}$ and $N = \{3, 4, 6, 9, 10\}$.

List the sets: **a** $M \cap N$ **b** $M \cup N$.

> To write down $M \cup N$, start with M then add to it the elements of N which are not in M.

a $M \cap N = \{3, 9\}$ since 3 and 9 are elements of both sets.

b Every element which is in either M or N is in the union of M and N.

∴ $M \cup N = \{2, 3, 4, 5, 6, 7, 8, 9, 10\}$

EXERCISE 2B

1 Find **i** $A \cap B$ **ii** $A \cup B$ for:

a $A = \{6, 7, 9, 11, 12\}$ and $B = \{5, 8, 10, 13, 9\}$

b $A = \{1, 2, 3, 4\}$ and $B = \{5, 6, 7, 8\}$

c $A = \{1, 3, 5, 7\}$ and $B = \{1, 2, 3, 4, 5, 6, 7, 8, 9\}$

d $A = \{0, 3, 5, 8, 14\}$ and $B = \{1, 4, 5, 8, 11, 13\}$

2 Determine whether the sets are disjoint:

a $A = \{3, 5, 7, 9\}$ and $B = \{2, 4, 6, 8\}$

b $P = \{3, 5, 6, 7, 8, 10\}$ and $Q = \{4, 9, 10\}$

3 Let $A = \{$even numbers between 20 and 30$\}$, $B = \{$odd numbers between 20 and 30$\}$, and $C = \{$composite numbers between 20 and 30$\}$.

a Which pair of sets is disjoint? Justify your answer.

b List the elements of $A \cap C$. Is $A \subset C$?

c Find $n(B \cup C)$.

4 Determine whether each statement is true or false. Explain your answers.

a If R and S are two non-empty sets and $R \cap S = \varnothing$ then R and S are disjoint.

b For any sets A and B, $n(A \cap B) \leqslant n(A)$ and $n(A \cap B) \leqslant n(B)$.

c If $A \cap B = A \cup B$ then $A = B$.

C   COMPLEMENT OF A SET

When we are dealing with sets:

> The **universal set** U is the set of all elements we are considering.

For example, if we are considering the digits we write whole numbers with, the universal set is $U = \{0, 1, 2, 3, 4, 5, 6, 7, 8, 9\}$.

From this universal set we can define subsets of U, such as $C - \{\text{composites}\} = \{4, 6, 8, 9\}$ and $P = \{\text{primes}\} = \{2, 3, 5, 7\}$.

> The **complement** of a set A is the set of all elements of U that are *not* elements of A.
>
> The complement of A is written A'.

For example, if $U = \{1, 2, 3, 4, 5, 6, 7, 8\}$ and $A = \{1, 3, 5, 7, 8\}$, then $A' = \{2, 4, 6\}$.

We can make three immediate observations about complementary sets:

> For any set A with complement A':
> - $A \cap A' = \varnothing$ as A' and A have no common members.
> - $A \cup A' = U$ as all elements of A and A' combined make up U.
> - $n(A) + n(A') = n(U)$ provided U is finite.

EXERCISE 2C

1 Let $U = \{1, 2, 3, 4, 5, 6, 7, 8, 9\}$.
 a Find the complement of $A = \{2, 3, 6, 7, 8\}$.
 b If $P = \{\text{prime numbers}\}$, is $P' = \{\text{composite numbers}\}$? Explain your answer.

2 Let $U = \{\text{months of the year}\}$. Find the complement of:
 a $M = \{\text{months starting with J}\}$ **b** $A = \{\text{months containing the letter A}\}$.

3 Let $U = \{\text{whole numbers between 10 and 20 inclusive}\}$, $A = \{\text{factors of 120}\}$, and $B = \{\text{multiples of 3}\}$.
List the elements of:
 a A **b** B **c** A' **d** B' **e** $A \cap B$ **f** $A \cup B$
 g $A' \cap B$ **h** $A' \cup B$ **i** $A \cap B'$ **j** $A \cup B'$ **k** $A' \cap B'$ **l** $A' \cup B'$

4 **a** Suppose $U = \{2, 3, 4, 5, 6, 7, 8\}$, $A = \{3, 5, 7\}$, and $B = \{2, 4, 7, 8\}$. Find:
   i $n(U)$ **ii** $n(A)$ **iii** $n(A')$ **iv** $n(B)$ **v** $n(B')$.
 b Copy and complete: For any set S within a universal set U, $n(S) + n(S') = \ldots\ldots$

5 Suppose P and Q' are subsets of U. $n(U) = 15$, $n(P) = 6$, and $n(Q') = 4$. Find:
 a $n(P')$ **b** $n(Q)$.

D   SPECIAL NUMBER SETS

Following is a list of some special number sets you should be familiar with. They are all endless, so they are infinite sets.

- $\mathbb{N} = \{0, 1, 2, 3, 4, 5, 6, 7, ...\}$ is the set of all **natural** or **counting numbers**.

- $\mathbb{Z} = \{0, \pm 1, \pm 2, \pm 3, \pm 4, ...\}$ is the set of all **integers**.

- $\mathbb{Z}^+ = \{1, 2, 3, 4, 5, 6, 7, ...\}$ is the set of all **positive integers**.

- $\mathbb{Q}$ is the set of all **rational numbers**, or numbers which can be written in the form $\frac{p}{q}$ where p and q are integers, $q \neq 0$.

  For example:
  - $\frac{3}{8}$ and $\frac{-7}{5}$ are rational
  - $-3\frac{2}{3}$ is rational as $-3\frac{2}{3} = \frac{-11}{3}$
  - $0.\overline{3}$ is rational as $0.\overline{3} = \frac{3}{9} = \frac{1}{3}$
  - $\sqrt{16}$ is rational as $\sqrt{16} = \frac{4}{1}$
  - All decimal numbers that terminate or recur are rational numbers.

- $\mathbb{Q}'$ is the set of all **irrational numbers**, or numbers which cannot be written in rational form.

  For example: $\sqrt{3}$ and π are irrational.

- $\mathbb{R}$ is the set of all **real numbers**, which are all numbers which can be placed on the number line.

Notice that $\mathbb{R} = \mathbb{Q} \cup \mathbb{Q}'$.

$\frac{1}{0}$ and $\sqrt{-2}$ cannot be placed on a number line, and so are not real.

HISTORICAL NOTE

The $\mathbb{Z}$ used for the set of all integers stands for *zahlen*, which is German for "numbers".

The earliest use of this notation is often attributed to **Nicolas Bourbaki** in the 1930s. Bourbaki was not actually a person, but rather a group of French mathematicians aiming to unify mathematics via set theory.

EXERCISE 2D

1   Copy and complete:

Number	$\mathbb{N}$	$\mathbb{Z}$	$\mathbb{Q}$	$\mathbb{R}$
6	✓	✓	✓	✓
$-\frac{3}{8}$				
1.8				
$1.\overline{8}$				
-17				
$\sqrt{64}$				
$\frac{\pi}{2}$				
$\sqrt{-3}$				
$-\sqrt{3}$				

2   Determine whether each statement is true or false:

a $-7 \in \mathbb{Z}^+$ b $\frac{2}{3} \notin \mathbb{Z}$ c $-\sqrt{4} \in \mathbb{Z}$ d $\sqrt{3} \in \mathbb{Q}$

e $\frac{7}{9} \in \mathbb{Q}$ f $0.201 \in \mathbb{Z}$ g $\frac{7}{0.31} \in \mathbb{Q}$ h $\sqrt{|-1|} \in \mathbb{R}$

3   Determine whether each statement is true or false:

a $\mathbb{Z}^+ \subseteq \mathbb{N}$ b $\mathbb{N} \subset \mathbb{Z}$ c $\mathbb{N} = \mathbb{Z}^+$ d $\mathbb{Z}^- \subseteq \mathbb{Z}$

e $\mathbb{Q} \subset \mathbb{Z}$ f $\{0\} \subseteq \mathbb{Z}$ g $\mathbb{Z} \subseteq \mathbb{Q}$ h $\mathbb{Z}^+ \cup \mathbb{Z}^- = \mathbb{Z}$

4   Describe the following sets as either finite or infinite:

a   the set of integers between 10 and 20

b   the set of integers greater than 5

c   the set of all rational numbers between 0 and 1.

5   If $U = \mathbb{Z}$, find the complement of $\mathbb{Z}^+$.

THEORY OF KNOWLEDGE

A number is *rational* if and only if its decimal expansion eventually terminates or recurs.

Equivalently, a number is *irrational* if and only if its decimal expansion never terminates nor recurs.

If we begin to write the decimal expansion of $\sqrt{2}$, there is no indication that it will terminate or recur, and we might therefore suspect that $\sqrt{2}$ is irrational.

$1.414\,213\,562\,373\,095\,048\,801\,688\,724\,209\,698\,078\,569\,671\,875\,376\,948\,073\,....$

However, we cannot *prove* that $\sqrt{2}$ is irrational by writing out its decimal expansion, as we would have to write an infinite number of decimal places. We might therefore *believe* that $\sqrt{2}$ is irrational, but it may also seem impossible to *prove* it.

1   If something has not yet been proven, does that make it untrue?

2   Is the state of an idea being true or false dependent on our ability to prove it?

In fact, we can prove that $\sqrt{2}$ is irrational using a method called **proof by contradiction**. In this method we suppose that the opposite of what we want to show is true, and follow a series of logical steps until we arrive at a contradiction. The contradiction confirms that our original supposition must be false. Proof by contradiction is an **indirect** proof.

Proof: Suppose $\sqrt{2}$ is rational, so $\sqrt{2} = \dfrac{p}{q}$ for some (positive) integers p and q, $q \neq 0$.

We assume this fraction has been written in lowest terms, so p and q have no common factors.

Squaring both sides, $2 = \dfrac{p^2}{q^2}$

$$\therefore \quad p^2 = 2q^2 \quad \dots (1)$$

$\therefore \quad p^2$ is even, and so p must be even.

$\therefore \quad p = 2k$ for some $k \in \mathbb{Z}^+$.

Substituting into (1), $4k^2 = 2q^2$

$$\therefore \quad q^2 = 2k^2$$

$\therefore \quad q^2$ is even, and so q must be even.

Here we have a contradiction, as p and q have no common factors.

$\therefore \quad$ our original supposition is false, and $\sqrt{2}$ is irrational.

3   Is proof by contradiction unique to mathematics, or do we use it elsewhere?

4   Is it useful to be able to prove something in more than one way?

5   In what other fields of human endeavour is it necessary to establish truth?

E   INTERVAL NOTATION

To describe the set of all integers between -3 and 5, we can list the set as $\{-2,\ -1,\ 0,\ 1,\ 2,\ 3,\ 4\}$ or illustrate the set as points on a number line.

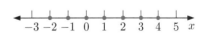

Alternatively, we can write the set using **interval notation** as $\{x \in \mathbb{Z} \mid -3 < x < 5\}$.

the set of all   such that

We read this as "the set of all integers x such that x lies between -3 and 5".

Interval notation is very useful if the set contains a large or infinite number of elements and listing them would be time consuming or impossible.

For example: $\{x \in \mathbb{R} \mid -2 \leqslant x < 4\}$ reads "the set of all real x such that x is greater than or equal to -2 and less than 4".

We represent this set on a number line as:

a filled in circle indicates   an open circle indicates 4
-2 is included   is not included

$$-2 \qquad 0 \qquad\qquad 4 \qquad x$$

We commonly write $\{x \mid -2 \leqslant x < 4\}$ in which case we *assume* that $x \in \mathbb{R}$.

Example 3

Suppose $A = \{x \in \mathbb{Z} \mid 3 < x \leqslant 10\}$.

a Write down the meaning of the interval notation.

b List the elements of set A.   **c** Find $n(A)$.

a The set of all x such that x is an integer between 3 and 10, including 10.

b $A = \{4,\ 5,\ 6,\ 7,\ 8,\ 9,\ 10\}$ **c** $n(A) = 7$

EXERCISE 2E

1 For the following sets:

   i Write down the meaning of the interval notation.

   ii If possible, list the elements of A.   **iii** Find $n(A)$.

   a $A = \{x \in \mathbb{Z} \mid -1 \leqslant x \leqslant 7\}$ **b** $A = \{x \in \mathbb{N} \mid -2 < x < 8\}$

   c $A = \{x \mid 0 \leqslant x \leqslant 1\}$ **d** $A = \{x \in \mathbb{Q} \mid 5 \leqslant x \leqslant 6\}$

2 Represent on a number line:

   a $\{x \in \mathbb{Z}^+ \mid x \leqslant 5\}$ **b** $\{x \in \mathbb{N} \mid x < 5\}$

   c $\{x \in \mathbb{Z} \mid -2 < x < 3\}$ **d** $\{x \in \mathbb{Z}^+ \mid 3 < x \leqslant 7\}$

   e $\{x \in \mathbb{R} \mid x \geqslant 3\}$ **f** $\{x \in \mathbb{R} \mid x < 6\}$

   g $\{x \in \mathbb{R} \mid 2 \leqslant x < 6\}$ **h** $\{x \mid 3.6 \leqslant x \leqslant 10.2\}$

   i $\{x \mid x < 3\} \cup \{x \mid x > 6\}$ **j** $\{x \mid x \leqslant 2\} \cup \{x \mid x > 4\}$

   k $\{x \mid x < 3\} \cup \{x \mid 7 < x < 12\}$ **l** $\{x \in \mathbb{Z}^+ \mid x \leqslant 6\} \cup \{x \in \mathbb{Z}^+ \mid 8 \leqslant x \leqslant 11\}$

3 Write in interval notation:

   a the set of all integers between -100 and 100

   b the set of all real numbers greater than 1000

   c the set of all rational numbers between 2 and 3 inclusive.

4 Write in interval notation:

a

b

c

d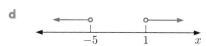

e

f

g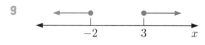

h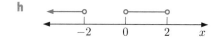

i

5 State whether $A \subseteq B$:

   a $A = \varnothing, \quad B = \{2, 5, 7, 9\}$ **b** $A = \{2, 5, 8, 9\}, \quad B = \{8, 9\}$

   c $A = \{x \in \mathbb{R} \mid 2 \leqslant x \leqslant 3\}, \quad B = \{x \in \mathbb{R}\}$

   d $A = \{x \in \mathbb{Q} \mid 3 \leqslant x \leqslant 9\}, \quad B = \{x \in \mathbb{R} \mid 0 \leqslant x \leqslant 10\}$

   e $A = \{x \in \mathbb{Z} \mid -10 \leqslant x \leqslant 10\}, \quad B = \{z \in \mathbb{Z} \mid 0 \leqslant z \leqslant 5\}$

   f $A = \{x \in \mathbb{Q} \mid 0 \leqslant x \leqslant 1\}, \quad B = \{y \in \mathbb{Q} \mid 0 < y \leqslant 2\}$

Example 4   ◀) Self Tutor

Suppose $U = \{x \in \mathbb{Z} \mid -5 \leqslant x \leqslant 5\}$, $A = \{x \in \mathbb{Z} \mid 1 \leqslant x \leqslant 4\}$, and
$B = \{x \in \mathbb{Z} \mid -3 \leqslant x < 2\}$. List the elements of:

   a A **b** B **c** A' **d** B'

   e $A \cap B$ **f** $A \cup B$ **g** $A' \cap B$ **h** $A' \cup B'$

---

   a $A = \{1, 2, 3, 4\}$ **b** $B = \{-3, -2, -1, 0, 1\}$

   c $A' = \{-5, -4, -3, -2, -1, 0, 5\}$ **d** $B' = \{-5, -4, 2, 3, 4, 5\}$

   e $A \cap B = \{1\}$ **f** $A \cup B = \{-3, -2, -1, 0, 1, 2, 3, 4\}$

   g $A' \cap B = \{-3, -2, -1, 0\}$ **h** $A' \cup B' = \{-5, -4, -3, -2, -1, 0, 2, 3, 4, 5\}$

---

6 Find the complement of C given:

   a $U = \mathbb{Z}$ and $C = \{x \in \mathbb{Z} \mid x \leqslant -5\}$

   b $U = \mathbb{Q}$ and $C = \{x \in \mathbb{Q} \mid x \leqslant 2\} \cup \{x \in \mathbb{Q} \mid x \geqslant 8\}$

7 Suppose $U = \{x \in \mathbb{Z} \mid 0 \leqslant x \leqslant 8\}$, $A = \{x \in \mathbb{Z} \mid 2 \leqslant x \leqslant 7\}$, and
$B = \{x \in \mathbb{Z} \mid 5 \leqslant x \leqslant 8\}$. List the elements of:

   a A **b** A' **c** B **d** B'

   e $A \cap B$ **f** $A \cup B$ **g** $A \cap B'$

Example 5   ◀) Self Tutor

Suppose $U = \mathbb{Z}^+$, $P = \{$multiples of 4 less than 50$\}$, and $Q = \{$multiples of 6 less than 50$\}$.

   a List P and Q.   **b** Find $P \cap Q$.   **c** Find $P \cup Q$.

   d Show that $n(P \cup Q) = n(P) + n(Q) - n(P \cap Q)$.

---

   a $P = \{4, 8, 12, 16, 20, 24, 28, 32, 36, 40, 44, 48\}$

        $Q = \{6, 12, 18, 24, 30, 36, 42, 48\}$

   b $P \cap Q = \{12, 24, 36, 48\}$

   c $P \cup Q = \{4, 6, 8, 12, 16, 18, 20, 24, 28, 30, 32, 36, 40, 42, 44, 48\}$

   d $n(P \cup Q) = 16$ and $n(P) + n(Q) - n(P \cap Q) = 12 + 8 - 4 = 16$

        $\therefore \quad n(P \cup Q) = n(P) + n(Q) - n(P \cap Q)$

8 Suppose $U = \mathbb{Z}^+$, $P = \{x \in \mathbb{Z}^+ \mid 9 \leqslant x < 16\}$, and $Q = \{2, 4, 5, 11, 12, 15\}$.

    a List P.   **b** Find $P \cap Q$.   **c** Find $P \cup Q$.

    d Show that $n(P \cup Q) = n(P) + n(Q) - n(P \cap Q)$.

9 Suppose $U = \{x \in \mathbb{Z} \mid 0 \leqslant x \leqslant 40\}$, $P = \{\text{factors of } 28\}$, and $Q = \{\text{factors of } 40\}$.

    a List P and Q.   **b** Find $P \cap Q$.   **c** Find $P \cup Q$.

    d Show that $n(P \cup Q) = n(P) + n(Q) - n(P \cap Q)$.

10 Suppose $U = \{x \in \mathbb{Z} \mid 30 < x < 60\}$, $M = \{\text{multiples of 4 between 30 and 60}\}$, and $N = \{\text{multiples of 6 between 30 and 60}\}$.

    a List M and N.   **b** Find $M \cap N$.   **c** Find $M \cup N$.

    d Show that $n(M \cup N) = n(M) + n(N) - n(M \cap N)$.

11 Suppose $U = \mathbb{Z}$, $R = \{x \in \mathbb{Z} \mid -2 \leqslant x \leqslant 4\}$, and $S = \{x \in \mathbb{Z} \mid 0 \leqslant x < 7\}$.

    a List R and S.   **b** Find $R \cap S$.   **c** Find $R \cup S$.

    d Show that $n(R \cup S) = n(R) + n(S) - n(R \cap S)$.

12 Suppose $U = \mathbb{Z}$, $C = \{y \in \mathbb{Z} \mid -4 \leqslant y \leqslant -1\}$, and $D = \{y \in \mathbb{Z} \mid -7 \leqslant y < 0\}$.

    a List C and D.   **b** Find $C \cap D$.   **c** Find $C \cup D$.

    d Show that $n(C \cup D) = n(C) + n(D) - n(C \cap D)$.

13 Suppose $U = \mathbb{Z}^+$, $P = \{x \in \mathbb{Z} \mid 5 \leqslant x \leqslant 17\}$, $Q = \{x \in \mathbb{Z} \mid 10 \leqslant x \leqslant 20\}$, and $R = \{x \in \mathbb{Z} \mid 15 \leqslant x \leqslant 23\}$.

    a List the sets P, Q, and R.

    b Find: **i** $P \cap Q$ **ii** $P \cap R$ **iii** $Q \cap R$

                 iv $P \cup Q$ **v** $P \cup R$ **vi** $Q \cup R$

    c Find: **i** $P \cap Q \cap R$ **ii** $P \cup Q \cup R$

14 Suppose $U = \{x \in \mathbb{Z}^+ \mid x < 40\}$, $A = \{\text{multiples of 4 less than 40}\}$, $B = \{\text{multiples of 6 less than 40}\}$, and $C = \{\text{multiples of 12 less than 40}\}$.

    a List the sets A, B, and C.

    b Find: **i** $A \cap B$ **ii** $B \cap C$ **iii** $A \cap C$

                 iv $A \cap B \cap C$ **v** $A \cup B \cup C$

    c Show that
$$n(A \cup B \cup C) = n(A) + n(B) + n(C) - n(A \cap B) - n(B \cap C) - n(A \cap C) + n(A \cap B \cap C).$$

15 Suppose $U = \{x \in \mathbb{Z}^+ \mid x < 31\}$, $A = \{\text{multiples of 6 less than 31}\}$, $B = \{\text{factors of 30}\}$, and $C = \{\text{primes} < 30\}$.

    a List the sets A, B, and C.

    b Find: **i** $A \cap B$ **ii** $B \cap C$ **iii** $A \cap C$

                 iv $A \cap B \cap C$ **v** $A \cup B \cup C$

    c Show that
$$n(A \cup B \cup C) = n(A) + n(B) + n(C) - n(A \cap B) - n(B \cap C) - n(A \cap C) + n(A \cap B \cap C).$$

VENN DIAGRAMS

A **Venn diagram** consists of a universal set U represented by a rectangle, and subsets within it that are generally represented by circles.

The Venn diagram alongside shows set A within the universal set U.

The **complement** of A is the shaded region outside the circle.

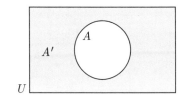

SUBSETS

If $B \subseteq A$ then every element of B is also in A.

The circle representing B is placed within the circle representing A.

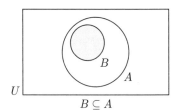

$B \subseteq A$

INTERSECTING SETS

For two sets A and B which have some elements in common, but where neither is a subset of the other, we draw the circles overlapping.

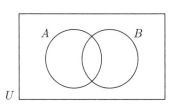

The **intersection** $A \cap B$ consists of all elements common to both A and B.

It is the region where the circles overlap.

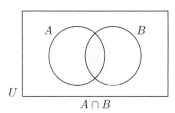

$A \cap B$

The **union** $A \cup B$ consists of all elements in A or B or both.

It is the region which includes the two circles.

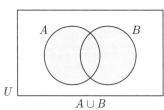

$A \cup B$

DISJOINT OR MUTUALLY EXCLUSIVE SETS

Disjoint sets do not have common elements.

They are represented by non-overlapping circles.

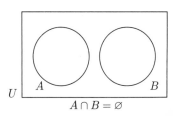

$A \cap B = \varnothing$

Example 6   ◀)) **Self Tutor**

Suppose $U = \{1, 2, 3, 4, 5, 6, 7, 8\}$. Illustrate on a Venn diagram the sets:

a $A = \{1, 3, 6, 8\}$ and $B = \{2, 3, 4, 5, 8\}$

b $A = \{1, 3, 6, 7, 8\}$ and $B = \{3, 6, 8\}$

c $A = \{2, 4, 8\}$ and $B = \{1, 3, 5\}$.

a $A \cap B = \{3, 8\}$

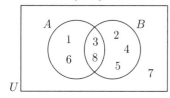

b $A \cap B = \{3, 6, 8\} = B$ and $B \neq A$, so $B \subset A$.

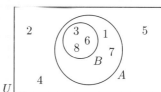

c $A \cap B = \varnothing$

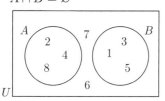

EXERCISE 2F

1 Represent sets A and B on a Venn diagram, given:

 a $U = \{2, 3, 4, 5, 6, 7\}$, $A = \{2, 4, 6\}$, and $B = \{5, 7\}$

 b $U = \{2, 3, 5, 7, 11, 13\}$, $A = \{2, 3, 7\}$, and $B = \{3, 5, 11\}$

 c $U = \{1, 2, 3, 4, 5, 6, 7\}$, $A = \{2, 4, 5, 6\}$, and $B = \{1, 4, 6, 7\}$

 d $U = \{1, 3, 4, 5, 7\}$, $A = \{3, 4, 5, 7\}$, and $B = \{3, 5\}$

2 Suppose $U = \{x \in \mathbb{Z} \mid 1 \leqslant x \leqslant 10\}$, $A = \{\text{odd numbers} < 10\}$, and $B = \{\text{primes} < 10\}$.

 a List sets A and B.   **b** Find $A \cap B$ and $A \cup B$.

 c Represent the sets A and B on a Venn diagram.

3 Suppose $U = \{x \in \mathbb{Z} \mid 1 \leqslant x \leqslant 9\}$, $A = \{\text{factors of 6}\}$, and $B = \{\text{factors of 9}\}$.

 a List sets A and B.   **b** Find $A \cap B$ and $A \cup B$.

 c Represent the sets A and B on a Venn diagram.

4 Suppose $U = \{\text{even numbers between 0 and 30}\}$, $P = \{\text{multiples of 4 less than 30}\}$,   and $Q = \{\text{multiples of 6 less than 30}\}$.

 a List sets P and Q.   **b** Find $P \cap Q$ and $P \cup Q$.

 c Represent the sets P and Q on a Venn diagram.

5 Suppose $U = \{x \in \mathbb{Z}^{+} \mid x \leqslant 30\}$, $R = \{\text{primes less than 30}\}$,   and $S = \{\text{composites less than 30}\}$.

 a List sets R and S.   **b** Find $R \cap S$ and $R \cup S$.

 c Represent the sets R and S on a Venn diagram.

6 Suppose $U = \mathbb{R}$.

Copy the Venn diagram and label the sets $\mathbb{Q}$, $\mathbb{Z}$, and $\mathbb{N}$.

Shade the region representing $\mathbb{Q}'$.

Place these numbers on the Venn diagram: $7, \frac{1}{5}, 2.\overline{8}, -\pi,$ $0, \sqrt{7}, -2, -0.35$.

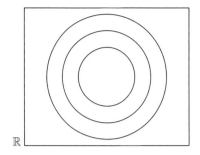

7 Display on a Venn diagram:

  a $U = \{$parallelograms$\}$, $R = \{$rectangles$\}$, $S = \{$squares$\}$

  b $U = \{$polygons$\}$, $Q = \{$quadrilaterals$\}$, $T = \{$triangles$\}$.

8

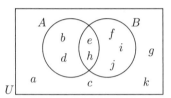

List the elements of set:

  a A **b** B **c** A'

  d B' **e** $A \cap B$ **f** $A \cup B$

  g $(A \cup B)'$ **h** $A' \cap B'$ **i** $A' \cup B'$

9 This Venn diagram consists of three overlapping circles A, B, and C.

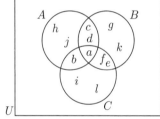

  a List the letters in set:

    i A **ii** B **iii** C

    iv $A \cap B$ **v** $A \cup B$ **vi** $B \cap C$

    vii $A \cap B \cap C$ **viii** $A \cup B \cup C$

  b Show that
$$n(A \cup B \cup C) = n(A) + n(B) + n(C) - n(A \cap B) - n(A \cap C) - n(B \cap C) + n(A \cap B \cap C).$$

10 Suppose $U = \{x \in \mathbb{Z}^+ \mid 40 \leqslant x \leqslant 60\}$,

$A = \{$multiples of $2\}$, $B = \{$multiples of $3\}$, and

$C = \{$multiples of $5\}$.

Display the elements of these sets using a Venn diagram.

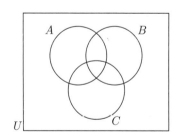

11

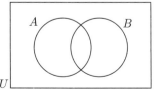

On separate Venn diagrams, shade regions for:

  a A **b** A'

  c $A \cap B$ **d** $A \cap B'$

  e $A' \cup B$ **f** $A \cup B'$

  g $(A \cap B)'$ **h** $(A \cup B)'$

PRINTABLE VENN DIAGRAMS (OVERLAPPING)

12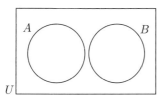

Suppose A and B are two disjoint sets. Shade on separate Venn diagrams:

PRINTABLE
VENN DIAGRAMS
(DISJOINT)

   a A **b** B **c** A'

   d B' **e** $A \cap B$ **f** $A \cup B$

   g $A' \cap B$ **h** $A \cup B'$ **i** $(A \cap B)'$

13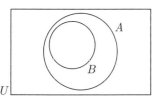

Suppose $B \subseteq A$. Shade on separate Venn diagrams:

PRINTABLE
VENN DIAGRAMS
(SUBSET)

   a A **b** B **c** A'

   d B' **e** $A \cap B$ **f** $A \cup B$

   g $A' \cap B$ **h** $A \cup B'$ **i** $(A \cap B)'$

14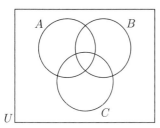

This Venn diagram consists of three intersecting sets. Shade on separate Venn diagrams:

PRINTABLE
VENN DIAGRAMS
(3 SETS)

   a A **b** B'

   c $B \cap C$ **d** $A \cup B$

   e $A \cap B \cap C$ **f** $A \cup B \cup C$

   g $(A \cap B \cap C)'$ **h** $(A \cup B) \cap C$

   i $(B \cap C) \cup A$ **j** $A' \cap (B \cup C)$

Click on the icon to practise shading regions representing various subsets. You can practise with both two and three intersecting sets.

VENN
DIAGRAMS

G   VENN DIAGRAM REGIONS

We have seen that there are four distinct regions on a Venn diagram which contains two intersecting sets A and B.

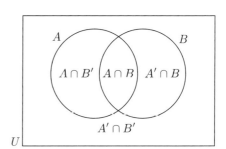

There are many situations where we are only interested in the **number of elements** of U that are in each region. We do not need to show all the elements on the diagram, so instead we write the number of elements in each region in brackets.

For example, the Venn diagram opposite shows there are 4 elements in both sets A and B, and 3 elements in neither set A nor B.

Every element in U belongs in only one region of the Venn diagram. So, in total there are $7 + 4 + 6 + 3 = 20$ elements in the universal set U.

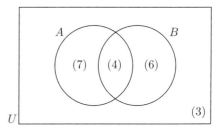

Example 7 **Self Tutor**

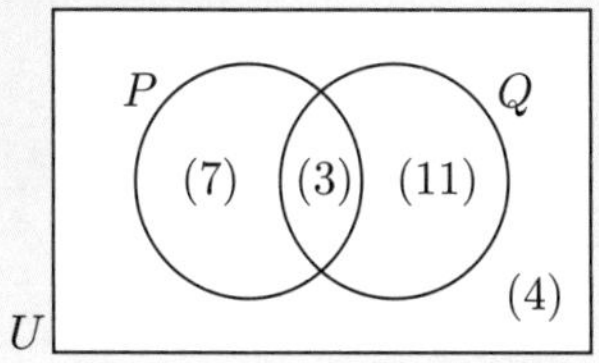

Use the Venn diagram to find the number of elements in:

a P **b** Q'
c $P \cup Q$ **d** P, but not Q
e Q, but not P **f** neither P nor Q.

a $n(P) = 7 + 3 = 10$ **b** $n(Q') = 7 + 4 = 11$
c $n(P \cup Q) = 7 + 3 + 11 = 21$ **d** $n(P\text{, but not }Q) = 7$
e $n(Q\text{, but not }P) = 11$ **f** $n(\text{neither }P\text{ nor }Q) = 4$

EXERCISE 2G

1

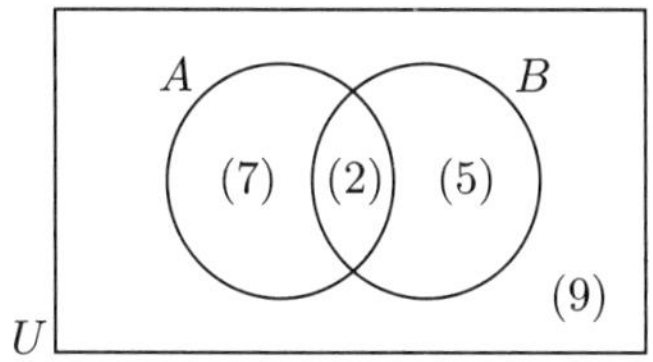

Use the Venn diagram to find the number of elements in:

a B **b** A'
c $A \cup B$ **d** A, but not B
e B, but not A **f** neither A nor B.

2

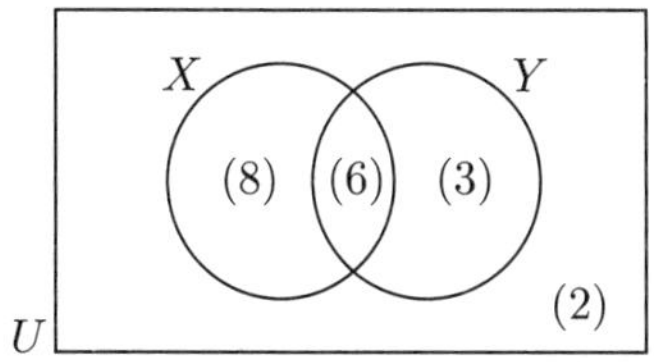

Find the number of elements in:

a X' **b** $X \cap Y$
c $X \cup Y$ **d** X, but not Y
e Y, but not X **f** neither X nor Y.

3

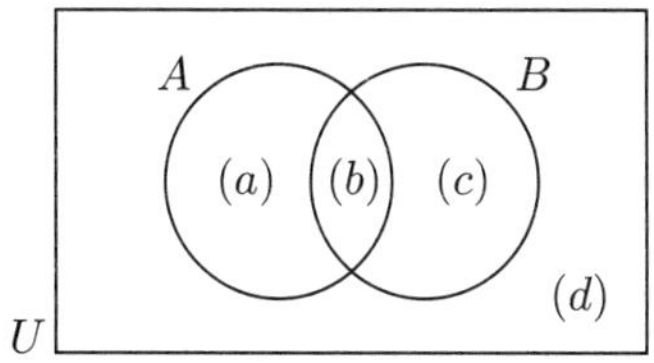

Use the Venn diagram to find:

a $n(B)$ **b** $n(A')$ **c** $n(A \cap B)$
d $n(A \cup B)$ **e** $n((A \cap B)')$ **f** $n((A \cup B)')$

4

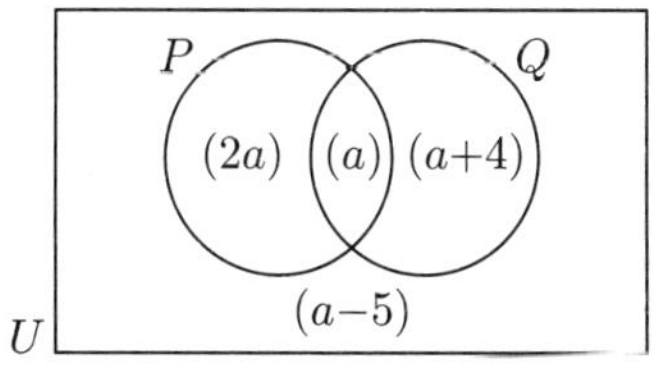

a Use the Venn diagram to find:
  i $n(P \cap Q)$ **ii** $n(P)$
  iii $n(Q)$ **iv** $n(P \cup Q)$
  v $n(Q')$ **vi** $n(U)$

b Find the value of a if:
  i $n(U) = 29$ **ii** $n(U) = 31$
  Comment on your results.

5

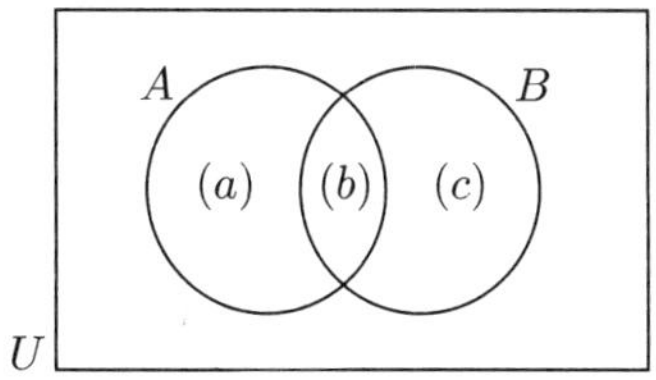

Use the Venn diagram to show that:

a $n(A \cup B) = n(A) + n(B) - n(A \cap B)$
b $n(A \cap B') = n(A) - n(A \cap B)$

6 Suppose A and B are disjoint sets. Use a Venn diagram to show that $n(A \cup B) = n(A) + n(B)$.

Example 8   ◀) **Self Tutor**

Given $n(U) = 30$, $n(A) = 14$, $n(B) = 17$, and $n(A \cap B) = 6$, find:

   a $n(A \cup B)$ **b** $n(A$, but not $B)$

We are given $n(A \cap B) = 6$

$\therefore$ $n(A \cap B') = 14 - 6 = 8$

and $n(A' \cap B) = 17 - 6 = 11$

$\therefore$ $n(A' \cap B') = 30 - 6 - 8 - 11 = 5$

  a $n(A \cup B) = 8 + 6 + 11 = 25$

  b $n(A \cap B') = 8$

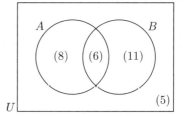

7 Given $n(U) = 26$, $n(A) = 11$, $n(B) = 12$, and $n(A \cap B) = 8$, find:

   a $n(A \cup B)$ **b** $n(B$, but not $A)$

8 Given $n(U) = 32$, $n(M) = 13$, $n(M \cap N) = 5$, and $n(M \cup N) = 26$, find:

   a $n(N)$ **b** $n((M \cup N)')$

9 Given $n(U) = 50$, $n(S) = 30$, $n(R) = 25$, and $n(R \cup S) = 48$, find:

   a $n(R \cap S)$ **b** $n(S$, but not $R)$

H PROBLEM SOLVING WITH VENN DIAGRAMS

When we solve problems with Venn diagrams, we are generally only interested in the number of individuals in each region, rather than where a particular individual is placed.

Example 9   ◀) **Self Tutor**

A squash club has 27 members. 19 have black hair, 14 have brown eyes, and 11 have both black hair and brown eyes.

  a Place this information on a Venn diagram.

  b Hence find the number of members with:

    i black hair or brown eyes

    ii black hair, but not brown eyes.

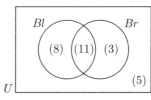

  a Let Bl represent those with black hair and Br represent those with brown eyes.

$n(Bl \cap Br) = 11$

$\therefore$ $n(Bl \cap Br') = 19 - 11 = 8$

and $n(Bl' \cap Br) = 14 - 11 = 3$

$\therefore$ $n(Bl' \cap Br') = 27 - 11 - 8 - 3 = 5$

  b **i** $n(Bl \cup Br) = 8 + 11 + 3 = 22$

         22 members have black hair or brown eyes.

    ii $n(Bl \cap Br') = 8$

         8 members have black hair, but not brown eyes.

EXERCISE 2H

1 Pelé has 14 cavies as pets. Five have long hair and eight are brown. Two are both brown and have long hair.

   a Place this information on a Venn diagram.

   b Hence find the number of cavies that:

     i do not have long hair

     ii have long hair and are not brown

     iii are neither long-haired nor brown.

2 During a 2 week period, Murielle took her umbrella with her on 8 days. It rained on 9 days, and Murielle took her umbrella on five of the days when it rained.

   a Display this information on a Venn diagram.

   b Hence find the number of days that:

     i Murielle did not take her umbrella and it rained

     ii Murielle did not take her umbrella and it did not rain.

Example 10   ◄ **Self Tutor**

A platform diving squad of 25 has 18 members who dive from 10 m, and 17 who dive from 4 m. How many dive from both platforms?

Let T represent those who dive from 10 m and
     F represent those who dive from 4 m.

Let $n(T \cap F) = x$

$\therefore \; n(T \cap F') = 18 - x$ and $n(T' \cap F) = 17 - x$

$n(T' \cap F') = 0$ since every diver in the squad must dive from at least one platform.

But $n(U) = 25$,   so $(18 - x) + x + (17 - x) = 25$

$$\therefore \; 35 - x = 25$$

$$\therefore \; x = 10$$

10 members dive from both platforms.

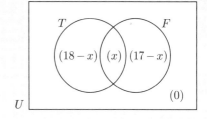

---

3 A badminton club has 31 playing members. 28 play singles and 16 play doubles. How many play both singles and doubles?

4 In a factory, 56 people work on the assembly line. 47 work day shifts and 29 work night shifts. How many work both day shifts and night shifts?

5 There are 38 stalls in a marketplace. 21 stalls sell food, 14 stalls sell craft, and 7 stalls sell neither food nor craft. Find the number of stalls which sell:

   a both food and craft   **b** food or craft but not both.

6 From the selection of 86 movies on a plane, Sandra has seen 13 and Robert has seen 14. 69 of the movies have been seen by neither. Find the number of movies seen by:

   a both Sandra and Robert   **b** Robert but not Sandra.

Example 11   ◀》 **Self Tutor**

The students at a school in Delhi were asked what modes of transportation they had used to travel to school in the past week. 46% had caught a bus, 37% had caught a train, and 31% had been driven in a car. 13% had caught a bus and a train, 5% had caught a bus and been driven in a car, and 9% had caught a train and been driven in a car. 11% of students used none of these modes of transport.

Find the percentage of students who used all three modes of transport.

Let B, T, and C represent the students taking a bus, train, and car respectively.

Let $n(B \cap T \cap C) = x$
∴ $n(B \cap T \cap C') = 13 - x$,
    $n(B \cap T' \cap C) = 5 - x$,
and $n(B' \cap T \cap C) = 9 - x$.

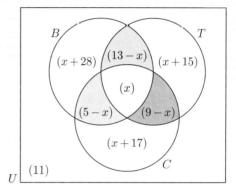

Now $n(B) = 46$, so $n(B \cap T' \cap C') = 46 - x - (13 - x) - (5 - x) = x + 28$
      $n(T) = 37$, so $n(B' \cap T \cap C') = 37 - x - (13 - x) - (9 - x) = x + 15$
and $n(C) = 31$, so $n(B' \cap T' \cap C) = 31 - x - (5 - x) - (9 - x) = x + 17$

∴ $(x + 28) + (13 - x) + x + (5 - x) + (x + 15) + (9 - x) + (x + 17) + 11 = 100$
                                                                          ∴ $x + 98 = 100$
                                                                          ∴ $x = 2$

2% of students used all three modes of transport.

---

7   In a year group of 63 students, 22 study Biology, 26 study Chemistry, and 25 study Physics. 18 study both Physics and Chemistry, 4 study both Biology and Chemistry, and 3 study both Physics and Biology. 1 student studies all three subjects.

   a   Display this information on a Venn diagram.

   b   How many students study:

      i   Biology only   **ii**   Physics or Chemistry

      iii   none of Biology, Physics, or Chemistry   **iv**   Physics but not Chemistry?

8   36 students participated in the mid-year adventure trip. 19 students went paragliding, 21 went abseiling, and 16 went white water rafting. 7 went abseiling and rafting, 8 went paragliding and rafting, and 11 went paragliding and abseiling. 5 students did all three activities. Find the number of students who:

   a   went paragliding or abseiling

   b   only went white water rafting

   c   did not participate in any of the activities mentioned

   d   did exactly two of the activities mentioned.

9 There are 29 students in the woodwind section of the school orchestra. 11 students can play the flute, 15 can play the clarinet, and 12 can play the saxophone. 4 can play the flute and the saxophone, 4 can play the flute and the clarinet, and 6 can play the clarinet and the saxophone. 3 students can play none of the three instruments.

   a Display the information on a Venn diagram.

   b Hence find the number of students in the woodwind section who can play:

   i all of the instruments mentioned   **ii** only the saxophone

   iii the saxophone and the clarinet, but not the flute

   iv exactly one of the clarinet, saxophone, or flute.

10 In a particular region, most farms have livestock and crops. A survey of 21 farms showed that 15 grow crops, 9 have cattle, and 11 have sheep. 4 have sheep and cattle, 7 have cattle and crops, and 8 have sheep and crops. 2 have neither animals nor crops.

   a Display the information on a Venn diagram.

   b Hence find the number of farms with:

   i only crops   **ii** only animals   **iii** exactly one type of animal, and crops.

11 A survey is conducted regarding the types of cardio equipment used by the 300 members of a fitness club.

   134 members use rowers (R), 92 use treadmills (T), and 144 use spin-bikes (S).

   23 members use rowers and treadmills only.

   28 members use treadmills and spin-bikes only.

   41 members use spin-bikes and rowers only.

   60 members do not use any type of cardio equipment.

   a Display the information on a Venn diagram.

   b Determine the number of fitness club members who:

   i use all three types of cardio equipment

   ii use exactly two of the three types of cardio equipment.

   c What percentage of the fitness club members use rowers, but do not use treadmills?

12 Answer the **Opening Problem** parts **a** to **c** on page **40**. Discuss part **d** with your class.

REVIEW SET 2A

1 Let A be the set of letters in the word VENN and B be the set of letters in the word DIAGRAM.

   a List the elements of A and B.

   b Find $n(A)$ and $n(B)$.

   c Find $A \cap B$ and comment on your answer.

   d Decide whether the statement is true or false:

   i $V \notin A$ **ii** $G \in B$ **iii** $n(A \cup B) = n(A) + n(B)$

2 If $U = \{\text{multiples of 6 less than 70}\}$ and $A = \{6, 6^2, 66\}$, find A'.

3 Decide whether each statement is true or false:

   a $\mathbb{N} \subset \mathbb{Q}$ **b** $0 \in \mathbb{Z}^+$ **c** $0 \in \mathbb{Q}$ **d** $\mathbb{R} \subseteq \mathbb{Q}$

4 Represent on a number line:

   a $\{x \in \mathbb{N} \mid x \leqslant 6\}$ **b** $\{x \in \mathbb{R} \mid -3 \leqslant x < 2\}$ **c** $\{x \mid 0 \leqslant x \leqslant 4\} \cup \{x \mid x \geqslant 10\}$

5 Let $U = \{x \in \mathbb{Z}^+ \mid x \leqslant 30\}$, $P = \{$factors of 24$\}$, and $Q = \{$factors of 30$\}$.

    a List the elements of:

        i P **ii** Q **iii** $P \cap Q$ **iv** $P \cup Q$

    b Show that $n(P \cup Q) = n(P) + n(Q) - n(P \cap Q)$.

6 Let $U = \{$the letters in the English alphabet$\}$, $A = \{$the letters in "springbok"$\}$, and $B = \{$the letters in "waterbuck"$\}$.

    a Describe each of these sets, and list their elements:

        i $A \cup B$ **ii** $A \cap B$ **iii** $A \cap B'$

    b Show U, A, and B on a Venn diagram.

7 On separate Venn diagrams like the one alongside, shade:

    a N' **b** $M \cap N$ **c** $M \cap N'$

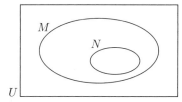

8

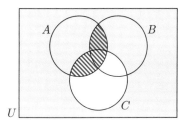

Write an expression for the region shaded in:

    a blue   **b** red.

9 Consider the sets $U = \{x \in \mathbb{Z}^+, \; x \leqslant 10\}$, $P = \{$odd numbers less than 10$\}$, and $Q = \{$even numbers less than 11$\}$.

    a List the sets P and Q.

    b What can be said about sets P and Q?

    c Illustrate sets P and Q on a Venn diagram.

10 The racquet sports offered at a local club are tennis (T), badminton (B), and squash (S). The Venn diagram shows the number of members involved in these activities. All of the members play at least one racquet sport.

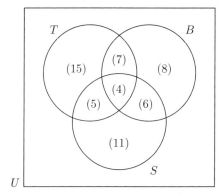

    a Write down the number of members in the club.

    b Write down the number of members who:

        i only play badminton

        ii do not play tennis

        iii play both tennis and squash, but not badminton.

    c Copy the diagram above, and shade the region that represents $S \cap (T \cup B)$.

    d Write down the number of members in $S \cap (T \cup B)'$.

11 A school has 564 students. During Term 1, 229 of them were absent for at least one day due to sickness, and 111 students missed some school because of family holidays. 296 students attended every day of Term 1.

    a Display this information on a Venn diagram.

    b Find how many students:

        i missed school for both illness and holidays

        ii were away for holidays but not sickness

        iii were absent during Term 1 for any reason.

12 The main courses at a restaurant all contain rice or onion. Of the 23 choices, 17 contain onion and 14 contain rice. How many dishes contain both rice and onion?

13 38 students were asked what life skills they had. 15 could swim, 12 could drive, and 23 could cook. 9 could cook and swim, 5 could swim and drive, and 6 could drive and cook. There was 1 student who could do all three. Find the number of students who:

    a could only cook   **b** could not do any of these things

    c had exactly two of these life skills.

REVIEW SET 2B

1 List the subsets of $\{1, 3, 5\}$.

2 S and T are disjoint sets. $n(S) = s$ and $n(T) = t$. Find: **a** $S \cap T$ **b** $n(S \cup T)$

3 Write in interval notation:

    a the real numbers between 5 and 12

    b the integers between -4 and 7, including -4

    c the natural numbers greater than 45.

State whether each set is finite or infinite.

4 Write in interval notation:

    a 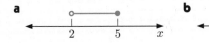   **b**    **c**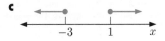

5 Let $S = \{x \in \mathbb{Z} \mid 2 < x \leqslant 7\}$.

    a List the elements of S.   **b** Display S on a number line.   **c** Find $n(S)$.

6 Determine whether $A \subseteq B$:

    a $A = \{2, 4, 6, 8\}$ and $B = \{x \in \mathbb{Z} \mid 0 < x < 10\}$

    b $A = \varnothing$ and $B = \{x \mid 2 < x < 3\}$

    c $A = \{x \in \mathbb{Q} \mid 2 < x \leqslant 4\}$ and $B = \{x \in \mathbb{R} \mid 0 \leqslant x < 4\}$

    d $A = \{x \mid x < 3\}$ and $B = \{x \mid x \leqslant 4\}$

7 Find the complement of X given that:

    a $U = \{$the 7 colours of the rainbow$\}$ and $X = \{$red, indigo, violet$\}$

    b $U = \{x \in \mathbb{Z} \mid -5 \leqslant x \leqslant 5\}$ and $X = \{-4, -1, 3, 4\}$

    c $U = \{x \in \mathbb{Q}\}$ and $X = \{x \in \mathbb{Q} \mid x < -8\}$

8 Let $U = \{x \in \mathbb{Z} \mid 0 < x < 10\}$, $A = \{$the even integers between 0 and 9$\}$, and
 $B = \{$the factors of 8$\}$.

   a List the elements of: **i** A **ii** $A \cap B$ **iii** $(A \cup B)'$

   b Represent this information on a Venn diagram.

9 Consider the sets $U = \{x \in \mathbb{Z}^+ \mid x \leqslant 40\}$, $A = \{$factors of 40$\}$, and $B = \{$factors of 20$\}$.

   a List the sets A and B.   **b** What can be said about sets A and B?

   c Illustrate sets A and B on a Venn diagram.

10 Consider $P = \{x \in \mathbb{Z} \mid 3 \leqslant x < 10\}$, $Q = \{2, 9, 15\}$, and
  $R = \{$multiples of 3 less than 12$\}$.

   a List the elements of P.   **b** Write down $n(P)$.

   c State whether P is finite or infinite.

   d Explain why: **i** $Q \not\subset P$ **ii** $R \subset P$

   e List the elements of: **i** $P \cap Q$ **ii** $R \cap Q$ **iii** $R \cup Q$

11 On Venn diagrams like the one shown, shade
the regions which are described by:

   a $(A \cup B)' \cap C$

   b $C' \cap B$

   c $B' \cap (A \cap C)$.

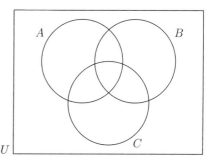

12 In a car club, 13 members drive a manual car and 15 members have a car with a sunroof. 5 have
manual cars with a sunroof, and 4 have neither.

   a Display this information on a Venn diagram.

   b How many members:

     i are in the club   **ii** drive a manual car without a sunroof

     iii do not drive a manual car?

13 All of the 30 students on a camp left something at home. 11 forgot to bring their towel.
23 forgot their hat. How many had neither a hat nor a towel?

14 At a conference, the 58 delegates speak many different
languages. 28 speak Arabic, 27 speak Chinese, and
39 speak English. 12 speak Arabic and Chinese, 16
speak both Chinese and English, and 17 speak Arabic
and English. 2 speak all three languages. How many
delegates speak:

   a Chinese only

   b none of these languages

   c neither Arabic nor Chinese?

Chapter 3

Surds and exponents

Contents:

OPENING PROBLEM

Sir Joseph John Thomson (1856 - 1940) won the Nobel Prize in Physics in 1906 for his experiments in the conduction of electricity through gases. He is also credited with the discovery of the first subatomic particle.

The table below shows the mass and electric charge for the three subatomic particles which, for many decades, were thought to be the smallest parts of an atom.

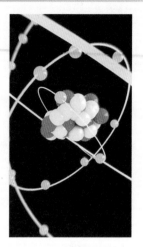

Particle	Mass (kg)	Charge (coulombs)
electron	$9.109\,383\,56 \times 10^{-31}$	$-1.602\,176\,620\,8 \times 10^{-19}$
proton	$1.672\,621\,898 \times 10^{-27}$	$+1.602\,176\,620\,8 \times 10^{-19}$
neutron	$1.674\,927\,471 \times 10^{-27}$	0

Things to think about:

a Most of the numbers in the table are written in a form involving a power of 10. Why would we choose to write numbers in this form?

b How many times more massive is:

   i a neutron than an electron   **ii** a proton than an electron

   iii a neutron than a proton?

c An atom of silver has 47 protons, has no charge, and has mass $1.791\,193\,4 \times 10^{-25}$ kg. Find how many electrons and neutrons it has.

d A large bolt of lightning transfers 350 coulombs of charge. How many electrons does it transfer?

In this Chapter we consider **surds** and **radicals**, and see how they relate to **exponents**. We will review the **laws of exponents** and apply them in algebra and to very large and very small numbers.

SURDS AND OTHER RADICALS

A **radical** is any number which is written with the **radical sign** $\sqrt{}$.

A **surd** is a real, irrational radical.

For example:
- $\sqrt{2}$, $\sqrt{3}$, $\sqrt{5}$, and $\sqrt{6}$ are surds.
- $\sqrt{4}$ is a radical but not a surd, since $\sqrt{4} = 2$.
- $\sqrt{\frac{1}{4}}$ is a radical but not a surd, since $\sqrt{\frac{1}{4}} = \frac{1}{2}$.

By definition, $\sqrt{a}$ is the non-negative number such that $\sqrt{a} \times \sqrt{a} = a$.

Notice that:
- $\sqrt{a}$ is never negative, so $\sqrt{a} \geqslant 0$.
- $\sqrt{a}$ is only real if $a \geqslant 0$.

INVESTIGATION   PROPERTIES OF RADICALS

What to do:

1 **a** Discuss each step of this argument with your class to make sure you are convinced it is valid:

$$(\sqrt{2 \times 3})^2 = 2 \times 3 \qquad \{\text{definition of square root}\}$$
$$= (\sqrt{2} \times \sqrt{2}) \times (\sqrt{3} \times \sqrt{3}) \qquad \{\text{definition of square root}\}$$
$$= (\sqrt{2} \times \sqrt{3}) \times (\sqrt{2} \times \sqrt{3}) \qquad \{\text{changing order of multiplication}\}$$
$$= (\sqrt{2} \times \sqrt{3})^2 \qquad \{\text{definition of perfect square}\}$$

$\therefore$ since square roots are non-negative, $\sqrt{2 \times 3} = \sqrt{2} \times \sqrt{3}$.

b Use the same argument to write a direct proof that $\sqrt{a \times b} = \sqrt{a} \times \sqrt{b}$ for any $a \geqslant 0$, $b \geqslant 0$.

2 **a** Discuss each step of this argument with your class to make sure you are convinced it is valid.

$$\left(\sqrt{\frac{2}{3}}\right)^2 = \frac{2}{3} \qquad \{\text{definition of square root}\}$$

$$= \frac{\sqrt{2} \times \sqrt{2}}{\sqrt{3} \times \sqrt{3}} \qquad \{\text{definition of square root}\}$$

$$= \frac{\sqrt{2}}{\sqrt{3}} \times \frac{\sqrt{2}}{\sqrt{3}} \qquad \{\text{multiplication of fractions}\}$$

$$= \left(\frac{\sqrt{2}}{\sqrt{3}}\right)^2$$

$\therefore$ since square roots are non-negative, $\sqrt{\dfrac{2}{3}} = \dfrac{\sqrt{2}}{\sqrt{3}}$.

b Use the same argument to write a direct proof that $\sqrt{\dfrac{a}{b}} = \dfrac{\sqrt{a}}{\sqrt{b}}$ for any $a \geqslant 0$, $b > 0$.

In the **Investigation** you should have proven that:

- $\sqrt{ab} = \sqrt{a} \times \sqrt{b}$ for $a \geqslant 0$ and $b \geqslant 0$.

- $\sqrt{\dfrac{a}{b}} = \dfrac{\sqrt{a}}{\sqrt{b}}$ for $a \geqslant 0$ and $b > 0$.

Example 1	◀) Self Tutor

Write as a single surd: **a** $\sqrt{2} \times \sqrt{3}$ **b** $\dfrac{\sqrt{18}}{\sqrt{6}}$

a $\sqrt{2} \times \sqrt{3}$
$= \sqrt{2 \times 3}$
$= \sqrt{6}$

b $\dfrac{\sqrt{18}}{\sqrt{6}}$
$= \sqrt{\dfrac{18}{6}}$
$= \sqrt{3}$

SIMPLEST FORM

A radical is in **simplest form** when the number under the radical sign is the smallest possible integer.

Example 2   ◀)) **Self Tutor**

Write $\sqrt{72}$ in simplest form.

$$\sqrt{72}$$
$$= \sqrt{36 \times 2} \qquad \{36 \text{ is the largest perfect square factor of } 72\}$$
$$= \sqrt{36} \times \sqrt{2}$$
$$= 6\sqrt{2}$$

EXERCISE 3A

1   Write as a single surd or rational number:

    a $\sqrt{11} \times \sqrt{11}$ **b** $\sqrt{3} \times \sqrt{5}$ **c** $(\sqrt{3})^2$ **d** $\sqrt{5} \times \sqrt{6}$

    e $\sqrt{2} \times \sqrt{6}$ **f** $2\sqrt{2} \times \sqrt{2}$ **g** $3\sqrt{2} \times 2\sqrt{2}$ **h** $3\sqrt{7} \times 2\sqrt{7}$

    i $(3\sqrt{5})^2$ **j** $3\sqrt{2} \times \sqrt{5}$ **k** $-2\sqrt{3} \times 3\sqrt{5}$ **l** $2\sqrt{6} \times \sqrt{12}$

2   Write as a single surd or rational number:

    a $\dfrac{\sqrt{12}}{\sqrt{2}}$ **b** $\dfrac{\sqrt{18}}{\sqrt{3}}$ **c** $\dfrac{\sqrt{20}}{\sqrt{5}}$ **d** $\dfrac{\sqrt{3}}{\sqrt{12}}$

    e $\dfrac{\sqrt{6}}{\sqrt{18}}$ **f** $\dfrac{\sqrt{6} \times \sqrt{10}}{\sqrt{12}}$ **g** $\dfrac{\sqrt{3}}{\sqrt{6} \times \sqrt{8}}$ **h** $\dfrac{\sqrt{5}}{2\sqrt{10} \times \sqrt{2}}$

3   Write in simplest form:

    a $\sqrt{8}$ **b** $\sqrt{12}$ **c** $\sqrt{20}$ **d** $\sqrt{32}$

    e $\sqrt{27}$ **f** $\sqrt{45}$ **g** $\sqrt{48}$ **h** $\sqrt{54}$

    i $\sqrt{50}$ **j** $\sqrt{80}$ **k** $\sqrt{96}$ **l** $\sqrt{108}$

4   Show that $\dfrac{\sqrt{125}}{\sqrt{5}} = 5$:

    a using the rule $\dfrac{\sqrt{a}}{\sqrt{b}} = \sqrt{\dfrac{a}{b}}$ **b** by first writing $\sqrt{125}$ in simplest form.

Example 3   ◀)) **Self Tutor**

Simplify:

    a $3\sqrt{3} + 5\sqrt{3}$ **b** $2\sqrt{2} - 5\sqrt{2}$

    a $\quad 3\sqrt{3} + 5\sqrt{3}$ **b** $\quad 2\sqrt{2} - 5\sqrt{2}$

        $= 8\sqrt{3}$ $= -3\sqrt{2}$

In **b**, compare with
$2x - 5x = -3x$

5 Simplify:

    a $2\sqrt{2} + 3\sqrt{2}$ **b** $2\sqrt{2} - 3\sqrt{2}$ **c** $5\sqrt{5} - 3\sqrt{5}$ **d** $5\sqrt{5} + 3\sqrt{5}$

    e $3\sqrt{5} - 5\sqrt{5}$ **f** $7\sqrt{3} + 2\sqrt{3}$ **g** $9\sqrt{6} - 12\sqrt{6}$ **h** $\sqrt{2} + \sqrt{2} + \sqrt{2}$

Example 4   ◀) **Self Tutor**

Simplify: $2\sqrt{75} - 5\sqrt{27}$

$$2\sqrt{75} - 5\sqrt{27}$$
$$= 2\sqrt{25 \times 3} - 5\sqrt{9 \times 3}$$
$$= 2 \times 5 \times \sqrt{3} - 5 \times 3 \times \sqrt{3}$$
$$= 10\sqrt{3} - 15\sqrt{3}$$
$$= -5\sqrt{3}$$

---

6 Simplify:

    a $4\sqrt{3} - \sqrt{12}$ **b** $3\sqrt{2} + \sqrt{50}$ **c** $3\sqrt{6} + \sqrt{24}$

    d $2\sqrt{27} + 2\sqrt{12}$ **e** $\sqrt{75} - \sqrt{12}$ **f** $\sqrt{2} + \sqrt{8} - \sqrt{32}$

Example 5   ◀) **Self Tutor**

Expand and simplify:

    a $\sqrt{5}(6 - \sqrt{5})$ **b** $(6 + \sqrt{3})(1 + 2\sqrt{3})$

    a $\sqrt{5}(6 - \sqrt{5})$ **b** $(6 + \sqrt{3})(1 + 2\sqrt{3})$

       $= \sqrt{5} \times 6 + \sqrt{5} \times (-\sqrt{5})$ $= 6 + 6(2\sqrt{3}) + \sqrt{3}(1) + \sqrt{3}(2\sqrt{3})$

       $= 6\sqrt{5} - 5$ $= 6 + 12\sqrt{3} + \sqrt{3} + 6$

                                                 $= 12 + 13\sqrt{3}$

---

7 Simplify:

    a $\sqrt{2}(3 - \sqrt{2})$ **b** $\sqrt{5}(\sqrt{5} + 1)$ **c** $\sqrt{10}(3 + 2\sqrt{10})$ **d** $\sqrt{7}(3\sqrt{7} - 4)$

    e $-\sqrt{3}(5 + \sqrt{3})$ **f** $2\sqrt{6}(\sqrt{6} - 7)$ **g** $-\sqrt{8}(\sqrt{8} - 5)$ **h** $-3\sqrt{2}(4 - 6\sqrt{2})$

8 Simplify:

    a $(5 + \sqrt{2})(4 + \sqrt{2})$ **b** $(7 + 2\sqrt{3})(4 + \sqrt{3})$ **c** $(9 - \sqrt{7})(4 + 2\sqrt{7})$

    d $(\sqrt{3} + 1)(2 - 3\sqrt{3})$ **e** $(\sqrt{8} - 6)(2\sqrt{8} - 3)$ **f** $(2\sqrt{5} - 7)(1 - 4\sqrt{5})$

Example 6   ◀) **Self Tutor**

Simplify:

    a $(5 - \sqrt{2})^2$ **b** $(7 + 2\sqrt{5})(7 - 2\sqrt{5})$

    a $(5 - \sqrt{2})^2$ **b** $(7 + 2\sqrt{5})(7 - 2\sqrt{5})$

       $= 5^2 + 2(5)(-\sqrt{2}) + (\sqrt{2})^2$ $= 7^2 - (2\sqrt{5})^2$

       $= 25 - 10\sqrt{2} + 2$ $= 49 - (4 \times 5)$

       $= 27 - 10\sqrt{2}$ $= 29$

9 Simplify:

    a $(3+\sqrt{2})^2$ **b** $(6-\sqrt{3})^2$ **c** $(\sqrt{5}+1)^2$

    d $(\sqrt{8}-3)^2$ **e** $(4+2\sqrt{3})^2$ **f** $(3\sqrt{5}+1)^2$

    g $(7-2\sqrt{10})^2$ **h** $(5\sqrt{6}-4)^2$ **i** $(-2+2\sqrt{2})^2$

10 Simplify:

    a $(3+\sqrt{7})(3-\sqrt{7})$ **b** $(\sqrt{2}+5)(\sqrt{2}-5)$ **c** $(4-\sqrt{3})(4+\sqrt{3})$

    d $(2\sqrt{2}+1)(2\sqrt{2}-1)$ **e** $(4+3\sqrt{8})(4-3\sqrt{8})$ **f** $(9\sqrt{3}-5)(9\sqrt{3}+5)$

B   DIVISION BY SURDS

Numbers like $\dfrac{6}{\sqrt{2}}$ and $\dfrac{9}{5+\sqrt{2}}$ involve division by a surd.

It is customary to "simplify" these numbers by rewriting them without the surd in the denominator.

For any fraction of the form $\dfrac{b}{\sqrt{a}}$, we can **rationalise the denominator** by multiplying by $\dfrac{\sqrt{a}}{\sqrt{a}}$.

Since $\dfrac{\sqrt{a}}{\sqrt{a}}=1$, this does not change the value of the number.

Example 7   ◀)) **Self Tutor**

Write with an integer denominator:

    a $\dfrac{6}{\sqrt{5}}$ **b** $\dfrac{35}{\sqrt{7}}$

    a $\dfrac{6}{\sqrt{5}}$ **b** $\dfrac{35}{\sqrt{7}}$

      $= \dfrac{6}{\sqrt{5}}\times\dfrac{\sqrt{5}}{\sqrt{5}}$ $= \dfrac{35}{\sqrt{7}}\times\dfrac{\sqrt{7}}{\sqrt{7}}$

      $= \dfrac{6\sqrt{5}}{5}$ $= \dfrac{\overset{5}{\cancel{35}}\sqrt{7}}{\underset{1}{\cancel{7}}}$

                                    $= 5\sqrt{7}$

> Multiplying the original number by $\dfrac{\sqrt{5}}{\sqrt{5}}$ or $\dfrac{\sqrt{7}}{\sqrt{7}}$ does not change its value.

For any fraction of the form $\dfrac{c}{a+\sqrt{b}}$, we can remove the surd

from the denominator by multiplying by $\dfrac{a-\sqrt{b}}{a-\sqrt{b}}$.

Expressions such as $a+\sqrt{b}$ and $a-\sqrt{b}$ are known as **radical conjugates**. They are identical except for the sign in front of the radical.

Example 8   ◄)) **Self Tutor**

Write $\dfrac{5}{3-\sqrt{2}}$ with an integer denominator.

$$\dfrac{5}{3-\sqrt{2}} = \left(\dfrac{5}{3-\sqrt{2}}\right)\left(\dfrac{3+\sqrt{2}}{3+\sqrt{2}}\right)$$

$$= \dfrac{5(3+\sqrt{2})}{3^2 - (\sqrt{2})^2} \quad \{\text{using the difference between two squares}\}$$

$$= \dfrac{15 + 5\sqrt{2}}{7}$$

The radical conjugate of $3 - \sqrt{2}$ is $3 + \sqrt{2}$.

EXERCISE 3B

1 Write with an integer denominator:

a $\dfrac{1}{\sqrt{3}}$ **b** $\dfrac{3}{\sqrt{3}}$ **c** $\dfrac{9}{\sqrt{3}}$ **d** $\dfrac{11}{\sqrt{3}}$

e $\dfrac{\sqrt{2}}{3\sqrt{3}}$ **f** $\dfrac{2}{\sqrt{2}}$ **g** $\dfrac{6}{\sqrt{2}}$ **h** $\dfrac{12}{\sqrt{2}}$

i $\dfrac{\sqrt{3}}{\sqrt{2}}$ **j** $\dfrac{1}{4\sqrt{2}}$ **k** $\dfrac{5}{\sqrt{5}}$ **l** $\dfrac{15}{\sqrt{5}}$

m $\dfrac{-3}{\sqrt{5}}$ **n** $\dfrac{200}{\sqrt{5}}$ **o** $\dfrac{1}{3\sqrt{5}}$ **p** $\dfrac{7}{\sqrt{7}}$

q $\dfrac{21}{\sqrt{7}}$ **r** $\dfrac{2}{\sqrt{11}}$ **s** $\dfrac{26}{\sqrt{13}}$ **t** $\dfrac{1}{(\sqrt{3})^3}$

2 Write with an integer denominator:

a $\dfrac{1}{3+\sqrt{2}}$ **b** $\dfrac{2}{3-\sqrt{2}}$ **c** $\dfrac{1}{2+\sqrt{5}}$ **d** $\dfrac{\sqrt{2}}{2-\sqrt{2}}$

e $\dfrac{10}{\sqrt{6}-1}$ **f** $\dfrac{\sqrt{3}}{\sqrt{7}+2}$ **g** $\dfrac{1+\sqrt{2}}{1-\sqrt{2}}$ **h** $\dfrac{\sqrt{3}}{4-\sqrt{3}}$

i $\dfrac{-2\sqrt{2}}{1-\sqrt{2}}$ **j** $\dfrac{1+\sqrt{5}}{2-\sqrt{5}}$ **k** $\dfrac{\sqrt{3}+2}{\sqrt{3}-1}$ **l** $\dfrac{\sqrt{10}-7}{\sqrt{10}+4}$

m $\dfrac{3+\sqrt{5}}{4+\sqrt{5}}$ **n** $\dfrac{6-\sqrt{2}}{5-\sqrt{2}}$ **o** $\dfrac{\sqrt{7}+5}{\sqrt{7}-2}$ **p** $\dfrac{\sqrt{11}-3}{4-\sqrt{11}}$

3 Write in the form $a + b\sqrt{2}$:

a $(\sqrt{2}-1)^2$ **b** $(3+\sqrt{2})^2$ **c** $\dfrac{\sqrt{2}-1}{\sqrt{2}+1}$ **d** $\dfrac{5-\sqrt{2}}{6-\sqrt{2}}$

e $\dfrac{1}{(\sqrt{2}+1)^2}$ **f** $\dfrac{1}{(3-\sqrt{2})^2}$ **g** $\dfrac{1}{3+2\sqrt{2}}$ **h** $\dfrac{1}{2\sqrt{2}-7}$

C   EXPONENTS

Rather than writing $3 \times 3 \times 3 \times 3 \times 3$, we can write this product as 3^5.

If n is a positive integer, then a^n is the product of n factors of a.

$$a^n = \underbrace{a \times a \times a \times a \times .... \times a}_{n \text{ factors}}$$

We say that a is the **base**, and n is the **exponent, power,** or **index**.

3^5

exponent, power, or index

base   index

NEGATIVE BASES

$(-1)^1 = -1$

$(-1)^2 = (-1) \times (-1) = 1$

$(-1)^3 = (-1) \times (-1) \times (-1) = -1$

$(-1)^4 = (-1) \times (-1) \times (-1) \times (-1) = 1$

$(-2)^1 = -2$

$(-2)^2 = (-2) \times (-2) = 4$

$(-2)^3 = (-2) \times (-2) \times (-2) = -8$

$(-2)^4 = (-2) \times (-2) \times (-2) \times (-2) = 16$

From the patterns above we can see that:

A **negative** base raised to an **odd** power is **negative**.
A **negative** base raised to an **even** power is **positive**.

EXERCISE 3C

1 List the first six powers of: **a** 2   **b** 3   **c** 4

2 Copy and complete the values of these common powers:

   a $5^1 = ...$, $5^2 = ...$, $5^3 = ...$, $5^4 = ...$

   b $6^1 = ...$, $6^2 = ...$, $6^3 = ...$, $6^4 = ...$

   c $7^1 = ...$, $7^2 = ...$, $7^3 = ...$, $7^4 = ...$

3 Simplify, then use a calculator to check your answer:

   a $(-1)^5$ **b** $(-1)^6$ **c** $(-1)^{14}$ **d** $(-1)^{19}$

   e $(\ 1)^8$ **f** -1^8 **g** $-(-1)^8$ **h** $(-2)^5$

   i -2^5 **j** $-(-2)^6$ **k** $(-5)^4$ **l** $-(-5)^4$

GRAPHICS CALCULATOR INSTRUCTIONS

4 Use your calculator to find the value of the following, recording the entire display:

   a 4^7 **b** 7^4 **c** -5^5 **d** $(-5)^5$ **e** 8^6

   f $(-8)^6$ **g** -8^6 **h** 2.13^9 **i** -2.13^9 **j** $(-2.13)^9$

5 Use your calculator to evaluate the following. Comment on your results.

   a 9^{-1} and $\dfrac{1}{9^1}$

   b 6^{-2} and $\dfrac{1}{6^2}$

   c 3^{-4} and $\dfrac{1}{3^4}$

   d 17^0 and $(0.366)^0$

6 Consider $3^1, 3^2, 3^3, 3^4, 3^5, ...$ Look for a pattern and hence find the last digit of 3^{101}.

7 What is the last digit of 7^{217}?

8 **Nicomachus** was born in Roman Syria (now Jerash, Jordan) around 100 AD. He wrote in Greek and was a Pythagorean. He discovered an interesting number pattern involving cubes and the sums of odd numbers.

$$1 = 1^3$$
$$3 + 5 = 8 = 2^3$$
$$7 + 9 + 11 = 27 = 3^3$$
$$\vdots$$

Find the series of odd numbers with sum equal to:

   a 5^3 **b** 7^3 **c** 12^3

D   LAWS OF EXPONENTS

When n is a positive integer, the notation a^n means a multiplied together n times.

From this definition, $a^m a^n = a^{m+n}$ and $(a^m)^n = a^{m \times n}$.

We observe that to transform a^n to a^{n+1}, we need to multiply by a.

So, to transform a^n to a^{n-1} we need to divide by a.

$\therefore$ we define $a^0 = \dfrac{a^1}{a} = 1$ to be consistent with the existing rules.

Dividing further by a, we find that $a^{-1} = \dfrac{1}{a}$, and more generally $a^{-n} = \dfrac{1}{a^n}$.

Using arguments like this, we arrive at the **laws of exponents** for $m,\ n \in \mathbb{Z}$:

$a^m \times a^n = a^{m+n}$	To **multiply** numbers with the **same base**, keep the base and **add** the exponents.
$\dfrac{a^m}{a^n} = a^{m-n}, \quad a \neq 0$	To **divide** numbers with the same base, keep the base and **subtract** the exponents.
$(a^m)^n = a^{m \times n}$	When **raising** a **power** to a **power**, keep the base and **multiply** the exponents.
$(ab)^n = a^n b^n$	The power of a product is the product of the powers.
$\left(\dfrac{a}{b}\right)^n = \dfrac{a^n}{b^n}, \quad b \neq 0$	The power of a quotient is the quotient of the powers.
$a^0 = 1, \quad a \neq 0$	Any non-zero number raised to the power zero is 1.

$a^{-n} = \dfrac{1}{a^n}$ and $\dfrac{1}{a^{-n}} = a^n$ and in particular $a^{-1} = \dfrac{1}{a}, \quad a \neq 0$.

Example 9		◀) **Self Tutor**

Simplify: **a** $7^4 \times 7^5$ **b** $p^6 \times p^2$

         a $7^4 \times 7^5$ **b** $p^6 \times p^2$
                   $= 7^{4+5}$ $= p^{6+2}$
                   $= 7^9$ $= p^8$

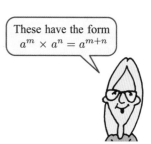

These have the form
$a^m \times a^n = a^{m+n}$

EXERCISE 3D

1 Simplify using $a^m \times a^n = a^{m+n}$:

  a $k^4 \times k^2$ **b** $5^2 \times 5^6$ **c** $d^3 \times d^7$

  d $11^4 \times 11^a$ **e** $p^6 \times p$ **f** $3^2 \times 3^{-1}$

  g $c^8 \times c^m$ **h** $x^k \times x^2$ **i** $x^3 \times x^0$

  j $5^{-6} \times 5^3$ **k** $r^2 \times r^5 \times r^4$ **l** $2^4 \times 2^{-2} \times 2^{-1}$

Example 10　　　　　　　🔊 **Self Tutor**

Simplify:

  a $\dfrac{5^6}{5^3}$ **b** $\dfrac{x^{11}}{x^6}$

  a $\dfrac{5^6}{5^3}$ **b** $\dfrac{x^{11}}{x^6}$

    $= 5^{6-3}$ $= x^{11-6}$

    $= 5^3$ $= x^5$

These have the form

$$\frac{a^m}{a^n} = a^{m-n}$$

---

2 Simplify using $\dfrac{a^m}{a^n} = a^{m-n}$:

  a $\dfrac{7^8}{7^3}$ **b** $\dfrac{b^7}{b^5}$ **c** $5^9 \div 5^6$ **d** $\dfrac{m^{10}}{m^4}$

  e $6^3 \div 6^5$ **f** $\dfrac{3^4}{3^4}$ **g** $\dfrac{k^{12}}{k^a}$ **h** $\dfrac{y^6}{y}$

  i $\dfrac{t^m}{t^4}$ **j** $\dfrac{x^{3a}}{x^2}$ **k** $\dfrac{x^{-2}}{x^3}$ **l** $\dfrac{a^3}{a^{-1}}$

Example 11　　　　　　　🔊 **Self Tutor**

Simplify:

  a $(3^5)^2$ **b** $(x^3)^k$

  a $(3^5)^2$ **b** $(x^3)^k$

    $= 3^{5 \times 2}$ $= x^{3 \times k}$

    $= 3^{10}$ $= x^{3k}$

These have the form

$(a^m)^n = a^{m \times n}$

---

3 Simplify using $(a^m)^n = a^{m \times n}$:

  a $(5^3)^2$ **b** $(c^4)^3$ **c** $(3^8)^4$

  d $(v^5)^5$ **e** $(7^6)^d$ **f** $(g^k)^8$

  g $(m^3)^t$ **h** $(11^x)^{2y}$ **i** $(3^0)^4$

  j $(2^4)^{-3}$ **k** $(x^{-2})^4$ **l** $(p^{-3})^{-2}$

4 Simplify:

   a $b^5 \times b^7$ **b** $\dfrac{t^9}{t^2}$ **c** $(p^6)^3$ **d** $\dfrac{7^6}{7^n}$

   e $(x^{2s})^3$ **f** $d^k \div d^3$ **g** $3^2 \times 3^7 \times 3^4$ **h** $(j^4)^{3x}$

   i $11^6 \times 11$ **j** $\dfrac{z^7}{z^{4t}}$ **k** $(13^c)^{5d}$ **l** $w^{7p} \div w$

Example 12   ◀» **Self Tutor**

Write as a power of 2:

  a 16   **b** $\frac{1}{16}$ **c** 1   **d** 4×2^n **e** $\dfrac{2^m}{8}$

  a 16   **b** $\quad\frac{1}{16}$ **c** $\quad 1$ **d** $\quad 4 \times 2^n$ **e** $\dfrac{2^m}{8}$

    $= 2 \times 2 \times 2 \times 2$ $= \dfrac{1}{2^4}$ $= 2^0$ $= 2^2 \times 2^n$ $= \dfrac{2^m}{2^3}$

    $= 2^4$ $= 2^{-4}$ $= 2^{2+n}$ $= 2^{m-3}$

---

5 Write as a power of 2:

   a 4   **b** $\frac{1}{4}$ **c** 8   **d** $\frac{1}{8}$ **e** 32   **f** $\frac{1}{32}$

   g 2   **h** $\frac{1}{2}$ **i** 64   **j** $\frac{1}{64}$ **k** 128   **l** $\frac{1}{128}$

6 Write as a power of 3:

   a 9   **b** $\frac{1}{9}$ **c** 27   **d** $\frac{1}{27}$ **e** 3   **f** $\frac{1}{3}$

   g 81   **h** $\frac{1}{81}$ **i** 1   **j** 243   **k** $\frac{1}{243}$

7 Write as a single power of 2:

   a 2×2^a **b** 4×2^b **c** 8×2^t **d** $(2^{x+1})^2$ **e** $(2^{1-n})^{-1}$

   f $\dfrac{2^c}{4}$ **g** $\dfrac{2^m}{2^{-m}}$ **h** $\dfrac{4}{2^{1-n}}$ **i** $\dfrac{2^{x+1}}{2^x}$ **j** $\dfrac{4^x}{2^{1-x}}$

8 Write as a single power of 3:

   a 9×3^p **b** 27^a **c** 3×9^n **d** 27×3^d **e** 9×27^t

   f $\dfrac{3^y}{3}$ **g** $\dfrac{3}{3^y}$ **h** $\dfrac{9}{27^t}$ **i** $\dfrac{9^a}{3^{1-a}}$ **j** $\dfrac{9^{n+1}}{3^{2n-1}}$

Example 13   ◀» **Self Tutor**

Express in exponent form with a prime number base:

  a 9^4 **b** $\dfrac{3^x}{9^y}$ **c** 25^x

> Decide first what the prime number base should be.

  a $9^4 = (3^2)^4$ **b** $\dfrac{3^x}{9^y} = \dfrac{3^x}{(3^2)^y}$ **c** $25^x = (5^2)^x$

      $= 3^{2 \times 4}$ $= \dfrac{3^x}{3^{2y}}$ $= 5^{2x}$

      $= 3^8$ $= 3^{x-2y}$

9 Express in exponent form with a prime number base:

a 32	**b** 49	**c** 25^3	**d** 4^5
e 16^p	**f** 27^t	**g** $5^a \times 25$	**h** $4^n \times 8^n$
i $\dfrac{8^m}{16^n}$	**j** $\dfrac{25^p}{5^4}$	**k** $\dfrac{2^{x+2}}{2^{x-1}}$	**l** 9^{t+2}
m 32^{2-r}	**n** $\dfrac{81}{3^{y+1}}$	**o** $\dfrac{16^k}{4^k}$	**p** $\dfrac{5^{a+1} \times 125}{25^{2a}}$

Example 14   ◀) **Self Tutor**

Write without brackets:

a $(3x)^3$ **b** $\left(\dfrac{x}{y}\right)^4$

a $(3x)^3$ **b** $\left(\dfrac{x}{y}\right)^4$
     $= 3^3 \times x^3$
     $= 27x^3$ $= \dfrac{x^4}{y^4}$

These have the form
$(ab)^n = a^n b^n$ or
$\left(\dfrac{a}{b}\right)^n = \dfrac{a^n}{b^n}$

---

10 Write without brackets:

a $(2a)^2$	**b** $(3n)^2$	**c** $(5m)^3$	**d** $(mn)^3$
e $\left(\dfrac{a}{2}\right)^3$	**f** $\left(\dfrac{3}{m}\right)^2$	**g** $\left(\dfrac{p}{q}\right)^4$	**h** $\left(\dfrac{t}{5}\right)^2$

Example 15   ◀) **Self Tutor**

Simplify:

a 7^0 **b** 3^{-2} **c** $3^0 - 3^{-1}$ **d** $\left(\tfrac{5}{3}\right)^{-2}$

a 7^0 **b** 3^{-2} **c** $3^0 - 3^{-1}$ **d** $\left(\tfrac{5}{3}\right)^{-2}$
     $= 1$ $= \dfrac{1}{3^2}$ $= 1 - \tfrac{1}{3}$ $= \left(\tfrac{3}{5}\right)^2$
                    $= \dfrac{1}{9}$ $= \tfrac{2}{3}$ $= \tfrac{9}{25}$

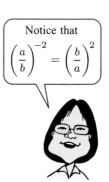

Notice that
$\left(\dfrac{a}{b}\right)^{-2} = \left(\dfrac{b}{a}\right)^2$

---

11 Simplify:

a 4^0	**b** 3^{-1}	**c** 7^{-2}	**d** $2^{-3} \times 2^4$
e $5^0 + 5^{-1}$	**f** $\left(\tfrac{5}{3}\right)^0$	**g** $\left(\tfrac{7}{4}\right)^{-1}$	**h** $\left(\tfrac{1}{6}\right)^{-1}$
i $\left(\tfrac{4}{3}\right)^{-2}$	**j** $2^1 + 2^{-1}$	**k** $\left(1\tfrac{2}{3}\right)^{-3}$	**l** $5^2 + 5^1 + 5^{-1}$

12 Write using powers of 2, 3, and/or 5:

a $\dfrac{1}{9}$	**b** $\dfrac{1}{16}$	**c** $\dfrac{1}{125}$	**d** $\dfrac{3}{5}$
e $\dfrac{4}{27}$	**f** $\dfrac{2^c}{8 \times 9}$	**g** $\dfrac{9^k}{10}$	**h** $\dfrac{6^p}{75}$

Example 16   ◀) **Self Tutor**

Write in simplest form, without brackets:

a $(-3a^2)^4$ b $\left(-\dfrac{2a^2}{b}\right)^3$

---

a $(-3a^2)^4$

   $= (-3)^4 \times (a^2)^4$

   $= 81 \times a^{2 \times 4}$

   $= 81a^8$

b $\left(-\dfrac{2a^2}{b}\right)^3$

   $= \dfrac{(-2)^3 \times (a^2)^3}{b^3}$

   $= \dfrac{-8a^6}{b^3}$

---

13 Write in simplest form, without brackets:

a $(2ab)^2$ b $(-2a)^2$ c $(6b^2)^2$ d $(-2a)^3$

e $(-3m^2n^2)^3$ f $(-2ab^4)^4$ g $\left(\dfrac{2a}{b}\right)^0$ h $\left(\dfrac{m}{3n}\right)^4$

i $\left(\dfrac{xy}{2}\right)^3$ j $\left(\dfrac{-2a^2}{b^2}\right)^3$ k $\left(\dfrac{-4a^3}{b}\right)^2$ l $\left(\dfrac{-3p^2}{q^3}\right)^2$

14 Expand the brackets and write in simplest form:

a $x^2(x^3 + x)$ b $x^2(x^2 - 2x + 3)$ c $x(x^2 + 1)(x^2 - 1)$

d $(x^3 - x^2)(x^2 + 2)$ e $(x^3 - x)^2$ f $x^2(x - 2 + x^{-1})$

g $x^{-1}(x^3 + x^2 - x)$ h $(x^2 + x^{-1})^2$ i $(x^2 + x^{-1})(x^2 - x^{-1})$

Example 17   ◀) **Self Tutor**

Simplify using the laws of exponents:

a $4x^3 \times 2x^6$ b $\dfrac{15t^7}{3t^5}$ c $\dfrac{k^2 \times k^6}{(k^3)^2}$

---

a $4x^3 \times 2x^6$

   $= 4 \times 2 \times x^3 \times x^6$

   $= 8 \times x^{3+6}$

   $= 8x^9$

b $\dfrac{15t^7}{3t^5}$

   $= \dfrac{15}{3} \times t^{7-5}$

   $= 5t^2$

c $\dfrac{k^2 \times k^6}{(k^3)^2}$

   $= \dfrac{k^{2+6}}{k^{3 \times 2}}$

   $= \dfrac{k^8}{k^6}$

   $= k^2$

---

15 Simplify using the laws of exponents:

a $\dfrac{4b^5}{b^2}$ b $2w^4 \times 3w$ c $\dfrac{12p^4}{3p^2}$ d $5c^7 \times 6c^4$

e $\dfrac{d^2 \times d^7}{d^5}$ f $\dfrac{18a^2b^3}{6ab}$ g $\dfrac{24m^2n^4}{6m^2n}$ h $\dfrac{t^5 \times t^8}{(t^2)^3}$

i $5s^2t \times 4t^3$ j $\dfrac{(k^4)^5}{k^3 \times k^6}$ k $\dfrac{12x^2y^5}{8xy^2}$ l $\dfrac{(b^3)^4 \times b^5}{b^2 \times b^6}$

Example 18   ◀) **Self Tutor**

Write without negative exponents:

a $(2c^3)^{-4}$
b $\dfrac{a^{-3}b^2}{c^{-1}}$

a $(2c^3)^{-4} = \dfrac{1}{(2c^3)^4}$
  $= \dfrac{1}{2^4 c^{3\times 4}}$
  $= \dfrac{1}{16c^{12}}$

b $a^{-3} = \dfrac{1}{a^3}$ and $\dfrac{1}{c^{-1}} = c^1$
  $\therefore \quad \dfrac{a^{-3}b^2}{c^{-1}} = \dfrac{b^2 c}{a^3}$

16 Write without negative exponents:

a x^{-3}
b $2x^{-3}$
c ab^{-2}
d $(ab)^{-2}$

e $(2ab^{-1})^2$
f $(5m^2)^{-2}$
g $(3a^{-2}b)^2$
h $(3xy^4)^{-3}$

i $\dfrac{a^2 b^{-1}}{c^2}$
j $\dfrac{a^2 b^{-1}}{c^{-2}}$
k $\dfrac{1}{a^{-3}}$
l $\dfrac{a^{-2}}{b^{-3}}$

m $\dfrac{2a^{-1}}{d^2}$
n $\dfrac{12a}{m^{-3}}$
o $\dfrac{(2a)^{-1}}{a^{-3}}$
p $\dfrac{8x^{-2}}{(2x)^2}$

Example 19   ◀) **Self Tutor**

Write $\dfrac{1}{2^{1-n}}$ without a fraction.

$\dfrac{1}{2^{1-n}} = 2^{-(1-n)}$
  $= 2^{-1+n}$
  $= 2^{n-1}$

17 Write without a fraction:

a $\dfrac{1}{a^n}$
b $\dfrac{5}{a^m}$
c $\dfrac{1}{b^{-n}}$
d $\dfrac{1}{2^{n-3}}$

e $\dfrac{1}{3^{2-n}}$
f $\dfrac{3}{a^{4-m}}$
g $\dfrac{a^n}{b^{-m}}$
h $\dfrac{a^{-n}}{a^{2+n}}$

18 Write without fractions:

a $\dfrac{1}{x^2}$
b $\dfrac{2}{x}$
c $x + \dfrac{1}{x}$
d $x^2 - \dfrac{2}{x^3}$

e $\dfrac{1}{x} + \dfrac{3}{x^2}$
f $\dfrac{4}{x} - \dfrac{5}{x^3}$
g $7x - \dfrac{4}{x} + \dfrac{5}{x^2}$
h $\dfrac{3}{x} - \dfrac{2}{x^2} + \dfrac{5}{x^4}$

Example 20   ◀)) **Self Tutor**

Write without fractions:

a $\dfrac{x^2 + 3x + 2}{x}$

b $\dfrac{2x^5 + x^2 + 3x}{x^{-2}}$

a $\dfrac{x^2 + 3x + 2}{x}$

$= \dfrac{x^2}{x} + \dfrac{3x}{x} + \dfrac{2}{x}$

$= x + 3 + 2x^{-1}$

b $\dfrac{2x^5 + x^2 + 3x}{x^{-2}}$

$= \dfrac{2x^5}{x^{-2}} + \dfrac{x^2}{x^{-2}} + \dfrac{3x}{x^{-2}}$

$= 2x^{5-(-2)} + x^{2-(-2)} + 3x^{1-(-2)}$

$= 2x^7 + x^4 + 3x^3$

19 Write without fractions:

a $\dfrac{x+3}{x}$

b $\dfrac{3-2x}{x}$

c $\dfrac{5-x}{x^2}$

d $\dfrac{x+2}{x^3}$

e $\dfrac{x^2+5}{x}$

f $\dfrac{x^2+x-2}{x}$

g $\dfrac{2x^2-3x+4}{x}$

h $\dfrac{x^3-3x+5}{x^2}$

i $\dfrac{5-x-x^2}{x}$

j $\dfrac{8+5x-2x^3}{x}$

k $\dfrac{16-3x+x^3}{x^2}$

l $\dfrac{5x^4-3x^2+x+6}{x^2}$

20 Write without fractions:

a $\dfrac{4+2x}{x^{-1}}$

b $\dfrac{5-4x}{x^{-2}}$

c $\dfrac{6+3x}{x^{-3}}$

d $\dfrac{x^2+3}{x^{-1}}$

e $\dfrac{x^2+x-4}{x^{-2}}$

f $\dfrac{x^3-3x+6}{x^{-3}}$

g $\dfrac{x^3-6x+10}{x^{-2}}$

E ▏ SCIENTIFIC NOTATION

Many people doing scientific work deal with very large or very small numbers. To avoid having to write and count lots of zeros, they write these numbers using **scientific notation** or **standard form**.

Scientific notation or **standard form** involves writing any given number as a number between 1 inclusive and 10, multiplied by a power of 10.

The result has the form $a \times 10^k$ where $1 \leqslant a < 10$ and $k \in \mathbb{Z}$.

Example 21   ◀)) **Self Tutor**

Express in scientific notation: a 37 600   b 0.000 008 6

a $37\,600 = 3.76 \times 10\,000$ {shift decimal point 4 places to the
  $= 3.76 \times 10^4$ left and $\times 10\,000$}

b $0.000\,008\,6 = 8.6 \div 10^6$ {shift decimal point 6 places to the
  $= 8.6 \times 10^{-6}$ right and $\div 1\,000\,000$}

A number such as 4.62 is already between 1 and 10. We write it in scientific notation as 4.62×10^0 since $10^0 = 1$.

EXERCISE 3E

1 Which of the following numbers are *not* written in scientific notation?

   A 3.7×10^4 **B** 4.2×10^{-7} **C** 0.3×10^5 **D** 21×10^{11}

2 Write in scientific notation:

   a 259
   b 259 000
   c 2 590 000 000
   d 2.59
   e 0.259
   f 0.000 259
   g 40.7
   h 4070
   i 0.0407
   j 407 000
   k 407 000 000
   l 0.000 040 7

3 Write each number in scientific notation:

   a The mass of the R.M.S Titanic was approximately 47 450 000 kg.

   b The ball bearing in a pen nib has diameter 0.003 m.

   c There are about 2 599 000 different 5-card poker hands which can be dealt.

   d The wavelength of blue light is about 0.000 000 47 m.

Example 22   ◀◎ **Self Tutor**

Write as an ordinary number:

  a 3.2×10^2 **b** 5.76×10^{-5}

  a 3.2×10^2 **b** 5.76×10^{-5}

       $= 3.\overparen{20} \times 100$ $= 0\overparen{00005}.76 \div 10^5$

       $= 320$ $= 0.000\,057\,6$

---

4 Write as an ordinary number:

   a 4×10^3 **b** 5×10^2 **c** 2.1×10^3 **d** 7.8×10^4
   e 3.8×10^5 **f** 8.6×10^1 **g** 4.33×10^7 **h** 6×10^7

5 Write as an ordinary number:

   a 4×10^{-3} **b** 5×10^{-2} **c** 2.1×10^{-3} **d** 7.8×10^{-4}
   e 3.8×10^{-5} **f** 8.6×10^{-1} **g** 4.33×10^{-7} **h** 6×10^{-7}

6 Write as a decimal number:

   a It is estimated that the population of the world in 2020 will be 7.4×10^9 people.

   b The mass of a Ryukyu mouse is 1.12×10^{-2} kg.

   c The bacterium *bordetella pertussis* is about 5×10^{-7} m long.

   d The Eiffel tower in Paris weighs approximately 7.3×10^6 kg.

7 Write these calculator displays in scientific notation and as decimal numbers:

a [4.5E07]   **b** [3.8E-04]   **c** [2.1E05]   **d** [4.0E-03]

e [6.1E03]   **f** [1.6E-06]   **g** [3.9E04]   **h** [6.7E-02]

GRAPHICS
CALCULATOR
INSTRUCTIONS

In an exam it is **not** acceptable to write your answer as a calculator display.

8 Use your calculator to evaluate the following, giving your answer in scientific notation:

a $680\,000 \times 73\,000\,000$

b $0.0006 \div 15\,000$

c $(0.0007)^3$

d $(3.42 \times 10^5) \times (4.8 \times 10^4)$

e $(6.42 \times 10^{-2})^2$

f $\dfrac{3.16 \times 10^{-10}}{6 \times 10^7}$

g $(9.8 \times 10^{-4}) \div (7.2 \times 10^{-6})$

h $\dfrac{1}{3.8 \times 10^5}$

i $(1.2 \times 10^3)^3$

9 Last year a peanut farmer produced 6×10^4 kg of peanuts. If the average weight of the peanuts was 8×10^{-4} kg, how many peanuts did the farm produce? Give your answer in scientific notation.

10 A bacterial cell is 4.6×10^{-7} m long. Behind it are flagella 2.15×10^{-6} m long which allow the bacterium to move. Find the total length of the bacterium.

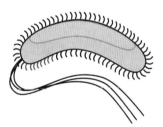

11 The closest distance between Earth and Venus in their orbits is about 3.8×10^9 m.
The closest distance between Venus and Mercury in their orbits is about 7.7×10^9 m.
A spacecraft is sent from Earth to Venus, waits for the opportune time, then travels on to Mercury.

a Find the minimum distance the spacecraft must travel.

b Discuss the assumptions you have made in your answer.

12 In a vacuum, light travels at approximately 2.9979×10^8 m s^{-1}.

a How far will light travel in:
  i 1 minute   **ii** 1 day?

b Assuming a year ≈ 365.25 days, calculate one **light-year**, the distance light will travel in a vacuum in a year.

c Apart from our own sun, the closest star to Earth is Proxima Centauri, which is an average distance of 4.22 light-years from Earth. Write this length in metres.

d The table alongside compares the sizes of some galaxies.

Galaxy	Diameter (light-years)
Milky Way	100 000
M87	980 000
Hercules A	1 500 000

   i Write the diameter of M87 in metres.

   ii If Hercules A was mapped on a scale diagram 26 cm wide, what would be the scale factor of the diagram?

   iii If a spaceship was able to travel at $100\,000$ km h^{-1}, how long would it take to cross the Milky Way?

13 Answer the **Opening Problem** on page **64**.

DISCUSSION

The product of the first n integers can be written using **factorial notation**:

$$n! = 1 \times 2 \times 3 \times \, ... \, \times (n-1) \times n$$

When a Mahjong set is arranged ready for play, the total number of orders in which the tiles can be selected is $\dfrac{144!}{(4!)^{34}} \approx 6.563 \times 10^{202}$.

Can your calculator evaluate numbers this large? If not, how can we evaluate expressions like $\dfrac{144!}{(4!)^{34}}$?

REVIEW SET 3A

1 Simplify:

   a $7\sqrt{5} - 3\sqrt{5}$

   b $2\sqrt{6} - \sqrt{54}$

   c $5\sqrt{3}(4 - \sqrt{3})$

   d $(1 + \sqrt{2})(2 + \sqrt{2})$

   e $(6 - 5\sqrt{2})^2$

   f $(3 + \sqrt{5})(3 - \sqrt{5})$

2 Simplify:

   a $-(-1)^{10}$

   b $-(-3)^3$

   c $3^0 - 3^{-1}$

3 Simplify:

   a $x^4 \times x^2$

   b $\left(2^{-1}\right)^7$

   c $\left(ab^3\right)^6$

4 Write without negative exponents:

   a 3^{-3}

   b $x^{-1}y$

   c $\left(\dfrac{a}{b}\right)^{-1}$

5 Express in exponent form with a prime number base:

   a 27

   b 9^t

   c $\dfrac{4}{2^{m-1}}$

6 Simplify using the laws of exponents:

   a $\dfrac{15xy^2}{3y^4}$

   b $\dfrac{j^6}{j^5 \times j^8}$

   c $\dfrac{36g^3h^5}{12h^2}$

7 Express in simplest form, without brackets:

    a $\left(\dfrac{t}{4s}\right)^3$ **b** $\left(\dfrac{m^2}{5n}\right)^0$ **c** $\left(5p^3q\right)^2$

8 Write without fractions:

    a $\dfrac{x^2+8}{x}$ **b** $\dfrac{4+x+x^3}{x^{-2}}$ **c** $\dfrac{k^{-x}}{k^{x+6}}$

9 Simplify using the laws of exponents:

    a $a^4b^5 \times a^2b^2$ **b** $6xy^5 \div 9x^2y^5$ **c** $\dfrac{5(x^2y)^2}{(5x^2)^2}$

10 Write as a decimal number:

    a 4.6×10^{11} **b** 1.9×10^0 **c** 3.2×10^{-3}

11 Write in scientific notation:

    a The diameter of the Earth is approximately 12.74 million metres.

    b An extremely fine needle tip has width 0.000 12 m.

12 Sheets of paper are 3.2×10^{-4} m thick. How many sheets are required to make a pile of paper 10 cm high?

13 At a particular moment, Earth is 4.3×10^9 km from Neptune and 1.5×10^9 km from Saturn. How much further away is Neptune than Saturn?

REVIEW SET 3B

1 Simplify:

    a $4\sqrt{11} - 5\sqrt{11}$ **b** $\sqrt{32} - 3\sqrt{2}$

    c $(7 + 2\sqrt{3})(5 - 3\sqrt{3})$ **d** $(6 + 2\sqrt{2})(6 - 2\sqrt{2})$

2 Write with an integer denominator:

    a $\dfrac{2}{\sqrt{3}}$ **b** $\dfrac{\sqrt{7}}{\sqrt{5}}$ **c** $\dfrac{3}{\sqrt{3}+2}$ **d** $\dfrac{1}{4+\sqrt{7}}$

3 Simplify:

    a $\dfrac{m^9}{m^5}$ **b** y^0 **c** $\left(\dfrac{7z}{w}\right)^{-2}$

4 Simplify:

    a $\dfrac{k^x}{k^2}$ **b** $11^r \times 11^{-4}$ **c** 9×3^b

5 Write without fractions:

    a $\dfrac{1}{11}$ **b** $\dfrac{a}{b^2}$ **c** $\dfrac{jk^4}{l^a}$

6 Express in exponent form with a prime number base:

    a $\dfrac{1}{16}$ **b** $3^k \times 81$ **c** $\dfrac{125^a}{5^b}$

Write in simplest rational form:

a 2^{-3}

b 7^0

c $3^{-1} + 3^1$

8 Express in simplest form, without brackets:

a $\left(\dfrac{2a^6}{8b^2}\right)^3$

b $\left(5d \times d^{-5}\right)^2$

c $\dfrac{16z^2 \times z^5}{(2z)^3}$

9 Write without brackets or negative exponents:

a $x^{-2} \times x^{-3}$

b $2(ab)^{-2}$

c $2ab^{-2}$

10 Write as a single power of 3:

a $\dfrac{27}{9^a}$

b $81^{1-x} \times 9^{1-2x}$

11 Express as a decimal number:

a Jupiter has a radius of 1.43×10^5 km.

b The ebola virus is about 8.2×10^{-8} m wide.

12 Sound travels along a telephone cable at 1.91×10^8 m s^{-1}. Find how long it takes Tetsuo's voice to travel from his office phone in Tokyo to:

a his wife's phone, 3740 m away

b his brother in Beijing, 2.1×10^6 m away.

13 Gold is special not just for its looks, but also its properties. Just 3 g of gold can be beaten out to form 1 m^2 of gold leaf approximately 1.8×10^{-7} m thick. By comparison, a US dime has a thickness of approximately 1.35×10^{-3} m. How many sheets of gold leaf would you need to create a stack the same height as the dime?

Chapter

4

Equations

Contents:

OPENING PROBLEM

Consider the equation $2x(x + 4) = 8(x + k)$ where k is a constant.

Things to think about:

a Suppose $k = 9$. Can you solve the equation:

    i using algebra   **ii** by graphing each side of the equation on the same set of axes?

b Can you show that for any value of k, the equation can be written in the form $x^2 = 4k$?

c For what values of k does the equation have:

    i two real solutions   **ii** one real solution   **iii** no real solutions?

In this Chapter we consider several types of equations and methods for finding their **solutions** or **roots**.

These methods are also used to find the **zeros** of an algebraic expression, which are the values of the variable for which the expression is equal to zero.

For example: • The **roots** of $x^2 + x - 2 = 0$ are $x = 1$ and $x = -2$.

          • The **zeros** of $x^2 + x - 2$ are 1 and -2.

We pay particular attention to quadratic equations, considering several methods for their solution. These are useful because we see many examples of quadratic equations in problem solving, and because the analysis of these equations teaches us principles we can apply elsewhere. We also solve equations using technology, giving us a tool for solving much harder problems.

A   EQUATIONS OF THE FORM $x^2 = k$

You should have seen in previous years that:

If $x^2 = k$ then $\begin{cases} x = \pm\sqrt{k} & \text{if } k > 0 \\ x = 0 & \text{if } k = 0 \\ \text{there are no real solutions if } k < 0. \end{cases}$

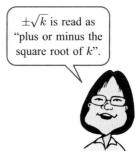
$\pm\sqrt{k}$ is read as "plus or minus the square root of k".

We often need to rearrange an equation into this form. We do this by performing operations on both sides of the equation, maintaining the balance just as we did for linear equations.

Example 1	◀) **Self Tutor**

Solve for x:

    a $3x^2 - 1 = 8$ **b** $5 - 2x^2 = 11$

---

a $3x^2 - 1 = 8$

    $\therefore \ 3x^2 = 9$ $\{+1 \text{ to both sides}\}$

    $\therefore \ x^2 = 3$ $\{\div \text{ both sides by 3}\}$

    $\therefore \ \ x = \pm\sqrt{3}$

b $5 - 2x^2 = 11$

    $\therefore \ -2x^2 = 6$ $\{-5 \text{ from both sides}\}$

    $\therefore \ \ x^2 = -3$ $\{\div \text{ both sides by } -2\}$

    which has no real solutions as x^2 cannot be negative.

The same principle can be applied to other perfect squares, in particular equations written in the form $(x + a)^2 = k$.

Example 2   ◀》 **Self Tutor**

Solve for x:

   a $(x+3)^2 = 36$ **b** $(x-4)^2 = 7$

> For equations of the form $(x+a)^2 = k$ we do not need to expand the brackets.

   a $(x+3)^2 = 36$

     $\therefore \ x+3 = \pm\sqrt{36}$

     $\therefore \ x+3 = \pm 6$

     $\therefore \ \ \ x = -3 \pm 6$

     $\therefore \ \ \ x = 3 \text{ or } -9$

   b $(x-4)^2 = 7$

     $\therefore \ x-4 = \pm\sqrt{7}$

     $\therefore \ \ \ x = 4 \pm \sqrt{7}$

EXERCISE 4A

1   Solve for x:

   a $x^2 = 4$ **b** $3x^2 = 48$ **c** $4x^2 = 4$

   d $5x^2 = 35$ **e** $2x^2 = -10$ **f** $6x^2 = 0$

   g $4x^2 - 5 = 15$ **h** $7 - 3x^2 = 19$ **i** $\frac{1}{2}x^2 - \frac{1}{8} = 1$

2   Solve for x:

   a $(x-3)^2 = 16$ **b** $(x+1)^2 = 9$ **c** $(x+4)^2 = -25$

   d $(x-2)^2 = 10$ **e** $(x+4)^2 = 13$ **f** $(x-7)^2 = 0$

   g $(2x-3)^2 = 25$ **h** $\frac{1}{2}(3x+1)^2 = 7$ **i** $(x-\sqrt{2})^2 = 2$

   j $(x+\sqrt{2})^2 = 1$ **k** $(2x-\sqrt{3})^2 = 2$ **l** $(2x+1)^2 = 7$

3   For what values of n does the equation $x^2 = n$ have:

   a   two real solutions   **b**   one real solution   **c**   no real solutions?

B   POWER EQUATIONS

A **power equation** is an equation which can be written in the form $x^n = k$, $n \neq 0$.

For example, $x^3 = 5$ and $2x^4 = 20$ are power equations.

In **Section A** we saw that $x^2 = k$ has two real solutions if $k > 0$, and no real solutions if $k < 0$. This is, in fact, true for all power equations with an *even power*.

If a power equation has an *odd power*, there will always be one real solution.

For $n > 0$, we write our solutions in terms of the nth root of k.

- If $x^n = k$ where n is **even**, then

$$\begin{cases} x = \pm\sqrt[n]{k} & \text{if } k > 0 \\ x = 0 & \text{if } k = 0 \\ \end{cases}$$
$$\text{there are no real solutions if } k < 0.$$

> $\sqrt[n]{k}$ is the nth root of k.

- If $x^n = k$ where n is **odd**, then $x = \sqrt[n]{k}$.

Example 3   ◀)) **Self Tutor**

Solve for x:

   a $\ x^3 = -27$ **b** $\ x^4 + 5 = 15$ **c** $\ (x-2)^5 = 11$

---

  a $\quad x^3 = -27$ **b** $\quad x^4 + 5 = 15$ **c** $\quad (x-2)^5 = 11$

     $\therefore\ x = \sqrt[3]{-27}$ $\therefore\ x^4 = 10$ $\therefore\ x - 2 = \sqrt[5]{11}$

     $\therefore\ x = -3$ $\therefore\ x = \pm\sqrt[4]{10}$ $\therefore\ x = 2 + \sqrt[5]{11}$

For $\ n < 0,\ $ we begin by using the laws of exponents to remove the negative exponent.

EXERCISE 4B

1   Solve for x:

  a $\ x^3 = 27$ **b** $\ x^4 = 16$ **c** $\ x^6 = -10$

  d $\ x^5 = -13$ **e** $\ x^3 + 8 = 0$ **f** $\ 2x^3 = 14$

  g $\ 5x^4 = 30$ **h** $\ x^3 = \frac{8}{27}$ **i** $\ x^4 = \frac{1}{16}$

  j $\ 3x^5 = 1$ **k** $\ 4x^3 + 5 = -19$ **l** $\ 2x^4 - 55 = 107$

2   Solve for x:

  a $\ (x-1)^3 = 17$ **b** $\ (x+3)^5 = -1$ **c** $\ (x-2)^4 = 20$

  d $\ (x+5)^4 = -16$ **e** $\ 2(x+4)^5 = -24$ **f** $\ 3(x-3)^4 = 15$

  g $\ (3x-1)^6 = 1$ **h** $\ (2x-3)^4 = 15$ **i** $\ \frac{1}{4}(1-x)^5 = 8$

3   Find the zeros of:

  a $\ 3x^3 - 24$ **b** $\ (x-1)^4 - 11$ **c** $\ (2x+3)^5 + 1$

Example 4   ◀)) **Self Tutor**

Solve for x:

   a $\ x^{-5} = -\frac{1}{32}$ **b** $\ x^{-4} = 256$

---

  a $\quad x^{-5} = -\frac{1}{32}$ **b** $\quad x^{-4} = 256$

     $\therefore\ x^5 = -32$ $\therefore\ x^4 = \frac{1}{256}$

     $\therefore\ x = \sqrt[5]{-32}$ $\therefore\ x = \pm\sqrt[4]{\frac{1}{256}}$

     $\therefore\ x = -2$ $\therefore\ x = \pm\frac{1}{4}$

---

4   Solve for x:

  a $\ x^{-1} = \frac{1}{6}$ **b** $\ x^{-2} = \frac{1}{9}$ **c** $\ x^{-3} = -\frac{1}{27}$

  d $\ x^{-2} = 49$ **e** $\ x^{-4} = \frac{1}{16}$ **f** $\ x^{-3} = -64$

  g $\ (x-3)^{-2} = 25$ **h** $\ (x+1)^{-2} = -4$ **i** $\ (2x-5)^{-3} = \frac{1}{5}$

C | EQUATIONS IN FACTORED FORM

An equation is written in **factored form** if one side of the equation is fully factorised and the other side is zero.

For example, $ab = 0$, $x(x + 1) = 0$, $(x + 2)(x - 3) = 0$ are all written in factored form.

If an equation is written in factored form, we can apply the **null factor law**:

> If the product of two (or more) numbers is zero then at least one of them must be zero.
>
> So, if $ab = 0$ then $a = 0$ or $b = 0$.

Example 5　　　　　　　　　　　　　　　　　　　　　　　　◀) **Self Tutor**

Solve for x using the null factor law:

　a $3x(x - 5) = 0$　　　　　　　　　　　**b** $(x - 4)(3x + 7) = 0$

a $\qquad 3x(x - 5) = 0$	**b** $\qquad (x - 4)(3x + 7) = 0$
$\therefore \;\; 3x = 0 \;$ or $\; x - 5 = 0$	$\therefore \;\; x - 4 = 0 \;$ or $\; 3x + 7 = 0$
$\therefore \qquad x = 0$ or 5	$\therefore \qquad x = 4 \;$ or $\; 3x = -7$
	$\therefore \qquad x = 4$ or $-\frac{7}{3}$

EXERCISE 4C

1 Solve using the null factor law:

　a $3x = 0$　　　　　**b** $a \times 8 = 0$　　　　　**c** $-7y = 0$　　　　　**d** $ab = 0$

　e $2xy = 0$　　　　**f** $a^2 = 0$　　　　　　**g** $xyz = 0$　　　　**h** $2abc = 0$

2 Solve for x using the null factor law:

　a $x(x - 5) = 0$　　　　　　　　　　　**b** $2x(x + 3) = 0$

　c $(x + 1)(x - 3) = 0$　　　　　　　　**d** $(x - 4)(x + 7) = 0$

　e $3x(7 - x) = 0$　　　　　　　　　　**f** $-2x(x + 1) = 0$

　g $4(x + 6)(2x - 3) = 0$　　　　　　　**h** $(2x + 1)(2x - 1) = 0$

　i $11(x + 2)(x - 7) = 0$　　　　　　　**j** $-6(x - 5)(3x + 2) = 0$

　k $x^2(x + 5) = 0$　　　　　　　　　　**l** $4(5 - x)^2 = 0$

　m $-3(3x - 1)^2 = 0$　　　　　　　　　**n** $x(x + 1)(x - 2) = 0$

　o $(x - 1)(x + 2)(x - 3) = 0$　　　　　**p** $3(x + 2)(x + 4)(2x - 1) = 0$

3 Solve, if possible, using the null factor law:

　a $\dfrac{a}{b} = 0$　　　　　**b** $\dfrac{3xy}{z} = 0$　　　　　**c** $\dfrac{2}{xy} = 0$　　　　　**d** $-\dfrac{x}{2y} = 0$

D QUADRATIC EQUATIONS

A **quadratic equation** is an equation which can be written in the form $ax^2 + bx + c = 0$ where a, b, and c are constants, $a \neq 0$.

We have seen that a linear equation such as $2x + 3 = 11$ will usually have *one* solution. In contrast, a quadratic equation may have *two*, *one*, or *zero* solutions.

Here are some quadratic equations which show the truth of this statement:

Equation	$ax^2 + bx + c = 0$ form	Solutions	Number of solutions
$(x+2)(x-2) = 0$	$x^2 + 0x - 4 = 0$	$x = 2$ or $x = -2$	**two**
$(x-2)^2 = 0$	$x^2 - 4x + 4 = 0$	$x = 2$	**one**
$x^2 = -4$	$x^2 + 0x + 4 = 0$	none as x^2 is always $\geqslant 0$	**zero**

METHODS FOR SOLVING QUADRATIC EQUATIONS

To solve quadratic equations we have the following methods to choose from:
- rewrite the quadratic into **factored form** then use the **null factor law**
- rewrite the quadratic into **completed square form** then solve $(x - h)^2 = k$
- use the **quadratic formula**
- use **technology**.

SOLVING BY FACTORISATION

Step 1: If necessary, rearrange the equation so one side is zero.

Step 2: Fully factorise the other side.

Step 3: Use the null factor law: If $ab = 0$ then $a = 0$ or $b = 0$.

Step 4: Solve the resulting linear equations.

Example 6   ◀) Self Tutor

Solve for x:

a $\quad 3x^2 + 5x = 0$

b $\quad x^2 = 5x + 6$

a
$$3x^2 + 5x = 0$$
$$\therefore x(3x + 5) = 0$$
$$\therefore x = 0 \text{ or } 3x + 5 = 0$$
$$\therefore x = 0 \text{ or } x = -\tfrac{5}{3}$$

b
$$x^2 = 5x + 6$$
$$\therefore x^2 - 5x - 6 = 0$$
$$\therefore (x - 6)(x + 1) = 0$$
$$\therefore x = 6 \text{ or } -1$$

Example 7   ◀) **Self Tutor**

Solve for x:

a $\quad 4x^2 + 1 = 4x$ $\qquad\qquad$ b $\quad 6x^2 = 11x + 10$

a $\qquad\qquad 4x^2 + 1 = 4x$

$\therefore\quad 4x^2 - 4x + 1 = 0$

$\therefore\quad (2x - 1)^2 = 0$

$\therefore\qquad x = \frac{1}{2}$

b $\qquad\qquad 6x^2 = 11x + 10$

$\therefore\quad 6x^2 - 11x - 10 = 0$

$\therefore\quad (2x - 5)(3x + 2) = 0$

$\therefore\qquad x = \frac{5}{2} \text{ or } -\frac{2}{3}$

Caution:

- Do not be tempted to divide both sides by an expression involving x.
  If you do this then you may lose one of the solutions.

  For example, consider $\quad x^2 = 5x$.

  We cannot divide by 0.
  In dividing both sides
  by x, we assume $x \neq 0$.
  For this reason, the
  solution $x = 0$ is lost.

Correct solution	*Incorrect solution*
$x^2 = 5x$	$x^2 = 5x$
$\therefore\quad x^2 - 5x = 0$	$\therefore\quad \dfrac{x^2}{x} = \dfrac{5x}{x}$
$\therefore\quad x(x - 5) = 0$	$\therefore\quad x = 5$
$\therefore\quad x = 0 \text{ or } 5$	

- Be careful when taking square roots of both sides of an equation.
  If you do this then you may lose one of the solutions.

  For example, consider $\quad (2x - 7)^2 = (x + 1)^2$.

  Correct solution

  $(2x - 7)^2 = (x + 1)^2$

  $\therefore\quad (2x - 7)^2 - (x + 1)^2 = 0$

  $\therefore\quad (2x - 7 + x + 1)(2x - 7 - x - 1) = 0$

  $\therefore\quad (3x - 6)(x - 8) = 0$

  $\therefore\quad x = 2 \text{ or } 8$

  Incorrect solution

  $(2x - 7)^2 = (x + 1)^2$

  $\therefore\quad 2x - 7 = x + 1$

  $\therefore\quad x = 8$

  If $a^2 = b^2$ then $a = \pm b$.
  If we take the square root of
  both sides, we consider only
  the case $a = b$. The solution
  from $a = -b$ is lost.

EXERCISE 4D.1

1 Solve for x:

  a $\quad 4x^2 + 7x = 0$ $\qquad$ b $\quad 6x^2 + 2x = 0$ $\qquad$ c $\quad 3x^2 - 7x = 0$

  d $\quad 2x^2 - 11x = 0$ $\qquad$ e $\quad 3x^2 = 8x$ $\qquad$ f $\quad 9x = 6x^2$

2 Solve for x:

  a $\quad x^2 - 5x + 6 = 0$ $\qquad$ b $\quad x^2 - 2x + 1 = 0$ $\qquad$ c $\quad x^2 + 2x - 8 = 0$

  d $\quad x^2 + 7x + 12 = 0$ $\qquad$ e $\quad x^2 = 2x + 8$ $\qquad$ f $\quad x^2 + 21 = 10x$

  g $\quad 9 + x^2 = 6x$ $\qquad$ h $\quad x^2 + x = 12$ $\qquad$ i $\quad x^2 + 8x = 33$

3 Solve for x:

    a $9x^2 - 12x + 4 = 0$ **b** $2x^2 - 13x - 7 = 0$ **c** $3x^2 = 16x + 12$

    d $3x^2 + 5x = 2$ **e** $2x^2 + 3 = 5x$ **f** $3x^2 + 8x + 4 = 0$

    g $3x^2 = 10x + 8$ **h** $4x^2 + 4x = 3$ **i** $4x^2 = 11x + 3$

    j $12x^2 = 11x + 15$ **k** $7x^2 + 6x = 1$ **l** $15x^2 + 2x = 56$

Example 8   ◀)) **Self Tutor**

Solve for x: $3x + \dfrac{2}{x} = -7$

$$3x + \frac{2}{x} = -7$$

$\therefore \ 3x^2 + 2 = -7x$ {multiplying both sides by x}

$\therefore \ 3x^2 + 7x + 2 = 0$ {making the RHS $= 0$}

$\therefore \ (x + 2)(3x + 1) = 0$ {factorising}

$\therefore \ x = -2$ or $-\frac{1}{3}$

RHS is short for Right Hand Side.

---

4 Solve for x:

    a $(x + 1)^2 = 2x^2 - 5x + 11$ **b** $(x + 2)(1 - x) = -4$

    c $5 - 4x^2 = 3(2x + 1) + 2$ **d** $x + \dfrac{2}{x} = 3$

    e $2x - \dfrac{1}{x} = -1$ **f** $\dfrac{x + 3}{1 - x} = -\dfrac{9}{x}$

    g $(x + 3)(2 - x) = 4$ **h** $(x - 4)(x + 2) = 16$

    i $(x - 5)(x + 3) = 20$ **j** $(4x - 5)(4x - 3) = 143$

LEARNING ALGEBRA

SOLVING BY "COMPLETING THE SQUARE"

As you would be aware by now, not all quadratics factorise easily.

For example, $x^2 + 4x + 1$ cannot be factorised by easily identifying factors. In particular, we cannot write $x^2 + 4x + 1$ in the form $(x - a)(x - b)$ where a and b are rational numbers.

An alternative method is to rewrite the equation in the form $(x - h)^2 = k$. We refer to this process as "completing the square".

        Start with the quadratic equation in the form $ax^2 + bx + c = 0$.

        Step 1:   If $a \neq 1$, divide both sides by a.

        Step 2:   Rearrange the equation so that only the constant is on the RHS.

        Step 3:   Add to both sides $\left(\dfrac{\text{coefficient of } x}{2} \right)^2$.

        Step 4:   Factorise the LHS.

        Step 5:   Use the rule: If $X^2 = k$ then $X = \pm\sqrt{k}$.

Example 9 🔊 **Self Tutor**

Solve exactly for x: $x^2 + 4x + 1 = 0$

$$x^2 + 4x + 1 = 0$$
$$\therefore \ x^2 + 4x = -1 \qquad \text{\{writing the constant on the RHS\}}$$
$$\therefore \ x^2 + 4x + 2^2 = -1 + 2^2 \quad \text{\{completing the square\}}$$
$$\therefore \ (x + 2)^2 = 3 \qquad \text{\{factorising the LHS\}}$$
$$\therefore \ x + 2 = \pm\sqrt{3}$$
$$\therefore \ x = -2 \pm \sqrt{3}$$

The squared number we add to both sides is
$$\left(\frac{\text{coefficient of } x}{2}\right)^2$$

Example 10 🔊 **Self Tutor**

Solve exactly for x: $-3x^2 + 12x + 5 = 0$

$$-3x^2 + 12x + 5 = 0$$
$$\therefore \ x^2 - 4x - \tfrac{5}{3} = 0 \qquad \text{\{dividing both sides by } -3\text{\}}$$
$$\therefore \ x^2 - 4x = \tfrac{5}{3} \qquad \text{\{writing the constant on the RHS\}}$$
$$\therefore \ x^2 - 4x + (-2)^2 = \tfrac{5}{3} + (-2)^2 \quad \text{\{completing the square\}}$$
$$\therefore \ (x - 2)^2 = \tfrac{17}{3} \qquad \text{\{factorising the LHS\}}$$
$$\therefore \ x - 2 = \pm\sqrt{\tfrac{17}{3}}$$
$$\therefore \ x = 2 \pm \sqrt{\tfrac{17}{3}}$$

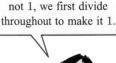

If the coefficient of x^2 is not 1, we first divide throughout to make it 1.

EXERCISE 4D.2

1 Solve exactly by completing the square:

   a $x^2 - 4x + 1 = 0$ **b** $x^2 + 6x + 2 = 0$ **c** $x^2 - 14x + 46 = 0$

   d $x^2 = 4x + 3$ **e** $x^2 + 6x + 7 = 0$ **f** $x^2 = 2x + 6$

   g $x^2 + 6x = 2$ **h** $x^2 + 10 = 8x$ **i** $x^2 + 6x = -11$

2 Solve exactly by completing the square:

   a $2x^2 + 4x + 1 = 0$ **b** $2x^2 - 10x + 3 = 0$ **c** $3x^2 + 12x + 5 = 0$

   d $3x^2 = 6x + 4$ **e** $5x^2 - 15x + 2 = 0$ **f** $4x^2 + 4x = 5$

3 Solve for x:

   a $3x - \dfrac{2}{x} = 4$ **b** $1 - \dfrac{1}{x} = -5x$ **c** $3 + \dfrac{1}{x^2} = -\dfrac{5}{x}$

4 Suppose $ax^2 + bx + c = 0$ where a, b, and c are constants, $a \neq 0$.
   Solve for x by completing the square.

LEARNING
ALGEBRA

THE QUADRATIC FORMULA

HISTORICAL NOTE   THE QUADRATIC FORMULA

Thousands of years ago, people knew how to calculate the area of a rectangular shape given its side lengths. When they wanted to find the side lengths necessary to give a certain area, however, they ended up with a quadratic equation which they needed to solve.

The first known solution of a quadratic equation is written on the Berlin Papyrus from the Middle Kingdom (2160 - 1700 BC) in Egypt. By 400 BC, the Babylonians were using the method of "completing the square".

Pythagoras and **Euclid** both used geometric methods to explore the problem. Pythagoras noted that the square root was not always an integer, but he refused to accept that irrational solutions existed. Euclid also discovered that the square root was not always rational, but concluded that irrational numbers *did* exist.

A major jump forward was made in India around 700 AD, when Hindu mathematician **Brahmagupta** devised a general (but incomplete) solution for the quadratic equation $ax^2 + bx = c$ which was equivalent to $x = \dfrac{\sqrt{4ac + b^2} - b}{2a}$. Taking into account the sign of c, this is one of the two solutions we know today.

Brahmagupta also added *zero* to our number system!

The final, complete solution as we know it today first came around 1100 AD, by another Hindu mathematician called **Bhaskhara**. He was the first to recognise that any positive number has two square roots, which could be negative or irrational. In fact, the quadratic formula is known in some countries today as "Bhaskhara's Formula".

While the Indians had knowledge of the quadratic formula even at this early stage, it took somewhat longer for the quadratic formula to arrive in Europe.

Around 820 AD, the Islamic mathematician **Muhammad bin Musa Al-Khwarizmi**, who was familiar with the work of Brahmagupta, recognised that for a quadratic equation to have real solutions, the value $b^2 - 4ac$ could not be negative.

From the name Al-Khwarizmi we get the word "algorithm".

Al-Khwarizmi's work was brought to Europe by the Jewish mathematician and astronomer **Abraham bar Hiyya** (also known as Savasorda) who lived in Barcelona around 1100 AD.

By 1545, **Girolamo Cardano** had blended the algebra of Al-Khwarizmi with Euclidean geometry. His work allowed for the existence of roots which are not real, as well as negative and irrational roots.

At the end of the 16th Century the mathematical notation and symbolism was introduced by **François Viète** in France.

In 1637, when **René Descartes** published *La Géométrie*, the quadratic formula adopted the form we see today.

In many cases, factorising a quadratic or completing the square can be long or difficult. We can instead use the **quadratic formula**:

$$\text{If }\ ax^2 + bx + c = 0, \ \ a \neq 0, \ \ \text{then}\ \ x = \frac{-b \pm \sqrt{b^2 - 4ac}}{2a}.$$

Proof:

$$\text{If }\ ax^2 + bx + c = 0, \ \ a \neq 0$$

$$\text{then}\ \ x^2 + \frac{b}{a}x + \frac{c}{a} = 0 \qquad \text{\{dividing each term by } a, \text{ as }\ a \neq 0\}$$

$$\therefore \ \ x^2 + \frac{b}{a}x \ \ \ = -\frac{c}{a}$$

$$\therefore \ \ x^2 + \frac{b}{a}x + \left(\frac{b}{2a}\right)^2 = -\frac{c}{a} + \left(\frac{b}{2a}\right)^2 \qquad \text{\{completing the square\}}$$

$$\therefore \ \ \left(x + \frac{b}{2a}\right)^2 = \frac{b^2 - 4ac}{4a^2} \qquad \text{\{factorising\}}$$

$$\therefore \ \ x + \frac{b}{2a} = \pm\sqrt{\frac{b^2 - 4ac}{4a^2}}$$

$$\therefore \ \ x = \frac{-b \pm \sqrt{b^2 - 4ac}}{2a}$$

Example 11 ◀)) **Self Tutor**

Solve for x:

  a $x^2 - 2x - 6 = 0$ **b** $2x^2 + 3x - 6 = 0$

a $x^2 - 2x - 6 = 0$ has
$a = 1, \ b = -2, \ c = -6$

$$\therefore \ \ x = \frac{-(-2) \pm \sqrt{(-2)^2 - 4(1)(-6)}}{2(1)}$$

$$\therefore \ \ x = \frac{2 \pm \sqrt{28}}{2}$$

$$\therefore \ \ x = \frac{2 \pm 2\sqrt{7}}{2} = 1 \pm \sqrt{7}$$

b $2x^2 + 3x - 6 = 0$ has
$a = 2, \ b = 3, \ c = -6$

$$\therefore \ \ x = \frac{-3 \pm \sqrt{3^2 - 4(2)(-6)}}{2(2)}$$

$$\therefore \ \ x = \frac{-3 \pm \sqrt{57}}{4}$$

EXERCISE 4D.3

1 Use the quadratic formula to solve exactly for x:

  a $x^2 - 4x - 3 = 0$ **b** $x^2 + 6x + 7 = 0$ **c** $x^2 + 1 = 4x$

  d $x^2 + 4x = 1$ **e** $x^2 - 4x + 2 = 0$ **f** $2x^2 - 2x - 3 = 0$

  g $3x^2 - 5x - 1 = 0$ **h** $-x^2 + 4x + 6 = 0$ **i** $-2x^2 + 7x - 2 = 0$

2 Rearrange the following equations so they are written in the form $ax^2 + bx + c = 0$, then use the quadratic formula to solve exactly for x.

  a $(x + 2)(x - 1) = 2 - 3x$ **b** $(2x + 1)^2 = 3 - x$ **c** $(x - 2)^2 = 1 + x$

  d $(3x + 1)^2 = -2x$ **e** $(x + 3)(2x + 1) = 9$ **f** $(2x + 3)(2x - 3) = x$

  g $\dfrac{x - 1}{2 - x} = 2x + 1$ **h** $x - \dfrac{1}{x} = 1$ **i** $2x - \dfrac{1}{x} = 3$

THE DISCRIMINANT OF A QUADRATIC

We can determine how many real solutions a quadratic equation has, without actually solving the equation.

In the quadratic formula, the quantity $b^2 - 4ac$ under the square root sign is called the **discriminant**.

The symbol **delta** Δ is used to represent the discriminant, so $\Delta = b^2 - 4ac$.

The quadratic formula becomes $x = \dfrac{-b \pm \sqrt{\Delta}}{2a}$ where Δ replaces $b^2 - 4ac$.

- If $\Delta > 0$, $\sqrt{\Delta}$ is a positive real number, so there are **two distinct real roots**
$$x = \frac{-b + \sqrt{\Delta}}{2a} \quad \text{and} \quad x = \frac{-b - \sqrt{\Delta}}{2a}.$$

- If $\Delta = 0$, $x = \dfrac{-b}{2a}$ is the **only solution**, which we call a **repeated root**.

- If $\Delta < 0$, $\sqrt{\Delta}$ is not a real number and so there are **no real roots**.

- If a, b, and c are rational and Δ is a **square** then the equation has two rational roots which can be found by factorisation.

Example 12   ◀) **Self Tutor**

Use the discriminant to determine the nature of the roots of:

  a $2x^2 - 2x + 3 = 0$ b $3x^2 - 4x - 2 = 0$

a $\Delta = b^2 - 4ac$
$\quad = (-2)^2 - 4(2)(3)$
$\quad = -20$
Since $\Delta < 0$, there are no real roots.

b $\Delta = b^2 - 4ac$
$\quad = (-4)^2 - 4(3)(-2)$
$\quad = 40$
Since $\Delta > 0$, but 40 is not a square, there are 2 distinct irrational roots.

EXERCISE 4D.4

1 Consider the quadratic equation $x^2 - 7x + 9 = 0$.

  a   Find the discriminant.

  b   Hence state the nature of the roots of the equation.

  c   Check your answer to **b** by solving the equation.

2 Consider the quadratic equation $4x^2 - 4x + 1 = 0$.

  a   Find the discriminant.

  b   Hence state the nature of the roots of the equation.

  c   Check your answer to **b** by solving the equation.

3 a   Without using the discriminant, explain why the equation $x^2 + 5 = 0$ has no real roots.

  b   Check that $\Delta < 0$ for this equation.

4 Using the discriminant only, state the nature of the solutions of:

  a $x^2 + 7x - 3 = 0$ b $x^2 - 3x + 2 = 0$ c $3x^2 + 2x - 1 = 0$

  d $5x^2 + 4x - 3 = 0$ e $x^2 + x + 5 = 0$ f $16x^2 - 8x + 1 = 0$

5 Using the discriminant only, determine which of the following quadratic equations have rational roots which can be found by factorisation.

a $6x^2 - 5x - 6 = 0$ **b** $2x^2 - 7x - 5 = 0$ **c** $3x^2 + 4x + 1 = 0$

d $6x^2 - 47x - 8 = 0$ **e** $4x^2 - 3x + 2 = 0$ **f** $8x^2 + 2x - 3 = 0$

Example 13 ◀) **Self Tutor**

Consider $x^2 - 2x + m = 0$. Find the discriminant Δ, and hence find the values of m for which the equation has:

a a repeated root **b** two distinct real roots **c** no real roots.

$x^2 - 2x + m = 0$ has $a = 1$, $b = -2$, and $c = m$

$$\therefore \ \Delta = b^2 - 4ac$$
$$= (-2)^2 - 4(1)(m)$$
$$= 4 - 4m$$

a For a repeated root	**b** For two distinct real roots	**c** For no real roots
$\Delta = 0$	$\Delta > 0$	$\Delta < 0$
$\therefore \ 4 - 4m = 0$	$\therefore \ 4 - 4m > 0$	$\therefore \ 4 - 4m < 0$
$\therefore \ 4 = 4m$	$\therefore \ -4m > -4$	$\therefore \ -4m < -4$
$\therefore \ m = 1$	$\therefore \ m < 1$	$\therefore \ m > 1$

---

6 For each of the following quadratic equations, find the discriminant Δ in simplest form. Hence find the values of m for which the equation has:

i a repeated root **ii** two distinct real roots **iii** no real roots.

a $x^2 + 4x + m = 0$ **b** $mx^2 + 3x + 2 = 0$, $m \neq 0$ **c** $mx^2 - 3x + 1 = 0$, $m \neq 0$

E   SOLVING POLYNOMIAL EQUATIONS USING TECHNOLOGY

We have already seen that:

- a **linear** equation can be written in the form $ax + b = 0$, $a \neq 0$
- a **quadratic** equation can be written in the form $ax^2 + bx + c = 0$, $a \neq 0$.

These are the first two members of a family called **polynomial equations**.

The next two members of the family are:

- a **cubic** equation which can be written in the form $ax^3 + bx^2 + cx + d = 0$, $a \neq 0$
- a **quartic** equation which can be written in the form $ax^4 + bx^3 + cx^2 + dx + e = 0$, $a \neq 0$.

The highest power of x in a polynomial equation is called its **degree**.

If a polynomial equation has degree n then it may have up to n real solutions.

You can use your graphics calculator to solve polynomial equations. You may need to first rearrange them into polynomial form.

Some calculator models will show exact solutions as well as numerical approximations.

GRAPHICS
CALCULATOR
INSTRUCTIONS

Example 14
🔊 **Self Tutor**

Use technology to solve:

a $2x^2 + 4x = 7$

b $x^3 + 4x^2 = 6 - x$

a $2x^2 + 4x = 7$

$\therefore\ 2x^2 + 4x - 7 = 0$

Using technology,

$x \approx 1.12$ or -3.12

Math Deg Norm1	d/c Real

aX² +bX+c=0

	a	b	c
[	2	4	-7]

-7

SOLVE DELETE CLEAR EDIT

Math Deg Norm1	d/c Real

aX² +bX+c=0

X1[1.1213]
X2[-3.121]

$\dfrac{-2+3\sqrt{2}}{2}$

REPEAT

b $x^3 + 4x^2 = 6 - x$

$\therefore\ x^3 + 4x^2 + x - 6 = 0$

Using technology,

$x = -3, -2,$ or 1

Math Deg Norm1	d/c Real

aX³ +bX²+cX+d=0

	a	b	c	d
[	1	4	1	-6]

-6

SOLVE DELETE CLEAR EDIT

Math Deg Norm1	d/c Real

aX³ +bX²+cX+d=0

X1[1]
X2[-2]
X3[-3]

1

REPEAT

EXERCISE 4E

1 Use technology to solve:

> A polynomial equation of degree n can have *up to* n real solutions.

  a $x^2 - 5x + 6 = 0$ **b** $x^2 + 9x + 14 = 0$

  c $x^2 - 8x + 16 = 0$ **d** $2x^2 - 6x + 5 = 0$

  e $8x^2 + 10x - 3 = 0$ **f** $4x^2 + x - 8 = 0$

  g $-5x^2 + x + 7 = 0$ **h** $\frac{1}{4}x^2 - 2x - \frac{3}{4} = 0$

2 Use technology to solve:

  a $x^2 + 6x = 7$ **b** $4x^2 + 4x = 15$ **c** $10x^2 + 63 = 53x$

  d $-3x^2 + 12x = 10$ **e** $x = 8 - 2x^2$ **f** $6 = 2x - 5x^2$

  g $4 = 3x^2 - 2x$ **h** $7x - 2 = 4x^2$ **i** $3.8x + 2.1x^2 = 52.6$

3 Solve for x:

  a $x(x + 5) + 2(x + 6) = 0$ **b** $x(1 + x) + x = 3$ **c** $(x - 1)(x + 9) = 5x$

  d $3x(x + 2) - 5(x - 3) = 18$ **e** $4x(x + 1) = -1$ **f** $2x(x - 6) = x - 25$

4 Use technology to solve:

  a $x^3 - 9x = 0$ **b** $x^3 - 2x^2 + 4 = 0$ **c** $x^3 - x^2 - 14x + 24 = 0$

  d $-x^3 + 2 = 2x - x^2$ **e** $2x^3 + x^2 = 3x - 1$ **f** $2x^3 + 8 = 5x^2 + 18x$

5 Use technology to solve:

   a $x^4 - x^3 + 2 = 0$ **b** $x^4 + 2x^3 - 3x^2 + x - 4 = 0$

   c $x^4 - 2x^2 + 1 = 0$ **d** $x^4 - x^3 + 3x^2 - x + 6 = 0$

6 Use technology to solve:

   a $x(x^2 - 1) = 2x$ **b** $(x - 2)(x + 1) = x^3$ **c** $(x^2 + 1)(x^2 - 2) = 10$

F SOLVING OTHER EQUATIONS USING TECHNOLOGY

In **Chapter 1** we solved simultaneous linear equations by graphing the equations on a set of axes, and finding the point of intersection. We can use this graphical method to solve more complicated equations.

- To solve an equation graphically, we graph each side of the equation on the same set of axes. The solutions to the equation are the x-coordinates of the points where the graphs meet.
- If one side of the equation is zero, we graph the other side of the equation. The solutions to the equation are the x-intercepts of the graph.

Example 15   🔊 Self Tutor

Use technology to solve:

   a $2^x = x + 3$ **b** $x^2 - \dfrac{5}{x} = 0$

   a We graph $y = 2^x$ and $y = x + 3$ on the same set of axes.

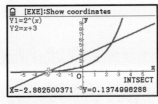

      The graphs intersect at $(-2.86, \ 0.137)$ and $(2.44, \ 5.44)$.

      $\therefore$ the solutions are $x \approx -2.86$ or 2.44.

   b We graph $y = x^2 - \dfrac{5}{x}$.

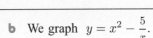
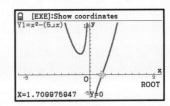

      The x-intercept is ≈ 1.71.

      $\therefore$ the solution is $x \approx 1.71$.

EXERCISE 4F

1 Solve the equation $x^2 - 5 = x + 1$ using:

   a algebra   **b** technology.

2 Use technology to solve:

   a $x = 5 - \sqrt{x}$ **b** $\dfrac{2}{x} = 3x + 4$ **c** $3^x = 15$

   d $5 \times 2^{x-1} = 90$ **e** $x^2 + 5 = 4x + \sqrt{x}$ **f** $(x + 1)(x - 3) = \sqrt{x + 3}$

3 Use technology to solve:

   a $x^2 + \dfrac{4}{x} = 0$ **b** $2^x - x^4 = 0$ **c** $x + \sqrt[3]{x} + 4 = 0$

   d $2x^2 - \sqrt{x+1} = 0$ **e** $x^4 + 2^{-x} - 30 = 0$ **f** $\dfrac{4}{x^2+5} - \dfrac{1}{x^2+1} = 0$

4   **a** Use technology to solve:

     i $2x^2 - 12x + 11 = 1$ **ii** $2x^2 - 12x + 11 = -7$ **iii** $2x^2 - 12x + 11 = -10$

  b For which values of k does the equation $2x^2 - 12x + 11 = k$ have:

     i two real solutions   **ii** one real solution   **iii** no real solutions?

DISCUSSION

Many polynomial equations need significant rearrangement before they are in a form suitable for the polynomial solver on a calculator.

For example, consider $(x - 4)(x^2 - 1) = (2 - x^2)(x + 1)$.

What are the advantages and disadvantages of:

- rearranging the equation using algebra and hence using the polynomial solver
- graphing both sides of the equation on the same set of axes then finding the x-coordinates of any points of intersection?

REVIEW SET 4A

1 Solve for x:

   a $2x^2 = 38$ **b** $(x - 2)^2 = 25$ **c** $3(x - \sqrt{2})^2 = 6$

2 Solve for x:

   a $x^4 = -9$ **b** $x^3 = \dfrac{1}{27}$ **c** $(x - 1)^5 = 2$

3 Solve for x using the null factor law:

   a $x(x + 2) = 0$ **b** $-(x + 3)(2x - 7) = 0$ **c** $(x + 5)(x + 1)(x - 6) = 0$

4 Solve for x:

   a $3x^2 - 5x = 0$ **b** $x^2 - 4x - 5 = 0$ **c** $x^2 + 6x + 9 = 0$

5 Solve for x:

   a $(x + 3)^2 = 5x + 29$ **b** $x(x - 4) - (x - 6) = 0$ **c** $(1 - 2x)(4 - x) = 39$

   d $4x - 3 = x^2$ **e** $3x^2 = 2 - 5x$ **f** $2x^2 - 108 = 6x$

6 Solve exactly by completing the square:

   a $x^2 - 6x + 4 = 0$ **b** $x^2 - 2x - 1 = 0$ **c** $2x^2 + 8x = 1$

7 Use the quadratic formula to solve:

   a $x^2 - 7x + 2 = 0$ **b** $-x^2 + 2x - 4 = 0$ **c** $-3x^2 - x + 3 = 0$

8 Write in the form $ax^2 + bx + c = 0$, and hence solve for x:

   a $x = \dfrac{9}{x}$ **b** $\dfrac{1}{x} = \dfrac{3}{x^2} - 2$ **c** $3x - 1 = \dfrac{2}{x}$

9   Consider the quadratic equation $6x^2 - x - 2 = 0$.

   a   Find the discriminant and hence state the nature of the roots of the equation.

   b   Check your answer to **a** by solving the equation.

10   Using the discriminant only, state the nature of the solutions of $2x^2 - 5x + 4 = 0$.

11   Use the quadratic formula to explain why the sum of the solutions to the equation

   $ax^2 + bx + c = 0$, $a \neq 0$, is always $-\dfrac{b}{a}$.

12   Solve for x:

   a $2x^3 - 3x^2 - 9x + 10 = 0$ **b** $3x^3 = x(7x - 2)$

   c $x^3 + 60 = 23x + 2x^2$ **d** $x^2(x^2 - 3) = 64 - 6x^3 - 14x$

13   Use technology to solve:

   a $10 \times 2^{x-1} = 35$ **b** $\sqrt{x} = \dfrac{4}{x} - 1$ **c** $x^3 - \sqrt[3]{x} + 5 = 0$

REVIEW SET 4B

1   Solve for x:

   a $-7x^2 = 0$ **b** $-4x^3 = \frac{125}{2}$ **c** $(x - \sqrt{3})^2 = 16$

2   Solve for x:

   a $x^4 = \frac{81}{16}$ **b** $x^5 = -18$ **c** $(x - 1)^{-2} = 4$

3   Solve, if possible, using the null factor law:

   a $\dfrac{p}{q} = 0$ **b** $\dfrac{2xz}{y} = 0$ **c** $-\dfrac{5}{ab} = 0$

4   Solve for x:

   a $2x^2 - 5x = 0$ **b** $3x^2 - 12x = 0$ **c** $x^2 - 7x + 6 = 0$

   d $x^2 + 4 = -4x$ **e** $x^2 - 12 = 4x$ **f** $3x^2 - x - 10 = 0$

5   Solve by completing the square:

   a $x^2 - 11x = 60$ **b** $x^2 + 5x + 5 = 0$ **c** $4x^2 - 5x = 6$

6   By completing the square, explain why $x^2 - 4x = -5$ has no real solutions.

7   Solve using the quadratic formula:

   a $x^2 + 5x + 3 = 0$ **b** $3x^2 + 11x - 2 = 0$ **c** $5x^2 + 4x - 2 = 0$

8   Using the discriminant only, state the nature of the solutions of:

   a $x^2 - 8x + 16 = 0$ **b** $2x^2 - x - 5 = 0$ **c** $3x^2 + 5x + 3 = 0$

9   Find the values of m for which $2x^2 - 3x + m = 0$ has:

   a   a repeated root   **b**   two distinct real roots   **c**   no real roots.

10   Answer the **Opening Problem** on page **84**.

11   Use technology to solve:

   a $2x^2 - 7 = 3x$ **b** $x(1 - x) = -10$ **c** $x(x - 2) + 4(x - 1) = 3$

12 Solve for x:

     a $x^3 - 15x = 2x^2$ **b** $x^3 - 4x^2 - 6x + 7 = 0$

     c $4x^4 - 4x^3 - 11x^2 - 8x + 6 = 0$

13 Use technology to solve:

     a $2^x = 7$ **b** $x^3 = 9 - 2\sqrt{x}$ **c** $\dfrac{x^2}{5} - \sqrt{x + 3} = 0$

Chapter 5

Sequences and series

Contents:

OPENING PROBLEM   THE LEGEND OF SISSA IBN DAHIR

Around 1260 AD, the Kurdish historian Ibn Khallikān recorded the following story about Sissa ibn Dahir and a chess game against the Indian King Shihram.

King Shihram was a tyrant king, and his subject Sissa ibn Dahir wanted to teach him how important all of his people were. He invented the game of chess for the king, and the king was greatly impressed. He insisted on Sissa ibn Dahir naming his reward, and the wise man asked for one grain of wheat for the first square, two grains of wheat for the second square, four grains of wheat for the third square, and so on, doubling the wheat on each successive square on the board.

The king laughed at first and agreed, for there was so little grain on the first few squares. By halfway he was surprised at the amount of grain being paid, and soon he realised his great error: that he owed more grain than there was in the world.

Things to think about:

a How can we describe the number of grains of wheat for each square?

b What expression gives the number of grains of wheat for the nth square?

c Find the total number of grains of wheat that the king owed.

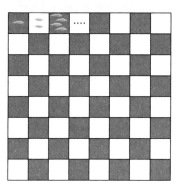

To help understand problems like the **Opening Problem**, we need to study **sequences** and their sums which are called **series**.

A   NUMBER SEQUENCES

In mathematics it is important that we can:

- **recognise** a pattern in a set of numbers
- **describe** the pattern in words
- **continue** the pattern.

A **number sequence** is an ordered list of numbers defined by a rule.

The numbers in a sequence are called the **terms** of the sequence.

Consider the illustrated tower of bricks:

The first row has 3 bricks.
The second row has 4 bricks.
The third row has 5 bricks.
The fourth row has 6 bricks.

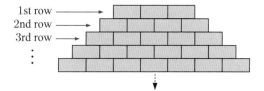

1st row
2nd row
3rd row

If we let u_n represent the number of bricks in the nth row, then $u_1 = 3$, $u_2 = 4$, $u_3 = 5$, and $u_4 = 6$.

The pattern could be continued forever, generating a **sequence** of numbers.

There are many ways to describe the sequence, including:

The string of dots indicates that the pattern continues forever.

- **listing the terms**:   3, 4, 5, 6, 7, ...

- using **words**:   "The sequence starts at 3, and increases by 1 each time".

- using the **explicit formula** $u_n = n + 2$ which gives the **nth term** or **general term** of the sequence in terms of n.
  We can use this formula to find, for example, the 20th term of the sequence, which is $u_{20} = 20 + 2 = 22$.

- a **graph** where each term of a sequence is represented by a dot. The dots *must not* be joined because n must be an integer.

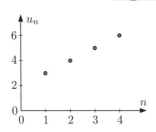

Example 1   ◄⑴ **Self Tutor**

Describe the sequence: 14, 17, 20, 23, ...   and write down the next two terms.

The sequence starts at 14, and each term is 3 more than the previous term.

The next two terms are 26 and 29.

THE GENERAL TERM OF A SEQUENCE

The **general term** or **nth term** of a sequence is represented by a symbol with a subscript, for example u_n, T_n, t_n, or A_n.

$\{u_n\}$ represents the sequence that can be generated by using u_n as the nth term.

Unless stated otherwise, we assume the first term of the sequence is u_1, and that the sequence is defined for $n \in \mathbb{Z}^+$. Sometimes we might choose for a sequence to start with u_0, particularly if n represents the number of time periods after the start of an experiment or investment.

You can use technology to help generate sequences from a formula.

GRAPHICS
CALCULATOR
INSTRUCTIONS

EXERCISE 5A

1   Write down the first four terms of the sequence if you start with:

    a   4 and add 9 each time
    b   45 and subtract 6 each time
    c   2 and multiply by 3 each time
    d   96 and divide by 2 each time.

2   The sequence of prime numbers is   2, 3, 5, 7, 11, 13, 17, 19, ...   Write down the value of:

    a u_2
    b u_5
    c u_{10}.

3 Consider the sequence 4, 7, 10, 13, 16, ...

    a Describe the sequence in words.   **b** Write down the values of u_1 and u_4.

    c Assuming the pattern continues, find the value of u_8.

4 Find the first four terms of the sequence defined by the explicit formula $u_n = 2n + 5$.

5 A sequence is defined by the explicit formula $u_n = 3n - 2$.   Find:

    a u_1 **b** u_5 **c** u_{27}.

6 Consider the number sequence $-9, -6, -1, 6, 15, ...$

    a Which of these is the correct explicit formula for this sequence?

      A $u_n = n - 10$ **B** $u_n = n^2 - 10$ **C** $u_n = n^3 - 10$

    b Use the correct formula to find the 20th term of the sequence.

7 Write a description of the sequence and find the next 2 terms:

    a 8, 16, 24, 32, ...   **b** 2, 5, 8, 11, ...   **c** 36, 31, 26, 21, ...

    d 96, 89, 82, 75, ...   **e** 1, 4, 16, 64, ...   **f** 2, 6, 18, 54, ...

    g 480, 240, 120, 60, ...   **h** 243, 81, 27, 9, ...   **i** 50 000, 10 000, 2000, 400, ...

8 Describe the sequence and write down the next 3 terms:

    a 1, 4, 9, 16, ...   **b** 1, 8, 27, 64, ...   **c** 2, 6, 12, 20, ...

9 Find the next two terms of the sequence:

    a 95, 91, 87, 83, ...   **b** 5, 20, 80, 320, ...   **c** 1, 16, 81, 256, ...

    d 2, 3, 5, 7, 11, ...   **e** 2, 4, 7, 11, ...   **f** 9, 8, 10, 7, 11, ...

10 Evaluate the first *five* terms of the sequence:

    a $\{2n\}$ **b** $\{2n - 3\}$ **c** $\{2n + 11\}$

    d $\{3 - 4n\}$ **e** $\{n^2 + 2n\}$ **f** $\{2^n\}$

    g $\{6 \times (\frac{1}{2})^n\}$ **h** $\{(-2)^n\}$ **i** $\{15 - (-2)^n\}$

RESEARCH   THE FIBONACCI SEQUENCE

Leonardo Pisano Bigollo, known commonly as **Fibonacci**, was born in Pisa around 1170 AD. He is best known for the **Fibonacci sequence** 1, 1, 2, 3, 5, 8, 13, 21, ... which starts with 1 and 1, and then each subsequent term of the sequence is the sum of the preceding two terms.

1 Can we write a formula for the general term u_n of the Fibonacci sequence?

2 Can the Fibonacci sequence be written using a formula which connects successive terms of the sequence?

3 Where do we see the Fibonacci sequence in nature?

4 **a** Calculate the ratio of consecutive terms of the Fibonacci sequence $\frac{2}{1}, \frac{3}{2}, \frac{5}{3}, \frac{8}{5}, \frac{13}{8}$, and so on. Where appropriate, round your answers to 5 decimal places.

    b What do you notice about the values in **a**?

    c Research the **golden ratio** and its connection with the Fibonacci sequence.

B   ARITHMETIC SEQUENCES

An **arithmetic sequence** is a sequence in which each term differs from the previous one by the same fixed number. We call this number the **common difference** d.

A sequence is arithmetic $\Leftrightarrow$ $u_{n+1} - u_n = d$ for all $n \in \mathbb{Z}^+$.

An arithmetic sequence can also be referred to as an **arithmetic progression**.

For example:

- the tower of bricks in the previous Section forms an arithmetic sequence with common difference 1

- 2, 5, 8, 11, 14, ... is arithmetic with common difference 3 since

  $5 - 2 = 3$
  $8 - 5 = 3$
  $11 - 8 = 3$, and so on.

- 30, 25, 20, 15, 10, ... is arithmetic with common difference -5 since

  $25 - 30 = -5$
  $20 - 25 = -5$
  $15 - 20 = -5$, and so on.

The name "arithmetic" is given because the middle term of any three consecutive terms is the **arithmetic mean** of the terms on either side.

If the terms are a, b, c, then $\quad b - a = c - b \quad$ {equating common differences}

$$\therefore \ 2b = a + c$$

$$\therefore \ b = \frac{a + c}{2} \quad \text{which is the arithmetic mean.}$$

THE GENERAL TERM FORMULA

If we know that a sequence is arithmetic, we can use a formula to find the value of any term of the sequence.

Suppose the first term of an arithmetic sequence is u_1 and the common difference is d.

Then $\quad u_2 = u_1 + d, \quad u_3 = u_1 + 2d, \quad u_4 = u_1 + 3d, \quad$ and so on.

Hence $\quad u_n = u_1 + \underbrace{(n-1)}\,d$

term number

the coefficient of d is
one less than the term number

> For an **arithmetic sequence** with **first term u_1** and **common difference d**,
> the **general term** or **nth term** is $\ u_n = u_1 + (n-1)d$.

Example 2   ◀⑴ Self Tutor

Consider the sequence 2, 9, 16, 23, 30, ...

a Show that the sequence is arithmetic.   **b** Find a formula for the general term u_n.

c Find the 100th term of the sequence.

d Is **i** 828 **ii** 2341 a term of the sequence?

---

a $9 - 2 = 7, \quad 16 - 9 = 7, \quad 23 - 16 = 7, \quad 30 - 23 = 7$

The difference between successive terms is constant.

$\therefore$ the sequence is arithmetic with $u_1 = 2$ and $d = 7$.

b $\quad u_n = u_1 + (n-1)d$

$\therefore \quad u_n = 2 + 7(n-1)$

$\therefore \quad u_n = 7n - 5$

c $\quad u_{100} = 7(100) - 5$

$\quad\quad\quad = 695$

d **i** Let $u_n = 828$

$\therefore \quad 7n - 5 = 828$

$\therefore \quad 7n = 833$

$\therefore \quad n = 119$

$\therefore \quad$ 828 is a term of the sequence, and in fact is the 119th term.

ii Let $u_n = 2341$

$\therefore \quad 7n - 5 = 2341$

$\therefore \quad 7n = 2346$

$\therefore \quad n = 335\frac{1}{7}$

But n must be an integer, so 2341 is not a member of the sequence.

EXERCISE 5B.1

1 Decide whether these sequences are arithmetic:

   a 7, 15, 23, 31, 39, ...

   b 10, 14, 18, 20, 24, ...

   c 41, 35, 29, 23, 17, ...

   d 6, 1, -6, -11, -16, ...

2 State the first term u_1 and common difference d for these arithmetic sequences:

   a 5, 9, 13, 17, 21, ...

   b -4, 3, 10, 17, 24, ...

   c 23, 18, 13, 8, 3, ...

   d -6, -15, -24, -33, ...

3 For each of these arithmetic sequences:

   i State u_1 and d.

   ii Find the formula for the general term u_n.

   iii Find the 15th term of the sequence.

   a 19, 25, 31, 37, ...

   b 101, 97, 93, 89, ...

   c 8, $9\frac{1}{2}$, 11, $12\frac{1}{2}$, ...

   d 31, 36, 41, 46, ...

   e 5, -3, -11, -19, ...

   f a, $a + d$, $a + 2d$, $a + 3d$, ...

4 Consider the sequence   6, 17, 28, 39, 50, ...

   a Show that the sequence is arithmetic.

   b Find the formula for its general term.

   c Find the 50th term.

   d Is 325 a member?

   e Is 761 a member?

5 Consider the sequence   87, 83, 79, 75, 71, ...

   a Show that the sequence is arithmetic.

   b Find the formula for its general term.

   c Find the 40th term.

   d Which term of the sequence is -297?

6 A sequence is defined by $u_n = 3n - 2$.

   a By finding $u_{n+1} - u_n$, prove that the sequence is arithmetic.

   b Find u_1 and d.

   c Find the 57th term.

   d What is the largest term of the sequence that is smaller than 450? Which term is this?

7 A sequence is defined by $u_n = \dfrac{71 - 7n}{2}$.

   a Prove that the sequence is arithmetic.

   b Find u_1 and d.

   c Find u_{75}.

   d For what values of n are the terms of the sequence less than -200?

8 Consider the arithmetic sequence $36, \ 35\frac{1}{3}, \ 34\frac{2}{3}, \ ....$

    a Find u_1 and d.
            b Which term of the sequence is -30?

9 An arithmetic sequence starts $23, \ 36, \ 49, \ 62, \ ....$ Find the first term of the sequence to exceed
    $100\,000$.

10 A sequence is defined by the formula $u_1 = -12, \quad u_{n+1} = u_n + 7, \quad n \geqslant 1.$

    a Prove that the sequence is arithmetic.
            b Find the 200th term of the sequence.

    c Is 1000 a member of the sequence?

11 What can you say about u_1 and d for an arithmetic sequence if:

    a all of the terms are even
            b all of the terms are odd?

Example 3　　　　　　　　　　　　　　　　　　　　　　🔊 **Self Tutor**

Find k given that $3k + 1, \ k, \ $ and $ \ -3$ are consecutive terms of an arithmetic sequence.

Since the terms are consecutive, $k - (3k + 1) = -3 - k$ {equating differences}

$$\therefore \quad k - 3k - 1 = -3 - k$$
$$\therefore \quad -2k - 1 = -3 - k$$
$$\therefore \quad -1 + 3 = -k + 2k$$
$$\therefore \quad k = 2$$

---

12 Find k given the consecutive arithmetic terms:

    a $32, \ k, \ 3$
            b $k, \ 7, \ 10$
            c $k, \ 2k - 1, \ 13$

    d $k, \ 2k + 1, \ 8 - k$
       e $2k + 7, \ 3k + 5, \ 5k - 4$
     f $2k + 18, \ -2 - k, \ 2k + 2$

    g $k, \ k^2, \ k^2 + 6$
         h $5, \ k, \ k^2 - 8$

Example 4　　　　　　　　　　　　　　　　　　　　　　🔊 **Self Tutor**

Find the general term u_n for an arithmetic sequence with $u_3 = 8$ and $u_8 = -17.$

$u_3 = 8 \qquad \therefore \ u_1 + 2d = 8 \qquad .... \ (1) \qquad$ {using $u_n = u_1 + (n - 1)d$}
$u_8 = -17 \quad \therefore \ u_1 + 7d = -17 \qquad .... \ (2)$

We now solve (1) and (2) simultaneously:

$$-u_1 - 2d = -8 \qquad \text{\{multiplying both sides of (1) by } -1\}$$
$$\underline{u_1 + 7d = -17}$$
$$\therefore \ 5d = -25 \qquad \text{\{adding the equations\}}$$
$$\therefore \ d = -5$$

So, in (1): $u_1 + 2(-5) = 8$ *Check*:

$$\therefore \ u_1 - 10 = 8 \qquad\qquad\qquad u_3 = 23 - 5(3)$$
$$\therefore \ u_1 = 18 \qquad\qquad\qquad\qquad = 23 - 15$$
$$\text{Now} \ \ u_n = u_1 + (n - 1)d \qquad\qquad = 8 \ \checkmark$$
$$\therefore \ u_n = 18 - 5(n - 1) \qquad u_8 = 23 - 5(8)$$
$$\therefore \ u_n = 18 - 5n + 5 \qquad\qquad = 23 - 40$$
$$\therefore \ u_n = 23 - 5n \qquad\qquad\qquad = -17 \ \checkmark$$

13   Find the general term u_n for an arithmetic sequence with:

    a $u_7 = 41$ and $u_{13} = 77$ **b** $u_5 = -2$ and $u_{12} = -12\frac{1}{2}$

    c   seventh term 1 and fifteenth term -39

    d   eleventh and eighth terms being -16 and $-11\frac{1}{2}$ respectively.

Example 5   **◄) Self Tutor**

Insert four numbers between 3 and 12 so that all six numbers are in arithmetic sequence.

Suppose the common difference is d.

∴   the numbers are $3,\ 3+d,\ 3+2d,\ 3+3d,\ 3+4d,$ and 12

$$\therefore\ 3 + 5d = 12$$
$$\therefore\ 5d = 9$$
$$\therefore\ d = \tfrac{9}{5} = 1.8$$

So, the sequence is   3, 4.8, 6.6, 8.4, 10.2, 12.

---

14   Insert three numbers between 5 and 10 so that all five numbers are in arithmetic sequence.

15   Insert six numbers between -1 and 32 so that all eight numbers are in arithmetic sequence.

16   **a**   Insert three numbers between 50 and 44 so that all five numbers are in arithmetic sequence.

    b   Assuming the sequence continues, find the first negative term of the sequence.

Example 6 **◄) Self Tutor**

Ryan is a cartoonist. His comic strip has just been bought by a newspaper, so he sends them the 28 comic strips he has drawn so far. Each week after the first he sends 3 more comic strips to the newspaper.

    a   Find the total number of comic strips sent after 1, 2, 3, and 4 weeks.

    b   Show that the total number of comic strips sent after n weeks forms an arithmetic sequence.

    c   Find the number of comic strips sent after 15 weeks.

    d   When does Ryan send his 120th comic strip?

a   *Week 1*:   28   comic strips
    Week 2: $28 + 3 = 31$ comic strips
    Week 3: $31 + 3 = 34$ comic strips
    Week 4: $34 + 3 = 37$ comic strips

b   Every week, Ryan sends 3 comic strips, so the difference between successive weeks is always 3. We have an arithmetic sequence with $u_1 = 28$ and common difference $d = 3$.

c $u_n = u_1 + (n-1)d$
       $= 28 + (n-1) \times 3$ ∴ $u_{15} = 25 + 3 \times 15$
       $= 25 + 3n$ $= 70$

After 15 weeks Ryan has sent 70 comic strips.

d   We want to find n such that $u_n = 120$
$$\therefore\ 25 + 3n = 120$$
$$\therefore\ 3n = 95$$
$$\therefore\ n = 31\tfrac{2}{3}$$

Ryan sends the 120th comic strip in the 32nd week.

17   A luxury car manufacturer sets up a factory for a new model vehicle. In the first month only 5 cars are made. After this, 13 cars are made every month.

    a   List the total number of cars that have been made by the end of each of the first six months.

    b   Explain why the total number of cars made after n months forms an arithmetic sequence.

    c   How many cars are made in the first year?

    d   How long is it until the 250th car is made?

18   At the start of the dry season, Yafiah's 3000 L water tank is full. She uses 183 L of water each week to water her garden.

    a   Find the amount of water left in the tank after 1, 2, 3, and 4 weeks.

    b   Explain why the amount of water left in the tank after n weeks forms an arithmetic sequence.

    c   When will Yafiah's tank run out of water?

APPROXIMATIONS USING ARITHMETIC SEQUENCES

In the real-world questions we have just seen, exactly the same number of items is added or subtracted in each time period. We can therefore use an arithmetic sequence to model the number of items exactly.

Most real-world scenarios will not be this exact. Instead, random variation may give us a sequence where the difference between terms is *similar*, but not the same. In these cases we can use an arithmetic sequence as an *approximation*.

For example, the table below shows the total mass of people in a lift as they walk in:

n (people)	1	2	3	4	5	6
Mass (kg)	86.2	147.5	210.1	298.4	385.0	459.8

No two people will have exactly the same mass, so the total mass of people will not form an exact arithmetic sequence. However, since the *average* mass of the people is $\frac{459.8}{6} \approx 76.6$ kg, a reasonable model for the total mass would be the arithmetic sequence $u_n = 76.6n$.

EXERCISE 5B.2

1   Halina is measuring the mass of oranges on a scale. When there are 8 oranges, the total mass is 1.126 kg.

    a   Find the average mass of the oranges on the scale.

    b   Hence write an arithmetic sequence for u_n, the approximate total mass when n oranges have been placed on the scale.

2   Nadir has placed an empty egg carton on a set of scales. Its mass is 32 g. When the carton is filled with 12 eggs, the total mass of eggs and carton is 743 g.

    a   Find the average mass of the eggs in the carton.

    b   Hence write an arithmetic sequence for u_n, the approximate total mass when n eggs have been added to the carton.

    c   For what values of n is your model valid?

3 A farmer has 580 square bales of hay in his shed with total mass 9850 kg.

The farm has 8 yards of animals. Each day, the farmer feeds out 2 bales of hay to each yard.

  a Write an arithmetic sequence for the number of bales of hay remaining after n days.

  b Write an arithmetic sequence which *approximates* the mass of hay remaining after n days.

4 Valéria joins a social networking website. After 1 week she has 34 online friends, and after 9 weeks she has 80 online friends.

  a Find the average number of online friends Valéria has made each week from week 1 to week 9.

  b Assuming that her total number of online friends after n weeks forms an arithmetic sequence, find a model which approximates the number of online friends after n weeks.

  c Do you think it is a problem that the common difference in your model is not an integer? Explain your answer.

  d Use your model to predict how many online friends Valéria will have after 20 weeks.

5 A wedding reception venue advertises all-inclusive venue hire and catering costs of €6950 for 50 guests or €11 950 for 100 guests.

Assume that the cost of venue hire and catering for n guests forms an arithmetic sequence.

  a Write a formula for the general term u_n of the sequence.

  b Explain the significance of:

    i the common difference   **ii** the constant term.

  c Estimate the cost of venue hire and catering for a reception with 85 guests.

C   GEOMETRIC SEQUENCES

A **geometric sequence** is a sequence in which each term can be obtained from the previous one by multiplying by the same non-zero number. We call this number the **common ratio** r.

A sequence is geometric $\Leftrightarrow \dfrac{u_{n+1}}{u_n} = r$ for all $n \in \mathbb{Z}^+$.

A geometric sequence can also be referred to as a **geometric progression**.

For example:

- 2, 10, 50, 250, ... is a geometric sequence as each term can be obtained by multiplying the previous term by 5.

  The common ratio is 5 since $\frac{10}{2} = \frac{50}{10} = \frac{250}{50} = 5$.

- 2, −10, 50, −250, ... is a geometric sequence with common ratio −5.

The name "geometric" is given because the middle term of any three consecutive terms is the **geometric mean** of the terms on either side.

If the terms are a, b, c then $\dfrac{b}{a} = \dfrac{c}{b}$ {common ratio}

$$\therefore b^2 = ac$$

$$\therefore b = \pm\sqrt{ac} \text{ where } \sqrt{ac} \text{ is the geometric mean.}$$

THE GENERAL TERM FORMULA

Suppose the first term of a geometric sequence is u_1 and the common ratio is r.

Then $u_2 = u_1 r$, $u_3 = u_1 r^2$, $u_4 = u_1 r^3$,   and so on.

Hence $u_n = u_1 r^{n-1}$

term number   The power of r is one less than the term number.

> For a **geometric sequence** with **first term u_1** and **common ratio r**,
> the **general term** or **nth term** is $u_n = u_1 r^{n-1}$.

Example 7   ◄)) **Self Tutor**

Consider the sequence $8, 4, 2, 1, \frac{1}{2}, \ldots$.

   a Show that the sequence is geometric.   **b** Find the general term u_n.

   c Hence find the 12th term as a fraction.

a $\dfrac{4}{8} = \dfrac{1}{2}$ $\dfrac{2}{4} = \dfrac{1}{2}$ $\dfrac{1}{2} = \dfrac{1}{2}$ $\dfrac{\frac{1}{2}}{1} = \dfrac{1}{2}$

Consecutive terms have a common ratio of $\frac{1}{2}$.

∴ the sequence is geometric with $u_1 = 8$ and $r = \frac{1}{2}$.

b $u_n = u_1 r^{n-1}$

∴ $u_n = 8\left(\frac{1}{2}\right)^{n-1}$ or $\begin{aligned}u_n &= 2^3 \times (2^{-1})^{n-1}\\ &= 2^3 \times 2^{-n+1}\\ &= 2^{3+(-n+1)}\\ &= 2^{4-n}\end{aligned}$

c $u_{12} = 8 \times \left(\frac{1}{2}\right)^{11}$

     $= \frac{1}{256}$

EXERCISE 5C

1 State the first term u_1 and common ratio r for these geometric sequences:

    a $5, 15, 45, 135, \ldots$ **b** $72, 36, 18, 9, \ldots$

    c $2, -8, 32, -128, \ldots$ **d** $6, -2, \frac{2}{3}, -\frac{2}{9}, \ldots$

2 For the geometric sequence with first two terms given, find b and c:

    a $2, 6, b, c, \ldots$ **b** $10, 5, b, c, \ldots$ **c** $12, -6, b, c, \ldots$

3 For each of these geometric sequences:

      i State u_1 and r.   **ii** Find the formula for the general term u_n.

      iii Find the 9th term of the sequence.

    a $3, 6, 12, 24, \ldots$ **b** $2, 10, 50, \ldots$ **c** $512, 256, 128, \ldots$

    d $1, 3, 9, 27, \ldots$ **e** $12, 18, 27, \ldots$ **f** $\frac{1}{16}, -\frac{1}{8}, \frac{1}{4}, -\frac{1}{2}, \ldots$

4 **a** Show that the sequence   5, 10, 20, 40, ...   is geometric.

    b Find u_n, and hence find the 15th term.

5 **a** Show that the sequence $12, -6, 3, -\frac{3}{2}, ...$ is geometric.

    b Find u_n, and hence write the 13th term as a rational number.

6 Show that the sequence   8, -6, 4.5, -3.375, ...   is geometric. Hence find the 10th term as a decimal.

7 Show that the sequence $8, 4\sqrt{2}, 4, 2\sqrt{2}, ...$ is geometric. Hence show that the general term of the sequence is $u_n = 2^{\frac{7}{2} - \frac{1}{2}n}$.

8 A sequence is defined by the formula $u_1 = \frac{4}{27}$, $u_{n+1} = 3 \times u_n$, $n \geqslant 1$.

    a Show that the sequence is geometric and find the common ratio.

    b Find the 10th term of the sequence.

    c How many terms of the sequence are *not* integers?

Example 8   ◀) **Self Tutor**

$k - 1$, $2k$, and $21 - k$ are consecutive terms of a geometric sequence. Find k.

Since the terms are geometric,

$$\frac{2k}{k - 1} = \frac{21 - k}{2k} \quad \text{\{equating the common ratio } r\text{\}}$$

$$\therefore \ 4k^2 = (21 - k)(k - 1)$$

$$\therefore \ 4k^2 = 21k - 21 - k^2 + k$$

$$\therefore \ 5k^2 - 22k + 21 = 0$$

$$\therefore \ (5k - 7)(k - 3) = 0$$

$$\therefore \ k = \tfrac{7}{5} \text{ or } 3$$

Check: If $k = \frac{7}{5}$ the terms are: $\frac{2}{5}, \frac{14}{5}, \frac{98}{5}$. ✓ $\{r = 7\}$

        If $k = 3$ the terms are: 2, 6, 18. ✓ $\{r = 3\}$

You could also solve the equation using technology.

---

9 Find k given that the following are consecutive terms of a geometric sequence:

    a $k, 3k, 54$ **b** $1000, 4k, k$ **c** $7, k, 28$

    d $18, k, \frac{2}{9}$ **e** $k, 12, \frac{k}{9}$ **f** $k, 20, \frac{25}{4}k$

    g $k, 3k, 20 - k$ **h** $k, k + 8, 9k$

10 The first three terms of a geometric sequence are $k - 1$,   6,   and $3k$.

    a Find the possible values of k.

    b For each value of k, find the next term in the sequence.

Example 9   ◀) **Self Tutor**

A geometric sequence has $u_2 = -6$ and $u_5 = 162$. Find its general term.

$$u_2 = u_1 r = -6 \quad \text{.... (1)}$$
$$\text{and} \quad u_5 = u_1 r^4 = 162 \quad \text{.... (2)}$$
$$\text{Now} \quad \frac{u_1 r^4}{u_1 r} = \frac{162}{-6} \quad \{(2) \div (1)\}$$
$$\therefore \quad r^3 = -27$$
$$\therefore \quad r = \sqrt[3]{-27}$$
$$\therefore \quad r = -3$$
$$\text{Using (1),} \quad u_1(-3) = -6$$
$$\therefore \quad u_1 = 2$$
$$\text{Thus} \quad u_n = 2 \times (-3)^{n-1}$$

11 Find the general term u_n of the geometric sequence which has:

a $u_4 = 24$ and $u_7 = 192$

b $u_3 = 8$ and $u_6 = -1$

c $u_7 = 24$ and $u_{15} = 384$

d $u_3 = 5$ and $u_7 = \frac{5}{4}$

Example 10   ◀) **Self Tutor**

Find the first term of the sequence $6, 6\sqrt{2}, 12, 12\sqrt{2}, ...$ which exceeds 1400.

The sequence is geometric with $u_1 = 6$ and $r = \sqrt{2}$
$$\therefore \quad u_n = 6 \times (\sqrt{2})^{n-1}$$

We need to find n such that $u_n > 1400$.

Using a graphics calculator with $Y_1 = 6 \times (\sqrt{2})^{\wedge}(X-1)$, we view a table of values:

GRAPHICS
CALCULATOR
INSTRUCTIONS

Math Deg Norm1	d/c Real
Y1=6×(√2)^(x−1)	

X	Y1
15	768
16	1086.1
17	1536
18	2172.2

1536

FORMULA DELETE ROW EDIT GPH-CON GPH-PLT

The first term to exceed 1400 is $u_{17} = 1536$.

12   a   Find the first term of the sequence $2, 6, 18, 54, ...$ which exceeds 10 000.

b   Find the first term of the sequence $4, 4\sqrt{3}, 12, 12\sqrt{3}, ...$ which exceeds 4800.

c   Find the first term of the sequence $12, 6, 3, 1.5, ...$ which is less than 0.0001.

D   GROWTH AND DECAY

We now turn our attention to applications of geometric sequences. We observe geometric sequences when a quantity increases or decreases by a fixed percentage of its size each time period.

Typical examples are in short term population growth models, and in longer term models of radioactive decay.

For most real-world situations, we have an **initial condition** corresponding to time zero. This may be an initial investment or an initial population. We therefore allow a "zeroeth" term u_0 to begin the sequence.

For situations where there is **growth** or **decay** in a geometric sequence:

$$u_n = u_0 \times r^n$$

where u_0 = initial amount

r = growth multiplier for each time period

n = number of time periods

u_n = amount after n time periods.

Example 11

◀) Self Tutor

The initial population of rabbits on a farm was 50. The population increased by 7% each week.

a How many rabbits were present after: **i** 15 weeks   **ii** 30 weeks?

b How long will it take for the population to reach 500?

There is a fixed percentage increase each week, so the population forms a geometric sequence.

$u_0 = 50$ and $r = 1.07$

$\therefore$ the population after n weeks is $u_n = 50 \times 1.07^n$.

a   **i** $u_{15} = 50 \times (1.07)^{15} \approx 137.95$ **ii** $u_{30} = 50 \times (1.07)^{30} \approx 380.61$

There were 138 rabbits.   There were 381 rabbits.

b   We need to find when $50 \times (1.07)^n = 500$.

Casio fx-CG50	TI-84 Plus CE	TI-*nspire*

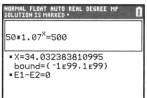

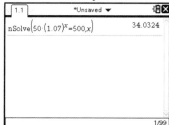

So, it will take approximately 34.0 weeks.

EXERCISE 5D

1   A nest of ants initially contains 500 individuals. The population is increasing by 12% each week.

a How many ants will there be after: **i** 10 weeks   **ii** 20 weeks?

b How many weeks will it take for the ant population to reach 2000?

2   The animal *Eraticus* is endangered. Since 2005 there has only been one colony remaining, and in 2005 the population of that colony was 555. The population has been steadily decreasing by 4.5% per year.

a Estimate the population in the year 2020.

b In what year do we expect the population to have declined to 50?

3 A herd of 32 deer is to be left unchecked in a new sanctuary. It is estimated that the size of the herd will increase each year by 18%.

    a Estimate the size of the herd after:

        i 5 years   **ii** 10 years.

    b How long will it take for the herd size to reach 5000?

4 An endangered species of marsupials has a population of 178. However, with a successful breeding program it is expected to increase by 32% each year.

    a Find the expected population size after: **i** 10 years   **ii** 25 years.

    b Estimate how long it will take for the population to reach 10 000.

5 Each year, a physicist measures the remaining radioactivity in a sample. She finds that it reduces by 18% each year. If there was 1.52 g of radioactive material left after 4 years:

    a Find the initial quantity of radioactive material.

    b How many *more* years will it take for the amount of radioactive material to reduce to 0.2 g?

6 Each year, Maria's salary is increased by 2.3%. She has been working for her company for 10 years, and she currently earns €49 852 per annum.

    a What was Maria's salary when she joined the company?

    b If she stays with the company for another 4 years, what will her salary be?

E   FINANCIAL MATHEMATICS

At some stage in life, most people need to either **invest** or **borrow** money. It is very important that potential investors and borrowers understand these procedures so they can make the right decisions according to their circumstances and their goals.

When money is lent, the person lending the money is known as the **lender**, and the person receiving the money is known as the **borrower**. The amount borrowed is called the **principal**.

The lender usually charges a fee called **interest** to the borrower. This fee represents the cost of using the other person's money. The borrower must repay the principal borrowed as well as the interest charged for using that money.

The rate at which interest is charged is usually expressed as a percentage of the principal. This percentage is known as the **interest rate**, and it is an important factor when deciding where to invest your money and where to borrow money from.

The total amount of interest charged on a loan depends on the principal, the time the money is borrowed for, and the interest rate.

COMPOUND INTEREST

When money is deposited in a bank, it will usually earn **compound interest**.

After a certain amount of time called the **period**, the bank pays interest, which is calculated as a percentage of the money already in the account.

It is called *compound* interest because the interest generated in one period will itself earn more interest in the next period.

For example, suppose you invest $1000 in the bank. The account pays an interest rate of 4% per annum (p.a.). The interest is added to your investment each year, so at the end of each year you will have $100\% + 4\% = 104\%$ of the value at its start. This corresponds to a *multiplier* of 1.04.

per annum means each year.

After one year your investment is worth $\$1000 \times 1.04 = \$1040$.

After two years it is worth

$\$1040 \times 1.04$

$= \$1000 \times 1.04 \times 1.04$

$= \$1000 \times (1.04)^2$

$= \$1081.60$

After three years it is worth

$\$1081.60 \times 1.04$

$= \$1000 \times (1.04)^2 \times 1.04$

$= \$1000 \times (1.04)^3$

$\approx \$1124.86$

Observe that:
$\begin{aligned} u_0 &= \$1000 &&= \text{initial investment} \\ u_1 &= u_0 \times 1.04 &&= \text{amount after 1 year} \\ u_2 &= u_0 \times (1.04)^2 &&= \text{amount after 2 years} \\ u_3 &= u_0 \times (1.04)^3 &&= \text{amount after 3 years} \\ &\vdots \\ u_n &= u_0 \times (1.04)^n &&= \text{amount after } n \text{ years} \end{aligned}$

So the amount in the account after each year forms a geometric sequence!

The value of a compound interest investment after n time periods is

$$u_n = u_0(1+i)^n$$

where u_0 is the initial investment

and i is the interest rate per compounding period.

The common ratio for this sequence is $r = (1 + i)$.

Example 12   ◀))) **Self Tutor**

$5000 is invested for 4 years at 7% p.a. interest compounded annually.

a   What will it amount to at the end of this period?

b   How much interest has been earned?

---

a   The interest is calculated annually, so $n = 4$ time periods.

$\begin{aligned} u_4 &= u_0 \times (1+i)^4 \\ &= 5000 \times (1.07)^4 \qquad \{7\% = 0.07\} \\ &\approx 6553.98 \end{aligned}$

The investment will amount to $6553.98.

b   The interest earned $= \$6553.98 - \$5000$

$= \$1553.98$

EXERCISE 5E.1

1 Lucy invested £7000 at 6% p.a. interest compounded annually. Find the value of this investment after 5 years.

2 What will an investment of £3000 at 4.8% p.a. interest compounded annually amount to after 3 years?

3 €2000 is invested for 4 years at 2.8% p.a. interest compounded annually.

    a What will it amount to at the end of this period?

    b How much interest has been earned?

4 How much compound interest is earned by investing €20 000 at 4.2% p.a. over a 4 year period?

5 How much compound interest is earned by investing $8000 at 2.9% p.a. over a 3 year period?

Example 13	◀》 **Self Tutor**

£5000 is invested for 4 years at 3% p.a. interest compounded quarterly. Find the value of the investment at the end of this period.

> Quarterly means 4 times per year.

There are $n = 4 \times 4 = 16$ time periods.

Each time period the investment increases by $i = \dfrac{3\%}{4} = 0.75\%$.

∴ the amount after 4 years is $u_{16} = u_0 \times (1+i)^{16}$
$$= 5000 \times (1.0075)^{16} \quad \{0.75\% = 0.0075\}$$
$$\approx 5634.96$$

The investment will amount to £5634.96.

---

6 $20 000 is invested at 4.8% p.a. interest compounded quarterly. Find the value of this investment after:

    a 1 year   **b** 3 years.

7 **a** What will an investment of €30 000 at 5.6% p.a. interest compounded annually amount to after 4 years?

    b How much of this is interest?

8 How much interest is earned by investing $80 000 at 4.4% p.a. for a 3 year period with interest compounded quarterly?

9 Jai recently inherited $92 000. He decides to invest it for 10 years before he spends any of it. The three banks in his town offer the following terms:

    Bank A: $5\frac{1}{2}\%$ p.a. compounded yearly.

    Bank B: $5\frac{1}{4}\%$ p.a. compounded quarterly.

    Bank C: 5% p.a. compounded monthly.

Which bank offers Jai the greatest interest on his inheritance?

Example 14   ◀)) **Self Tutor**

How much does Ivana need to invest now, to get a maturing value of $10 000 in 4 years' time, given interest at 8% p.a. compounded twice annually? Give your answer to the nearest dollar.

The initial investment u_0 is unknown.

There are $n = 4 \times 2 = 8$ time periods.

Each time period the investment increases by $i = \dfrac{8\%}{2} = 4\%$.

Now $u_8 = u_0 \times (1 + i)^8$

$\therefore \; 10\,000 = u_0 \times (1.04)^8$ $\{4\% = 0.04\}$

$\therefore \; u_0 = \dfrac{10\,000}{(1.04)^8} \approx 7306.90$

Ivana needs to invest $7307 now.

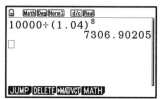

10   How much does Habib need to invest now, to get a maturing value of £20 000 in 4 years' time, given the money can be invested at a fixed rate of 7.5% p.a. compounded annually? Round your answer up to the next pound.

11   What initial investment is required to produce a maturing amount of $15 000 in 60 months' time given a guaranteed fixed interest rate of 5.5% p.a. compounded annually? Round your answer up to the next dollar.

12   How much should I invest now to yield $25 000 in 3 years' time, if the money can be invested at a fixed rate of 4.2% p.a. compounded quarterly?

13   What initial investment will yield ¥4 000 000 in 8 years' time if your money can be invested at 3.6% p.a. compounded monthly?

INFLATION

Inflation is the general increase in the price of goods and services over time. Inflation reduces the **purchasing power** of your money, because a fixed amount of money will buy less goods and services as prices rise over time.

Inflation needs to be taken into account when setting investment goals. For example, suppose you see a painting that you would like to buy, and it costs $5000 today. If it takes you 3 years to accumulate the $5000, the price of the painting is likely to have increased in that time. So, you will need to accumulate more than $5000 to purchase the painting.

To find how much you need to accumulate, you must **index** the value of the painting for inflation.

Example 15   ◀)) **Self Tutor**

Georgia would like to purchase a painting that is currently worth $5000. She makes monthly deposits into an investment account, so that she can purchase the painting in 3 years' time.

If inflation averages 2.5% per year, calculate the value of the painting indexed for inflation for 3 years.

To index the value of the painting for inflation, we increase it by 2.5% each year for 3 years.

$\therefore$ indexed value $= \$5000 \times (1.025)^3$

$\phantom{\therefore \text{ indexed value }} = \$5384.45$

EXERCISE 5E.2

1 If inflation averages 3% per year, calculate the value of:

    a $8000 indexed for inflation over 2 years

    b $14\,000 indexed for inflation over 5 years

    c $22\,500 indexed for inflation over 7 years.

2 Hoang currently requires $1000 per week to maintain his lifestyle. Assuming inflation averages 2% per year, how much will Hoang require per week for him to maintain his current lifestyle in:

    a 10 years' time   **b** 20 years' time

    c 30 years' time?

3 A holiday package is valued at $15\,000 today. If inflation averages 2% per year, calculate the value of the holiday package indexed for inflation over 4 years.

THE REAL VALUE OF AN INVESTMENT

To understand how well an investment will perform, we can consider its final value in terms of today's purchasing power. We call this the **real value** of the investment.

We have seen that to index a value for inflation, we *multiply* its value by the inflation multiplier each year. So, to consider the final value of an investment in today's dollars, we *divide* its value by the inflation multiplier each year.

Example 16	◀) Self Tutor

Gemma invested $4000 in an account for 5 years at 4.8% p.a. interest compounded half-yearly. Inflation over the period averaged 3% per year.

    a Calculate the value of the investment after 5 years.

    b Find the real value of the investment by indexing it for inflation.

a There are $n = 5 \times 2 = 10$ time periods.

Each period, the investment increases by $i = \dfrac{4.8\%}{2} = 2.4\%$.

$\therefore$ the amount after 5 years is $\quad u_{10} = u_0 \times (1 + i)^{10}$
$$= 4000 \times (1.024)^{10}$$
$$\approx 5070.60$$

The investment will amount to $5070.60.

b real value $\times (1.03)^5 = \$5070.60$

$\therefore$ real value $= \dfrac{\$5070.60}{(1.03)^5}$

$\qquad\qquad\quad = \$4373.94$

Inflation reduces the real value of an investment.

EXERCISE 5E.3

1 Ernie invested $5000 in an account for 3 years at 3.6% p.a. interest compounded quarterly. Inflation over the period averaged 2% per year.

   a Calculate the value of the investment after 3 years.

   b Find the real value of the investment by indexing it for inflation.

2 Gino invested €20 000 in an account for 4 years at 4.2% p.a. interest compounded monthly. Inflation over the period averaged 3.4% per year.

   a Find the value of Gino's investment after 4 years.

   b Find the real value of the investment.

3 Brooke invested $4000 in an account that pays 3% p.a. interest compounded half-yearly for 6 years.

   a Calculate the final value of the investment.

   b How much interest did Brooke earn?

   c Given that inflation averaged 3.2% per year over the investment period, find the real value of the investment.

   d Discuss the effectiveness of the investment once inflation has been considered.

DEPRECIATION

Assets such as computers, cars, and furniture lose value as time passes. This is due to wear and tear, technology becoming old, fashions changing, and other reasons.

Depreciation is the loss in value of an item over time.

Mathematically, depreciation is similar to compound interest. In the case of compound interest, the investment increases by a fixed percentage each time period. For depreciation, the value *decreases* by a fixed percentage each time period.

The value of an object after n years is $u_n = u_0(1 - d)^n$

where u_0 is the initial value of the object

  and d is the rate of depreciation per annum.

The common ratio for this sequence is $r = (1 - d)$.

Example 17	◀) **Self Tutor**

An industrial dishwasher was purchased for £2400 and depreciated by 15% each year.

   a Find its value after six years.   **b** By how much did it depreciate?

a $u_6 = u_0 \times (1 - d)^6$

      $= 2400 \times (0.85)^6$ $\{15\% = 0.15\}$

      ≈ 905.16

So, after 6 years the value is £905.16 .

b The depreciation $= £2400 - £905.16$

                  $= £1494.84$

EXERCISE 5E.4

1 A lathe is purchased by a workshop for €2500. It depreciates by 20% each year. Find the value of the lathe after 3 years.

2 A tractor was purchased for €110 000, and depreciates at 25% p.a. for 5 years.

    a Find its value at the end of this period.

    b By how much has it depreciated?

3 Suppose I buy a laptop for ¥87 500 and keep it for 3 years. During this time it depreciates at an annual rate of 30%.

    a Find its value after 3 years.

    b By how much has the laptop depreciated?

4 A printing press costing $250 000 was sold 4 years later for $80 000. At what yearly rate did it depreciate in value?

USING TECHNOLOGY FOR FINANCIAL MODELS

To solve more complicated problems involving financial models, we must use technology.

Most graphics calculators have an in-built **finance program** that can help with finance problems. This is called a **TVM Solver**, where **TVM** stands for **time value of money**.

The TVM Solver can be used to find any variable if all the other variables are given. For the **TI-84 Plus CE**, the abbreviations used are:

TI-84 Plus CE

- N represents the **number of compounding periods**
- $I\%$ represents the **interest rate per year**
- PV represents the **present value** of the investment
- PMT represents the **payment each time period**
- FV represents the **future value** of the investment
- P/Y is the **number of payments per year**
- C/Y is the **number of compounding periods per year**
- PMT : END BEGIN   lets you choose between payments at the end of a time period or payments at the beginning of a time period. Most interest payments are made at the end of the time periods.

Casio fx-CG50

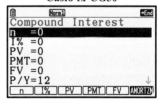

Click on the icon to obtain instructions for using the finance program on your calculator.

GRAPHICS
CALCULATOR
INSTRUCTIONS

When calculating compound interest using electronic technology, notice that:

- The initial investment is entered as a negative value, because that money is moving from you to the bank. The future value is the money you receive at the end of the investment, so FV is positive.
- N represents the number of compounding periods, not the number of years.
- I is always the percentage interest rate *per annum*.

Example 18   ◀ᴼ) **Self Tutor**

Sally invests $15 000 in an account that pays 4.25% p.a. compounded monthly. How much is her investment worth after 5 years?

$N = 5 \times 12 = 60, \quad I\% = 4.25, \quad PV = -15\,000, \quad PMT = 0,$
$P/Y = 12, \quad C/Y = 12$

$\therefore \quad FV \approx 18\,544.53$

Sally's investment is worth $18 544.53 after 5 years.

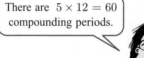

There are $5 \times 12 = 60$ compounding periods.

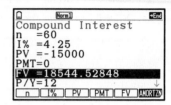

```
              Norm1              ►End
Compound Interest
n   =60
I%  =4.25
PV  =-15000
PMT=0
FV  =18544.52848
P/Y=12
  n   I%   PV   PMT   FV  AMORTZN
```

Example 19   ◀ᴼ) **Self Tutor**

Halena is investing money in a term deposit paying 5.2% p.a. compounded quarterly. How much does she need to deposit now, in order to collect $5000 at the end of 3 years?

$N = 3 \times 4 = 12, \quad I\% = 5.2, \quad PMT = 0, \quad FV = 5000, \quad P/Y = 4, \quad C/Y = 4$

$\therefore \quad PV \approx -4282.10$

Thus, $4282.10 needs to be deposited.

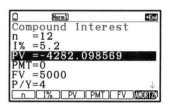

```
              Norm1              ►End
Compound Interest
n   =12
I%  =5.2
PV  =-4282.098569
PMT=0
FV  =5000
P/Y=4
  n   I%   PV   PMT   FV  AMORTZN
```

EXERCISE 5E.5

1   Enrique invests 60 000 pesos at 3.7% p.a. compounded annually. Find the value of his investment after 6 years.

2   I deposit $6000 in a bank account that pays 5% p.a. compounded monthly. How much will I have in my account after 2 years?

3   When my daughter was born, I deposited €2000 in a bank account paying 4% p.a. compounded half-yearly. How much will my daughter receive on her 18th birthday?

4   Kenneth sold his boat for $8000, and deposited the money in a bank account paying 5.6% p.a. compounded quarterly. How much will Kenneth have in his account after:

   a   3 years   b   8 years?

5   Drew invested €5000 in an account paying 4.2% p.a. interest compounded monthly.

   a   Find the amount in the account after 7 years.

   b   Calculate the interest earned.

6 Calculate the interest earned on an investment of £13 000 for 4 years at 7% p.a. compounded quarterly.

7 How much would you need to invest now in order to accumulate $2500 in 5 years' time, if the interest rate is 4.5% p.a. compounded monthly?

8 You have just won the lottery and decide to invest the money. Your accountant advises you to deposit your winnings in an account that pays 6.5% p.a. compounded annually. After four years your winnings have grown to $102 917.31. How much did you win in the lottery?

9 Donald bought a new stereo for $458. If it depreciated in value by 25% p.a., find its value after 5 years.

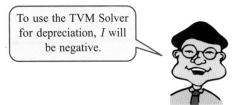

To use the TVM Solver for depreciation, I will be negative.

| **Example 20** | ◀⟩ **Self Tutor** |

For how long must Magnus invest $4000 at 6.45% p.a. compounded half-yearly, for it to amount to $10 000?

$I\% = 6.45$, $PV = -4000$, $PMT = 0$, $FV = 10\,000$, $P/Y = 2$, $C/Y = 2$

$\therefore$ $N \approx 28.9$

So, 29 half-years are required, which is 14.5 years.

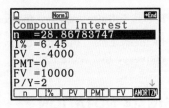

---

10 A couple inherited $40 000 and deposited it in an account paying $4\frac{1}{2}$% p.a. compounded quarterly. They withdrew the money as soon as they had over $45 000. How long did they keep the money in that account?

11 A business deposits €80 000 in an account that pays $5\frac{1}{4}$% p.a. compounded monthly. How long will it take before they double their money?

12 Farm vehicles are known to depreciate in value by 12% each year. If Susan buys a quadrunner for $6800, how long will it take for the value to reduce to $1000?

| **Example 21** | ◀⟩ **Self Tutor** |

Iman deposits $5000 in an account that compounds interest monthly. 2.5 years later, the account has balance $6000. What annual rate of interest has been paid?

$N = 2.5 \times 12 = 30$, $PV = -5000$, $PMT = 0$, $FV = 6000$, $P/Y = 12$, $C/Y = 12$

$\therefore$ $I\% \approx 7.32$

The interest rate is 7.32% p.a.

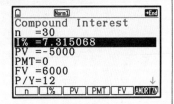

13 An investor has purchased rare medals for $10 000 and hopes to sell them 3 years later for $15 000. What must the annual percentage increase in the value of the medals be, in order for the investor's target to be reached?

14 I deposited €5000 into an account that compounds interest monthly. $3\frac{1}{2}$ years later the account has balance €6165. What annual rate of interest did the account pay?

15 A young couple invests their savings of $9000 in an account where the interest is compounded quarterly. Three years later the account balance is $10 493. What interest rate has been paid?

16 A new sports car devalues from £68 500 to £26 380 over 4 years. Find the annual rate of depreciation.

F   SERIES

There are many situations where we are interested in finding the sum of the terms of a number sequence.

A **series** is the sum of the terms of a sequence.

For a **finite** sequence with n terms, the corresponding series is $u_1 + u_2 + u_3 + \ldots + u_n$.

The sum of this series is $S_n = u_1 + u_2 + u_3 + \ldots + u_n$ and this will always be a finite real number.

For an **infinite** sequence the corresponding series is $u_1 + u_2 + u_3 + \ldots + u_n + \ldots$

In many cases, the sum of an infinite series cannot be calculated. In some cases, however, it does **converge** to a finite number.

SIGMA NOTATION

$u_1 + u_2 + u_3 + u_4 + \ldots + u_n$ can be written more compactly using **sigma notation** or **summation notation**.

The symbol $\sum$ is called **sigma**. It is the equivalent of capital S in the Greek alphabet.

We write $u_1 + u_2 + u_3 + u_4 + \ldots + u_n$ as $\displaystyle\sum_{k=1}^{n} u_k$.

$\displaystyle\sum_{k=1}^{n} u_k$ reads "the sum of all numbers of the form u_k where $k = 1, 2, 3, \ldots$, up to n".

Example 22	◀ᴺ **Self Tutor**

Consider the sequence   1, 4, 9, 16, 25, ...

    a Write down an expression for S_n.   **b** Find S_n for $n = 1, 2, 3, 4,$ and 5.

  a $S_n = 1^2 + 2^2 + 3^2 + 4^2 + \ldots + n^2$

        {all terms are squares}

      $= \displaystyle\sum_{k=1}^{n} k^2$

  b $S_1 = 1$

    $S_2 = 1 + 4 = 5$

    $S_3 = 1 + 4 + 9 = 14$

    $S_4 = 1 + 4 + 9 + 16 = 30$

    $S_5 = 1 + 4 + 9 + 16 + 25 = 55$

Example 23   🔊 **Self Tutor**

Expand and evaluate:

a $\displaystyle\sum_{k=1}^{7} (k+1)$ **b** $\displaystyle\sum_{k=1}^{5} \frac{1}{2^k}$

---

a $\displaystyle\sum_{k=1}^{7} (k+1)$ **b** $\displaystyle\sum_{k=1}^{5} \frac{1}{2^k}$

$\quad = 2 + 3 + 4 + 5 + 6 + 7 + 8$ $\quad = \frac{1}{2} + \frac{1}{4} + \frac{1}{8} + \frac{1}{16} + \frac{1}{32}$

$\quad = 35$ $\quad = \frac{31}{32}$

You can also use technology to evaluate the sum of a series in sigma notation. Click on the icon for instructions.

GRAPHICS
CALCULATOR
INSTRUCTIONS

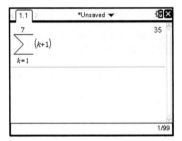

PROPERTIES OF SIGMA NOTATION

$$\sum_{k=1}^{n} (a_k + b_k) = \sum_{k=1}^{n} a_k + \sum_{k=1}^{n} b_k$$

If c is a constant, $\displaystyle\sum_{k=1}^{n} ca_k = c\sum_{k=1}^{n} a_k$ and $\displaystyle\sum_{k=1}^{n} c = cn.$

EXERCISE 5F

1 Consider the sequence of composite numbers   4, 6, 8, 9, 10, 12, 14, 15, 16, ...
Find:

   a S_3 **b** S_5 **c** S_{12}

2 Suppose a sequence has $S_4 = 13$ and $S_5 = 20$. Find the value of u_5.

3 Consider the sequence $u_n = \dfrac{1}{n}$.

   a Write down the first 5 terms of the sequence.

   b Find S_4 in rational form.

   c Find the values of n such that $S_n > 3$.

4 For each of the following sequences:

     i Write down an expression for S_n.

     ii Find S_5.

   a 3, 11, 19, 27, ...   **b** 42, 37, 32, 27, ...   **c** 12, 6, 3, $1\frac{1}{2}$, ...

   d 2, 3, $4\frac{1}{2}$, $6\frac{3}{4}$, ...   **e** 1, $\frac{1}{2}$, $\frac{1}{4}$, $\frac{1}{8}$, ...   **f** 1, 8, 27, 64, ...

5 Expand and evaluate:

a $\displaystyle\sum_{k=1}^{3} 4k$

b $\displaystyle\sum_{k=1}^{6} (k+1)$

c $\displaystyle\sum_{k=1}^{4} (3k-5)$

d $\displaystyle\sum_{k=1}^{5} (11-2k)$

e $\displaystyle\sum_{k=1}^{7} k(k+1)$

f $\displaystyle\sum_{k=1}^{5} 10 \times 2^{k-1}$

6 For $u_n = 3n - 1$, write $u_1 + u_2 + u_3 + \ldots + u_{20}$ using sigma notation and evaluate the sum.

7 Show that:

a $\displaystyle\sum_{k=1}^{n} c = cn$

b $\displaystyle\sum_{k=1}^{n} ca_k = c \sum_{k=1}^{n} a_k$

c $\displaystyle\sum_{k=1}^{n} (a_k + b_k) = \sum_{k=1}^{n} a_k + \sum_{k=1}^{n} b_k$

Example 24   ◀)) **Self Tutor**

a Expand $\displaystyle\sum_{k=1}^{n} 2k$ then write the expansion again underneath but with the terms in the reverse order.

b Add the terms vertically, and hence write an expression for the sum S_n of the first n even integers.

---

a $\displaystyle\sum_{k=1}^{n} 2k = 2 + \quad 4 \quad + \quad 6 \quad + \ldots + (2n-2) + 2n$

or $\quad 2n + (2n-2) + (2n-4) + \ldots + \quad 4 \quad + 2$

b $2 \displaystyle\sum_{k=1}^{n} 2k = (2n+2) + (2n+2) + (2n+2) + \ldots + (2n+2) + (2n+2)$

$\phantom{2 \sum_{k=1}^{n} 2k} = n(2n+2)$

$\phantom{2 \sum_{k=1}^{n} 2k} = 2n(n+1)$

$\therefore \displaystyle\sum_{k=1}^{n} 2k = n(n+1)$

---

8 **a** Expand $\displaystyle\sum_{k=1}^{n} k$ then write the expansion again underneath with the terms in the reverse order.

b Add the terms vertically, and hence write an expression for the sum S_n of the first n integers.

c Hence find a and b such that $\displaystyle\sum_{k=1}^{n} (ak+b) = 8n^2 + 11n$ for all positive integers n.

9 Write an expression for the sum of the first n positive odd integers.

10 Given that $\displaystyle\sum_{k=1}^{n} k = \frac{n(n+1)}{2}$ and $\displaystyle\sum_{k=1}^{n} k^2 = \frac{n(n+1)(2n+1)}{6}$, write $\displaystyle\sum_{k=1}^{n} (k+1)(k+2)$ in simplest form.

Check your answer in the case when $n = 10$.

G | ARITHMETIC SERIES

An **arithmetic series** is the sum of the terms of an arithmetic sequence.

For example: $21, 23, 25, 27, ..., 49$ is a finite arithmetic sequence.

$21 + 23 + 25 + 27 + ... + 49$ is the corresponding arithmetic series.

SUM OF A FINITE ARITHMETIC SERIES

Rather than adding all the terms individually, we can use a formula to find the sum of a finite arithmetic series.

If the first term is u_1, the final term is u_n, and the common difference is d, the terms are
$u_1, \ u_1 + d, \ u_1 + 2d, \ ...., \ (u_n - 2d), \ (u_n - d), \ u_n$.

$$\therefore \ S_n = u_1 + (u_1 + d) + (u_1 + 2d) + ... + (u_n - 2d) + (u_n - d) + u_n$$
$$\text{But} \quad S_n = u_n + (u_n - d) + (u_n - 2d) + ... + (u_1 + 2d) + (u_1 + d) + u_1 \quad \{\text{reversing them}\}$$

Adding these two equations vertically, we get:

$$2S_n = \underbrace{(u_1 + u_n) + (u_1 + u_n) + (u_1 + u_n) + ... + (u_1 + u_n) + (u_1 + u_n) + (u_1 + u_n)}_{n \text{ of these}}$$

$$\therefore \ 2S_n = n(u_1 + u_n)$$
$$\therefore \ S_n = \frac{n}{2}(u_1 + u_n) \quad \text{where} \quad u_n = u_1 + (n-1)d$$

The sum of a finite arithmetic series with first term u_1, common difference d, and last term u_n, is

$$S_n = \frac{n}{2}(u_1 + u_n) \qquad or \qquad S_n = \frac{n}{2}(2u_1 + (n-1)d).$$

Example 25 ◀) **Self Tutor**

Find the sum of $4 + 7 + 10 + 13 + ...$ to 50 terms.

The series is arithmetic with $u_1 = 4$, $d = 3$, and $n = 50$.

Now $S_n = \frac{n}{2}(2u_1 + (n-1)d)$

$\therefore \ S_{50} = \frac{50}{2}(2 \times 4 + 49 \times 3)$

$= 3875$

You can also use technology to evaluate series, although for some calculator models this is tedious.

GRAPHICS
CALCULATOR
INSTRUCTIONS

EXERCISE 5G

1 Find the sum of the arithmetic series $2 + 6 + 10 + 14 + 18 + 22 + 26 + 30$:

     a by direct addition   **b** using $S_n = \dfrac{n}{2}(u_1 + u_n)$

     c using $S_n = \dfrac{n}{2}(2u_1 + (n-1)d)$.

2 Find the sum of:

     a $7 + 9 + 11 + 13 + \ldots$ to 10 terms   **b** $3 + 7 + 11 + 15 + \ldots$ to 20 terms

     c $\frac{1}{2} + 3 + 5\frac{1}{2} + 8 + \ldots$ to 50 terms   **d** $100 + 93 + 86 + 79 + \ldots$ to 40 terms

     e $(-31) + (-28) + (-25) + (-22) + \ldots$ to 15 terms

     f $50 + 48\frac{1}{2} + 47 + 45\frac{1}{2} + \ldots$ to 80 terms.

Example 26   ◀) Self Tutor

Find the sum of $-6 + 1 + 8 + 15 + \ldots + 141$.

The series is arithmetic with $u_1 = -6$, $d = 7$, and $u_n = 141$.

First we need to find n.

$$\begin{aligned} \text{Now} \quad u_n &= 141 \\ \therefore \quad u_1 + (n-1)d &= 141 \\ \therefore \quad -6 + 7(n-1) &= 141 \\ \therefore \quad 7(n-1) &= 147 \\ \therefore \quad n - 1 &= 21 \\ \therefore \quad n &= 22 \end{aligned}$$

Using $S_n = \dfrac{n}{2}(u_1 + u_n)$,

$$\begin{aligned} S_{22} &= \tfrac{22}{2}(-6 + 141) \\ &= 11 \times 135 \\ &= 1485 \end{aligned}$$

---

3 Find the sum of:

     a $5 + 8 + 11 + 14 + \ldots + 101$ **b** $37 + 33 + 29 + 25 + \ldots + 9$

     c $50 + 49\frac{1}{2} + 49 + 48\frac{1}{2} + \ldots + (-20)$ **d** $8 + 10\frac{1}{2} + 13 + 15\frac{1}{2} + \ldots + 83$

4 Consider the arithmetic sequence $9, 15, 21, \ldots, 69, 75$.

     a Find the common difference d.

     b Find the number of terms in the sequence.

     c Find the sum of the terms in the sequence.

5 Evaluate these arithmetic series:

     a $\displaystyle\sum_{k=1}^{10} (2k + 5)$ **b** $\displaystyle\sum_{k=1}^{15} (k - 50)$ **c** $\displaystyle\sum_{k=1}^{20} \left(\dfrac{k+3}{2}\right)$

Check your answers using technology.

6 An arithmetic series has seven terms. The first term is 5 and the last term is 53. Find the sum of the series.

7 An arithmetic series has eleven terms. The first term is 6 and the last term is -27. Find the sum of the series.

8 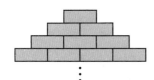   A bricklayer builds a triangular wall with layers of bricks as shown. If the bricklayer uses 171 bricks, how many layers did he build?

9 Vicki has 30 days to train for a swimming competition. She swims 20 laps on the first day, then each day after that she swims two more laps than the previous day. So, she swims 22 laps on the second day, 24 laps on the third day, and so on.

    a How many laps does Vicki swim on:

        i the tenth day   **ii** the final day?

    b How many laps does Vicki swim in total?

10 A woman deposits \$100 into her son's savings account on his first birthday. She deposits \$125 on his second birthday, \$150 on his third birthday, and so on.

    a Calculate the amount of money she will deposit into her son's account on his 15th birthday.

    b Find the total amount she will have deposited over the 15 years.

11 A football stadium has 25 sections of seating. Each section has 44 rows of seats, with 22 seats in the first row, 23 in the second row, 24 in the third row, and so on. How many seats are there in:

    a row 44 of one section   **b** each section   **c** the whole stadium?

12 Find the sum of:

    a the first 50 multiples of 11

    b the multiples of 7 between 0 and 1000

    c the integers from 1 to 100 which are not divisible by 3.

13 The sixth term of an arithmetic sequence is 21, and the sum of the first seventeen terms is 0. Find the first two terms of the sequence.

Example 27   ◀⧏ **Self Tutor**

An arithmetic sequence has first term 8 and common difference 2. The sum of the terms of the sequence is 170. Find the number of terms in the sequence.

The sequence is arithmetic with $u_1 = 8$ and $d = 2$.

Now $S_n = 170$, so $\dfrac{n}{2}(2u_1 + (n-1)d) = 170$

$$\therefore \ \frac{n}{2}(16 + 2(n-1)) = 170$$

$$\therefore \ 8n + n(n-1) = 170$$

$$\therefore \ n^2 + 7n - 170 = 0$$

$$\therefore \ (n+17)(n-10) = 0$$

$$\therefore \ n = 10 \quad \{as \ n > 0\}$$

$\therefore$ there are 10 terms in the sequence.

---

14 An arithmetic sequence has first term 4 and common difference 6. The sum of the terms of the sequence is 200. Find the number of terms in the sequence.

15 An arithmetic sequence has $u_1 = 7$ and $S_2 = 17$.

    a Find the common difference of the sequence.

    b Find n such that $S_n = 242$.

16 Consider the arithmetic sequence 13, 21, 29, 37, ... How many terms are needed for the sum of the sequence terms to exceed 1000?

17 Consider the series of odd numbers $1 + 3 + 5 + 7 + ...$

    a Write a formula for the nth term u_n.

    b Prove that the sum of the first n odd integers is n^2.

18 Prove that the sum of the first n integers is $\dfrac{n(n+1)}{2}$.

19 Three consecutive terms of an arithmetic sequence have a sum of 12 and a product of -80. Find the terms.

    Hint: Let the terms be $x - d$, x, and $x + d$.

20 The sum of the first 15 terms of an arithmetic sequence is 480. Find the 8th term of the sequence.

21 Five consecutive terms of an arithmetic sequence have a sum of 40. The product of the first, middle, and last terms is 224. Find the terms of the sequence.

22 The sum of the first n terms of an arithmetic sequence is $\dfrac{n(3n+11)}{2}$.

    a Find its first two terms.   **b** Find the twentieth term of the sequence.

23 Find $3 - 5 + 7 - 9 + 11 - 13 + 15 - ....$ to 80 terms.

24 Let $u_n = 3 + 2n$.

    a For $n = 1, ..., 4$, plot the points (n, u_n) on a graph, and draw rectangles with vertices (n, u_n), $(n+1, u_n)$, $(n, 0)$, and $(n+1, 0)$.

    b Explain how S_n relates to the areas of the rectangles.

    c Using your sketch, explain why: **i** $u_{n+1} = u_n + 2$ **ii** $S_{n+1} = S_n + u_{n+1}$.

ACTIVITY 1   STADIUM SEATING

A circular stadium consists of sections as illustrated, with aisles in between. The diagram shows the 13 tiers of concrete steps for the final section, Section K. Seats are placed along every concrete step, with each seat 0.45 m wide. The arc AB at the front of the first row is 14.4 m long, while the arc CD at the back of the back row is 20.25 m long.

1 How wide is each concrete step?

2 What is the length of the arc of the back of Row 1, Row 2, Row 3, and so on?

3 How many seats are there in Row 1, Row 2, Row 3, ..., Row 13?

4 How many sections are there in the stadium?

5 What is the total seating capacity of the stadium?

6 What is the radius r of the "playing surface"?

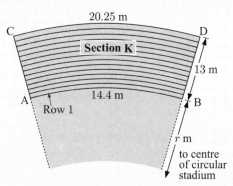

THEORY OF KNOWLEDGE

The sequence of odd numbers   1, 3, 5, 7, ...   is defined by $u_n = 2n - 1$, $n = 1, 2, 3, 4, ...$

By studying sums of the first few terms of the sequence, we might suspect that the sum of the first n odd numbers is n^2.

$$
\begin{aligned}
S_1 &= & 1 &= \ 1 = 1^2 \\
S_2 &= & 1 + 3 &= \ 4 = 2^2 \\
S_3 &= & 1 + 3 + 5 &= \ 9 = 3^2 \\
S_4 &= & 1 + 3 + 5 + 7 &= 16 = 4^2 \\
S_5 &= 1 + 3 + 5 + 7 + 9 &= 25 = 5^2
\end{aligned}
$$

But is this enough to *prove* that the statement is true for all positive integers n?

1 Can we prove that a statement is true in all cases by checking that it is true for some specific cases?

2 How do we know when we have proven a statement to be true?

In the case of the sum of the first n odd integers, you should have proven the result in the last Exercise using the known, proven formula for the sum of an arithmetic series.

However, in mathematics not all **conjectures** turn out to be true. For example, consider the sequence of numbers $u_n = n^2 + n + 41$.

We observe that:

$u_1 = 1^2 + 1 + 41 = 43$ which is prime

$u_2 = 2^2 + 2 + 41 = 47$ which is prime

$u_3 = 3^2 + 3 + 41 = 53$ which is prime

$u_4 = 4^2 + 4 + 41 = 61$ which is prime.

From this, we may *conjecture* that $n^2 + n + 41$ is prime for any positive integer n.

In fact, $n^2 + n + 41$ is prime for all positive integers n from 1 to 39.

However, $u_{40} = 40^2 + 40 + 41 = 41^2$, so u_{40} is composite.

Suppose we place n points around a circle such that when we connect each point with every other point, no three lines intersect at the same point. We then count the number of regions that the circle is divided into.

The first five cases are shown below:

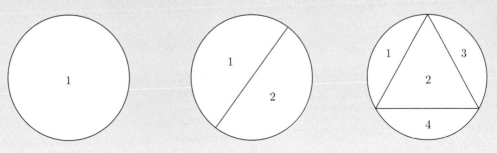

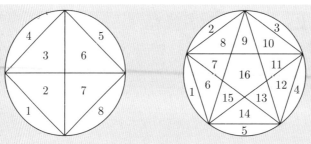

From these cases we *conjecture* that for n points, the circle is divided into 2^{n-1} regions.

Draw the case $n = 6$ and see if the conjecture is true!

3 Is it reasonable for a mathematician to assume a conjecture is true until it has been formally proven?

H   FINITE GEOMETRIC SERIES

A **geometric series** is the sum of the terms of a geometric sequence.

For example: 1, 2, 4, 8, 16, ..., 1024   is a finite geometric sequence.

$1 + 2 + 4 + 8 + 16 + ... + 1024$ is the corresponding finite geometric series.

If we are adding the first n terms of an infinite geometric sequence, we are then calculating a finite geometric series called the **nth partial sum** of the corresponding infinite series.

If we are adding all of the terms in an infinite geometric sequence, we have an **infinite geometric series**.

SUM OF A FINITE GEOMETRIC SERIES

If the first term is u_1 and the common ratio is r, then the terms are: $u_1, u_1r, u_1r^2, u_1r^3, ..., u_1r^{n-1}$.

So, $S_n = u_1 \; + \; u_1r \; + \; u_1r^2 \; + \; u_1r^3 \; + \; .... \; + \; u_1r^{n-2} \; + \; u_1r^{n-1}$

$$u_2 \qquad u_3 \qquad u_4 \qquad\qquad u_{n-1} \qquad u_n$$

For a finite geometric series with $r \neq 1$,

$$S_n = \frac{u_1(r^n - 1)}{r - 1} \quad or \quad S_n = \frac{u_1(1 - r^n)}{1 - r}.$$

Proof:

If $S_n = u_1 + u_1r + u_1r^2 + u_1r^3 + ... + u_1r^{n-2} + u_1r^{n-1}$ (*)

then $rS_n = (u_1r + u_1r^2 + u_1r^3 + u_1r^4 + ... + u_1r^{n-1}) + u_1r^n$

$\therefore \; rS_n = (S_n - u_1) + u_1r^n$ {from (*)}

$\therefore \; rS_n - S_n = u_1r^n - u_1$

$\therefore \; S_n(r - 1) = u_1(r^n - 1)$

$\therefore \; S_n = \dfrac{u_1(r^n - 1)}{r - 1}$ or $\dfrac{u_1(1 - r^n)}{1 - r}$ provided $r \neq 1$.

In the case $r = 1$ we have a sequence in which all terms are the same. The sequence is also arithmetic with $d = 0$, and $S_n = u_1 n$.

Example 28   ◀)) **Self Tutor**

Find the sum of $2 + 6 + 18 + 54 + ...$ to 12 terms.

The series is geometric with $u_1 = 2$, $r = 3$, and $n = 12$.

$$S_n = \frac{u_1(r^n - 1)}{r - 1}$$

$$\therefore \ S_{12} = \frac{2(3^{12} - 1)}{3 - 1} = 531\,440$$

Example 29   ◀)) **Self Tutor**

Find a formula for S_n, the sum of the first n terms of the series $9 - 3 + 1 - \frac{1}{3} + ...$

This answer cannot be simplified as we do not know if n is odd or even.

The series is geometric with $u_1 = 9$ and $r = -\frac{1}{3}$.

$$S_n = \frac{u_1(1 - r^n)}{1 - r} = \frac{9(1 - (-\frac{1}{3})^n)}{\frac{4}{3}}$$

$$\therefore \ S_n = \frac{27}{4}(1 - (-\frac{1}{3})^n)$$

EXERCISE 5H

1 Find the sum $3 + 6 + 12 + 24 + 48$:

   a by direct addition

   b using $S_n = \dfrac{u_1(r^n - 1)}{r - 1}$

2 Find the sum of the following series:

   a $2 + 6 + 18 + 54 + ...$ to 8 terms

   b $5 + 10 + 20 + 40 + ...$ to 10 terms

   c $12 + 6 + 3 + 1.5 + ...$ to 10 terms

   d $\sqrt{7} + 7 + 7\sqrt{7} + 49 + ...$ to 12 terms

   e $6 - 3 + 1\frac{1}{2} - \frac{3}{4} + ...$ to 15 terms

   f $1 - \frac{1}{\sqrt{2}} + \frac{1}{2} - \frac{1}{2\sqrt{2}} + ...$ to 20 terms

3 Find a formula for S_n, the sum of the first n terms of the series:

   a $\sqrt{3} + 3 + 3\sqrt{3} + 9 + ...$

   b $12 + 6 + 3 + 1\frac{1}{2} + ...$

   c $0.9 + 0.09 + 0.009 + 0.0009 + ...$

   d $20 - 10 + 5 - 2\frac{1}{2} + ...$

4 A geometric sequence has partial sums $S_1 = 3$ and $S_2 = 4$.

   a State the first term u_1.

   b Calculate the common ratio r.

   c Calculate the fifth term u_5 of the series.

   d Find the value of S_5.

5 Evaluate these geometric series:

   a $\displaystyle\sum_{k=1}^{10} 3 \times 2^{k-1}$

   b $\displaystyle\sum_{k=1}^{12} \left(\frac{1}{2}\right)^{k-2}$

   c $\displaystyle\sum_{k=1}^{25} 6 \times (-2)^k$

6   At the end of each year, a salesperson is paid a bonus of $2000 which is always deposited into the same account. It earns a fixed rate of interest of 6% p.a. with interest being paid annually. The total amount in the account at the end of each year will be:

$$A_1 = 2000$$
$$A_2 = A_1 \times 1.06 + 2000$$
$$A_3 = A_2 \times 1.06 + 2000 \quad \text{and so on.}$$

   a   Show that $A_3 = 2000 + 2000 \times 1.06 + 2000 \times (1.06)^2$.

   b   Show that $A_4 = 2000[1 + 1.06 + (1.06)^2 + (1.06)^3]$.

   c   Find the total bank balance after 10 years, assuming there are no fees or withdrawals.

7   Answer the **Opening Problem** on page **102**.

8   Paula has started renting an apartment. She paid $5000 rent in the first year, and the rent increased by 5% each year.

   a   Find, to the nearest $10, the rent paid by Paula in the 4th year.

   b   Write an expression for the total rent paid by Paula during the first n years.

   c   How much rent did Paula pay during the first 7 years? Give your answer to the nearest $10.

9   Consider $S_n = \frac{1}{2} + \frac{1}{4} + \frac{1}{8} + \frac{1}{16} + ... + \frac{1}{2^n}$.

   a   Find S_1, S_2, S_3, S_4, and S_5 in fractional form.

   b   Hence guess the formula for S_n.

   c   Find S_n using $S_n = \frac{u_1(1 - r^n)}{1 - r}$.

   d   Comment on S_n as n gets very large.

   e   Explain the relationship between the given diagram and **d**.

10   A geometric series has second term 6. The sum of its first three terms is -14. Find its fourth term.

Example 30   ◀ッ **Self Tutor**

A geometric sequence has first term 5 and common ratio 2. The sum of the first n terms of the sequence is 635. Find n.

The sequence is geometric with $u_1 = 5$ and $r = 2$.

$$\therefore \ S_n = \frac{u_1(r^n - 1)}{r - 1}$$
$$= \frac{5(2^n - 1)}{2 - 1}$$
$$= 5(2^n - 1)$$

To find n such that $S_n = 635$, we use a table of values with $Y_1 = 5 \times (2^\wedge X - 1)$:

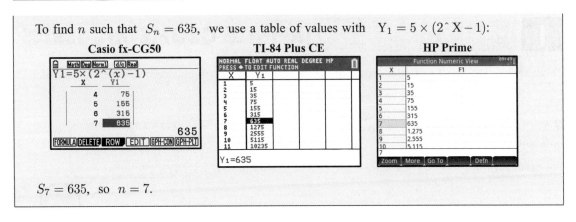

| Casio fx-CG50 | TI-84 Plus CE | HP Prime |

$S_7 = 635$, so $n = 7$.

11 A geometric sequence has first term 6 and common ratio 1.5. The sum of the first n terms of the sequence is 79.125. Find n.

12 Find n given that $\displaystyle\sum_{k=1}^{n} 2 \times 3^{k-1} = 177\,146$.

13 Consider the geometric sequence   160, 80, 40, 20, ...

   a Find, in decimal form, the 8th term of the sequence.

   b Find the sum of the first 8 terms of the sequence.

   c How many terms are required for the sum of the terms to exceed 319.9?

14 Felicity is offered a new job, and is given two salary options to choose from:

   Option A: $40\,000 in the first year, and 5% extra each subsequent year.

   Option B: $60\,000 in the first year, and $1000 more each subsequent year.

   a If Felicity believed that she would work for 3 years in this new job, explain why *Option B* would be best for her.

   b Write down an expression for the amount of money earned in the nth year if she selects:

     i *Option A*   **ii** *Option B*.

   c Find the minimum length of time Felicity would need to work before the amount of money earned per year from *Option A* exceeds that of *Option B*.

   d Felicity decides that the best way to compare the two options is to consider the *total* income accumulated after the first n years in each case. If T_A and T_B represent the total income earned over n years for *Options A* and *B* respectively, show that:

     i $T_A = 800\,000(1.05^n - 1)$ dollars   **ii** $T_B = 500n^2 + 59\,500n$ dollars

   e The graph alongside shows T_A and T_B graphed against n.

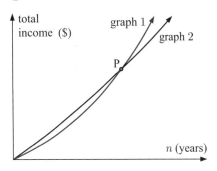

     i Which graph represents T_A and which graph represents T_B?

     ii Use technology to find the coordinates of the point P, where T_A and T_B intersect.

     iii Hence write down a time interval, in whole years, for which *Option B* provides the greater total income.

INFINITE GEOMETRIC SERIES

To examine the sum of all the terms of an infinite geometric sequence, we need to consider $S_n = \dfrac{u_1(1 - r^n)}{1 - r}$ when n gets very large.

If $|r| > 1$, the series is said to be **divergent** and the sum becomes infinitely large.

For example, when $r = 2$, $1 + 2 + 4 + 8 + 16 + ...$ is infinitely large.

$|r|$ is the *size* of r.
If $|r| > 1$ then
$r < -1$ or $r > 1$.

If $|r| < 1$, or in other words $-1 < r < 1$, then as n becomes very large, r^n approaches 0.

This means that S_n will get closer and closer to $\dfrac{u_1}{1 - r}$.

If $|r| < 1$, an infinite geometric series of the form $u_1 + u_1 r + u_1 r^2 + ... = \displaystyle\sum_{k=1}^{\infty} u_1 r^{k-1}$ will **converge** to the **limiting sum** $S = \dfrac{u_1}{1 - r}$.

Proof: If the first term is u_1 and the common ratio is r, the terms are $u_1, u_1 r, u_1 r^2, u_1 r^3, ...$

Suppose the sum of the corresponding infinite series is

$S = u_1 + u_1 r + u_1 r^2 + u_1 r^3 + ...$ $(*)$

$\therefore \ rS = u_1 r + u_1 r^2 + u_1 r^3 + u_1 r^4 + ...$

$\therefore \ rS = S - u_1$ {comparing with $(*)$}

$\therefore \ S(r - 1) = -u_1$

$\therefore \ S = \dfrac{u_1}{1 - r}$ {provided $r \neq 1$}

This result can be used to find the value of recurring decimals.

Example 31	◀》 **Self Tutor**

Write $0.\overline{7}$ as a rational number.

$0.\overline{7} = \dfrac{7}{10} + \dfrac{7}{100} + \dfrac{7}{1000} + \dfrac{7}{10\,000} + ...$ is an infinite geometric series with $u_1 = \dfrac{7}{10}$ and $r = \dfrac{1}{10}$.

$\therefore \ S = \dfrac{u_1}{1 - r} = \dfrac{\frac{7}{10}}{1 - \frac{1}{10}} = \dfrac{7}{9}$

$\therefore \ 0.\overline{7} = \dfrac{7}{9}$

EXERCISE 5I

1 **a** Explain why $0.\overline{3} = \dfrac{3}{10} + \dfrac{3}{100} + \dfrac{3}{1000} + ...$ is an infinite geometric series.

  b Hence show that $0.\overline{3} = \dfrac{1}{3}$.

2 Write as a rational number:

    a $0.\overline{4}$ **b** $0.\overline{16}$ **c** $0.\overline{312}$

3 Use $S = \dfrac{u_1}{1-r}$ to check your answer to **Exercise 5H** question **9 d**.

4 Find the sum of each of the following infinite geometric series:

    a $18 + 12 + 8 + \frac{16}{3} + ...$ **b** $18.9 - 6.3 + 2.1 - 0.7 + ...$

5 Find:

    a $\displaystyle\sum_{k=1}^{\infty} \frac{3}{4^k}$ **b** $\displaystyle\sum_{k=0}^{\infty} 6\left(-\frac{2}{5}\right)^k$

6 The sum of the first three terms of a convergent infinite geometric series is 19. The sum of the series is 27. Find the first term and the common ratio.

7 The second term of a convergent infinite geometric series is $\frac{8}{5}$. The sum of the series is 10. Show that there are two possible series, and find the first term and the common ratio in each case.

8 The sequence $x, \ x - 2, \ 2x - 7, \ ....$ is geometric.

    a Find x.

    b Does the sum of the corresponding infinite geometric series converge? Explain your answer.

9

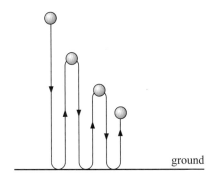

ground

When dropped, a ball takes 1 second to hit the ground. It then takes 90% of this time to rebound to its new height, and this continues until the ball comes to rest.

    a Show that the total time of motion is given by
$$1 + 2(0.9) + 2(0.9)^2 + 2(0.9)^3 + ...$$

    b Find S_n for the series in **a**.

    c How long does it take for the ball to come to rest?

10 When a ball is dropped, it rebounds 75% of its height after each bounce. If the ball travels a total distance of 490 cm, from what height was the ball dropped?

11   **a** Explain why $0.\overline{9} = 1$ exactly.

    b Show that if $u_n = \dfrac{9}{10^n}$, then $S_n = 1 - \dfrac{1}{10^n}$.

    c On a graph, plot the points $(n, \ u_n)$ and $(n, \ S_n)$ for $n = 1, 2, ..., 10$. Connect each set of points with a smooth curve.

12 Find x if $\displaystyle\sum_{k=1}^{\infty} \left(\frac{3x}{2}\right)^{k-1} = 4$.

ACTIVITY 2

Click on the icon to run a card game for sequences and series.

CARD GAME

ACTIVITY 3   VON KOCH'S SNOWFLAKE CURVE

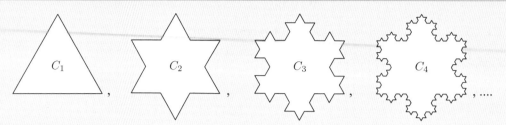

In this Activity we consider a **limit curve** named after the Swedish mathematician Niels Fabian Helge von Koch (1870 - 1924).

To draw **von Koch's snowflake curve** we:

- start with an equilateral triangle, C_1
- divide each side into 3 equal parts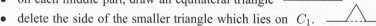
- on each middle part, draw an equilateral triangle
- delete the side of the smaller triangle which lies on C_1.

DEMO

The resulting curve is C_2. By repeating this process on every edge of C_2, we generate curve C_3.

We hence obtain a sequence of special curves C_1, C_2, C_3, C_4, ... and von Koch's curve is the limiting case when n is infinitely large.

Your task is to investigate the perimeter and area of von Koch's curve.

What to do:

1 **a** Suppose C_1 has perimeter 3 units. Find the perimeter of C_2, C_3, C_4, and C_5.

    Hint: _____ becomes $\wedge$ so 3 parts become 4 parts.

    b Remembering that von Koch's curve is C_n, where n is infinitely large, find the perimeter of von Koch's curve.

2 Suppose the area of C_1 is 1 unit^2.

    a Explain why the areas of C_2, C_3, C_4, and C_5 are:

$$A_2 = 1 + \tfrac{1}{3} \text{ units}^2 \qquad\qquad A_3 = 1 + \tfrac{1}{3}[1 + \tfrac{4}{9}] \text{ units}^2$$
$$A_4 = 1 + \tfrac{1}{3}[1 + \tfrac{4}{9} + (\tfrac{4}{9})^2] \text{ units}^2 \qquad A_5 = 1 + \tfrac{1}{3}[1 + \tfrac{4}{9} + (\tfrac{4}{9})^2 + (\tfrac{4}{9})^3] \text{ units}^2.$$

    b Use your calculator to find A_n where $n = 1, 2, 3, 4, 5, 6,$ and 7, giving answers which are as accurate as your calculator permits.

    c What do you think will be the area within von Koch's snowflake curve?

3 Is there anything remarkable about your answers to **1** and **2**?

4 Investigate the sequence of curves obtained by adding squares on successive curves from the middle third of each side. These are the curves C_1, C_2, C_3, ... shown below.

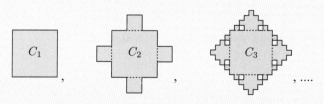

THEORY OF KNOWLEDGE

The German mathematician Leopold Kronecker (1823 - 1891) made important contributions in number theory and algebra. Several things are named after him, including formulae, symbols, and a theorem.

Kronecker made several well-known quotes, including:

"God made integers; all else is the work of man."

"A mathematical object does not exist unless it can be constructed from natural numbers in a finite number of steps."

Leopold Kronecker

1   What do you understand by the term *infinity*?

2   If the entire world were made of grains of sand, could you count them? Would the number of grains of sand be infinite?

3   There are clearly an infinite number of positive integers, and an infinite number of positive even integers.

    a   Construct an argument that:

        i   there are *more* positive integers than positive even integers

        ii   there is the *same number* of positive integers as positive even integers.

    b   Can the traditional notions of "more than", "less than", and "equal to" be extended to infinity?

Consider an infinite geometric series with first term u_1 and common ratio r.

If $|r| < 1$, the series will converge to the sum $S = \dfrac{u_1}{1 - r}$.

4   Can we explain through *intuition* how a sum of non-zero terms, which goes on and on for ever and ever, could actually be a finite number?

In the case $r = -1$, the terms are $u_1, -u_1, u_1, -u_1, \ldots$.

If we take partial sums of the series, the answer is always u_1 or 0.

5   What is the sum of the infinite series when $r = -1$? Is it infinite? Is it defined?

Substituting $r = -1$ into the formula above gives $S = \dfrac{u_1}{2}$. Could this possibly be the answer?

REVIEW SET 5A

1   Consider the number sequence $5, 9, 11, 12, 15, 19$.   Find:

    a u_2 **b** u_6 **c** S_4.

2   Identify each sequence as arithmetic, geometric, or neither:

    a $7, -1, -9, -17, \ldots$ **b** $4, -2, 1, -\frac{1}{2}, \ldots$ **c** $1, 1, 2, 3, 5, 8, \ldots$

3 Find k if $3k$, $k - 2$, and $k + 7$ are consecutive terms of an arithmetic sequence.

4 A sequence is defined by $u_n = 6\left(\frac{1}{2}\right)^{n-1}$.

   a Prove that the sequence is geometric.   **b** Find u_1 and r.

   c Find the 16th term of the sequence to 3 significant figures.

5 Determine the general term of a geometric sequence given that its sixth term is $\frac{16}{3}$ and its tenth term is $\frac{256}{3}$.

6 Insert six numbers between 23 and 9 so that all eight numbers are in arithmetic sequence.

7 An arithmetic series has nine terms. The first term is -2 and the last term is 54. Find the sum of the series.

8 Theodore is squeezing the juice from some lemons. When he has squeezed 6 lemons, he has collected 274.3 mL of juice.

   a Find the average amount of juice collected from each lemon.

   b Hence write an arithmetic sequence u_n which approximates the amount of juice collected from squeezing n lemons.

   c Predict the amount of juice collected from squeezing 13 lemons.

9 Find the sum of each of the following infinite geometric series:

   a $18 - 12 + 8 - ....$ **b** $8 + 4\sqrt{2} + 4 + ...$

10 Find the sum of:

   a $7 + 11 + 15 + 19 + ... + 99$ **b** $35 + 33\frac{1}{2} + 32 + 30\frac{1}{2} + ... + 20$

11 Each year, a school manages to use only 90% as much paper as the previous year. In the year 2010, they used 700 000 sheets of paper.

   a Find how much paper the school used in the years 2011 and 2012.

   b How much paper did the school use in total in the decade from 2008 to 2018?

12 Write a formula for the general term u_n of:

   a $86, 83, 80, 77, ...$ **b** $\frac{3}{4}, 1, \frac{7}{6}, \frac{9}{7}, ...$ **c** $100, 90, 81, 72.9, ...$

Hint: One of these sequences is neither arithmetic nor geometric.

13 Expand and hence evaluate:

   a $\displaystyle\sum_{k=1}^{7} k^2$ **b** $\displaystyle\sum_{k=1}^{4} \frac{k+3}{k+2}$

14 The sum of the first n terms of an infinite sequence is $\dfrac{3n^2 + 5n}{2}$ for all $n \in \mathbb{Z}^+$.

   a Find the nth term.   **b** Prove that the sequence is arithmetic.

15 £12 500 is invested in an account which pays 4.25% p.a. interest. Find the value of the investment after 5 years if the interest is compounded:

   a half-yearly   **b** monthly.

16 Jana invests €6000 in an account which pays 5.2% p.a. interest compounded quarterly for 6 years. Use technology to find:

    a the future value of the investment   **b** the interest the investment will earn.

17 4 years ago, Chelsea invested some money in an account paying 6.5% p.a. interest compounded quarterly. There is currently $6212.27 in the account. How much did Chelsea invest originally?

18 For how long must I invest £4000 at 8% p.a. compounded monthly if it is to amount to £10 000?

19 If inflation averages 2.5% per year, calculate the value of:

    a €6000 indexed for inflation over 4 years

    b €11 200 indexed for inflation over 7 years.

20 Georgina invested $20 000 in an account which paid 6.2% p.a. interest, compounded monthly for 3 years. Inflation averaged 1.8% per year over this time.

    a Calculate the future value of the investment.

    b Find the real value of the investment.

21 Show that 28, 23, 18, 13, ... is an arithmetic sequence. Hence find u_n and the sum S_n of its first n terms in simplest form.

22 Consider the arithmetic sequence 12, 19, 26, 33, ...

    a Find the 8th term of the sequence.

    b Find the sum of the first 10 terms of the sequence.

    c The sum of the first n terms is 915. Find the value of n.

23 A truck is purchased for $135 000. It depreciates at 15% p.a. for 5 years.

    a Find the value of the truck at the end of this period.

    b By how much has it depreciated?

24 **a** Determine the number of terms in the sequence 128, 64, 32, 16, ..., $\frac{1}{512}$.

    b Find the sum of these terms.

25 The sum of the first two terms of an infinite geometric series is 90. The third term is 24. Show that there are two possible series, and that both series converge.

26 After years of decline in his health, Tim has now realised that smoking is unhealthy. Until now, he has regularly smoked 120 cigarettes each week. To help him quit, he is determined to reduce this amount by 5 cigarettes every week from now on.

    a Explain why the number of cigarettes Tim smokes each week will form an arithmetic sequence with $u_1 = 115$. State the common difference for the sequence.

    b How many weeks will it take before Tim has smoked his last cigarette?

    c Find the total number of cigarettes Tim will smoke before he successfully quits.

27 A competition offers three options for the first prize, each of which pays the winner a monthly sum for 24 months.

    Option 1: $8000 per month.

    Option 2: $1000 in the first month, then each successive month pays $600 more than the previous month.

    Option 3: $500 in the first month, then each successive month pays 20% more than the previous month.

    a Calculate the total prize value for *Option 1*.

    b For *Option 2*:

        i Write down the amount won in each of the first three months.

        ii Calculate the total amount won over the 24 month period.

    c For *Option 3*:

        i Write down the amount won in each of the first three months.

        ii Calculate the total amount won over the 24 month period.

    d Which option is worth the greatest amount of money overall?

    e The amount won in the first month under *Option 3* is to be altered so that the total prize over 24 months is $250 000. Calculate the new initial amount, giving your answer to the nearest cent.

28 Consider the infinite geometric sequence $160, 80\sqrt{2}, 80, 40\sqrt{2}, ...$

    a Write the 12th term of the sequence in the form $k\sqrt{2}$ where $k \in \mathbb{Q}$.

    b Find, in the form $a + b\sqrt{2}$ where $a, b \in \mathbb{Z}$:

        i S_{10} **ii** the sum S of the infinite series.

REVIEW SET 5B

1 Evaluate the first five terms of the sequence:

    a $\{(\frac{1}{3})^n\}$ **b** $\{12 + 5n\}$ **c** $\left\{\dfrac{4}{n+2}\right\}$

2 A sequence is defined by $u_n = 68 - 5n$.

    a Prove that the sequence is arithmetic.

    b Find u_1 and d.

    c Find the 37th term of the sequence.

    d State the first term of the sequence which is less than -200.

3   **a** Show that the sequence $3, 12, 48, 192, ...$ is geometric.

    b Find u_n and hence find u_9.

4   **a** Find the general term of the arithmetic sequence with $u_7 = 31$ and $u_{15} = -17$.

    b Hence find the value of u_{34}.

5 Consider the sequence $24, 23\frac{1}{4}, 22\frac{1}{2}, ...$

    a Which term of the sequence is -36?

    b Find the value of u_{35}.

    c Find S_{40}, the sum of the first 40 terms of the sequence.

6 Find the sum of the first 12 terms of:

    a $3 + 9 + 15 + 21 + ...$ **b** $24 + 12 + 6 + 3 + ...$

7 Consider the sequence $24, a, 6, ...$
Find the value(s) of a if the sequence is:

    a arithmetic   **b** geometric.

8 Stacy runs a hot dog stand at a local fair. On the first day she served 25 customers and made £60 profit. On the second day she served 43 customers and made £135 profit.

    a Assuming that her profit from serving n customers forms an arithmetic sequence, find a model which approximates the profit from serving n customers.

    b Explain the significance of the common difference and the constant term in your model.

    c On the third day, Stacy served 36 customers. Use your model to estimate her profit.

9 Find the first term of the sequence 5, 10, 20, 40, ... which exceeds 10 000.

10 A ball bounces from a height of 3 metres and returns to 80% of its previous height on each bounce. Find the total distance travelled by the ball until it stops bouncing.

11 Find the final value of a compound interest investment of €8000 after 7 years at 3% p.a. with interest compounded annually.

12 $7000 is invested at 6% p.a. compound interest. Find the value of the investment after 3 years if interest is compounded:

    a annually   **b** quarterly   **c** monthly.

13 **a** Find k given that 4, k, and $k^2 - 1$ are consecutive terms of a geometric sequence.

    b For each value of k, find the common ratio of the sequence.

14 Seve is training for a long distance walk. He walks for 10 km in the first week, then each week thereafter he walks 500 m further than the previous week. If he continues this pattern for a year, how far does Seve walk:

    a in the last week   **b** in total?

15 Find the sum of the infinite geometric series:

    a $1.21 - 1.1 + 1 - ....$ **b** $\frac{14}{3} + \frac{4}{3} + \frac{8}{21} + ...$

16 Find the first term of the sequence 24, 8, $\frac{8}{3}$, $\frac{8}{9}$, ... which is less than 0.001 .

17 Vijay deposits 200 000 rupees in an account that compounds interest half-yearly. 6 years later, the account has balance 250 680 rupees. Use technology to calculate the annual rate of interest.

18 Frederik invests €5000 at 5.8% p.a. compounded monthly. Use technology to find how long it will take to amount to €12 000.

19 Richard sold his car for $7500. He invested the money in an account paying 3.7% p.a. interest compounded quarterly for 8 years. Inflation averaged 3.1% per year over this period.

    a Find the future value of Richard's investment.

    b Find the real value of Richard's investment.

20 A photocopier bought for $9800 will depreciate by 26% each year. Find its value after 5 years.

21 Evaluate:

a $\displaystyle\sum_{k=1}^{8} \left(\frac{31 - 3k}{2}\right)$

b $\displaystyle\sum_{k=1}^{15} 50(0.8)^{k-1}$

c $\displaystyle\sum_{k=7}^{\infty} 5 \left(\frac{2}{5}\right)^{k-1}$

22 A geometric sequence has $u_6 = 24$ and $u_{11} = 768$.

a Determine the general term of the sequence.

b Find the sum of the first 15 terms.

23 The nth term of a sequence is given by the formula $u_n = 4n - 7$.

a Find the value of u_{10}.

b Explain why the sequence is arithmetic.

c Evaluate $u_{15} + u_{16} + u_{17} + \ldots + u_{30}$.

24 Ena currently has £7800. She wants to buy a car valued at £9000. If she puts her money in an account paying 4.8% p.a. compounded quarterly, when will she be able to buy the car?

25 In 2004 there were 3000 iguanas on a Galapagos island. Since then, the population of iguanas on the island has increased by 5% each year.

a How many iguanas were on the island in 2007?

b In what year will the population first exceed 10 000?

26 a Under what conditions will the series $\displaystyle\sum_{k=1}^{\infty} 50(2x - 1)^{k-1}$ converge? Explain your answer.

b Find $\displaystyle\sum_{k=1}^{\infty} 50(2x - 1)^{k-1}$ if $x = 0.3$.

27 Michael is saving to buy a house and needs $400 000.

a Three years ago, he invested a sum of money in an account paying 6.5% p.a. interest compounded half-yearly. This investment has just matured at $100 000. How much did Michael invest three years ago?

b Michael decides to reinvest his $100 000 lump sum into an account for a period of n years at 6.0% p.a. interest compounded annually.

Copy and complete the table below showing the value V_n of Michael's investment after n years.

n (years)	0	1	2	3	4
V_n ($)	100 000	106 000	112 360		

c Write a formula for V_n in terms of n.

d Michael also decides to start an additional saving plan, whereby he deposits $6000 into a safe at the end of each year. Write down a formula for S_n, the amount of money in Michael's safe after n years.

e The total amount of money Michael has for his house after n years is given by $T_n = V_n + S_n$. Calculate the missing values in the table below.

n (years)	0	1	2	3	4
T_n ($)	100 000	112 000	124 360		

f After how many whole years will Michael have the $400 000 needed to buy his house?

Chapter 6

Measurement

Contents:

OPENING PROBLEM

A jewellery box is made of wood 4 mm thick.
When shut, its height is 88 mm.

Things to think about:

a What is the *external* surface area of the container?

b Why is it useful to specify the "external" surface area when talking about a container?

c Can you find:

  i the *volume* of jewellery the box can hold

  ii the *capacity* of the box

  iii the *volume* of wood used to make the box?

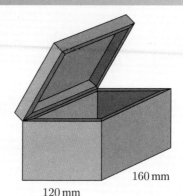

160 mm

120 mm

In previous years you should have studied measurement extensively.   In this Chapter we revise measurements associated with parts of a circle, as well as the surface area and volume of 3-dimensional shapes.

A   CIRCLES, ARCS, AND SECTORS

For a **circle** with radius r:

- the **circumference** $C = 2\pi r$
- the **area** $A = \pi r^2$.

An **arc** is a part of a circle which joins any two different points. It can be measured using the angle θ° subtended by the points at the centre.

Arc length $= \dfrac{\theta}{360} \times 2\pi r$

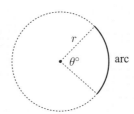

arc

A **sector** is the region between two radii of a circle and the arc between them.

Perimeter $=$ two radii $+$ arc length

$$= 2r + \dfrac{\theta}{360} \times 2\pi r$$

$$\text{Area} = \dfrac{\theta}{360} \times \pi r^2$$

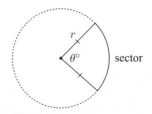

sector

Example 1   ◀》 **Self Tutor**

For the given figure, find to 3 significant figures:

  a   the length of the arc

  b   the perimeter of the sector

  c   the area of the sector.

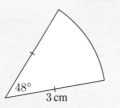

a   Arc length $= \dfrac{\theta}{360} \times 2\pi r$

$ = \dfrac{48}{360} \times 2\pi \times 3$ cm

$ \approx 2.51$ cm

c   Area $= \dfrac{\theta}{360} \times \pi r^2$

$ = \dfrac{48}{360} \times \pi \times 3^2$

$ \approx 3.77$ cm^2

b   Perimeter $= 2r +$ arc length

$ \approx 2 \times 3 + 2.51$ cm

$ \approx 8.51$ cm

EXERCISE 6A

1   Find the length of:

  a   the blue arc

  b   the red arc.

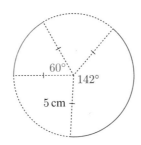

2   Find the perimeter of:

a   **b**   **c**

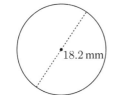
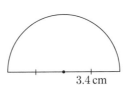
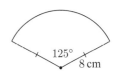

d   **e**   **f**

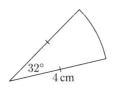
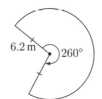
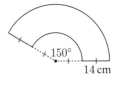

3   An arc of a circle makes a $36°$ angle at its centre. If the arc has length 26 cm, find the radius of the circle.

4   A sector of a circle makes a $127°$ angle at its centre. If the arc of the sector has length 36 mm, find the perimeter of the sector.

5 Find the area of:

a
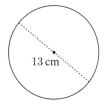
13 cm

b
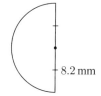
8.2 mm

c
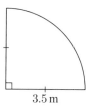
3.5 m

d
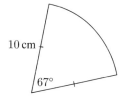
10 cm
67°

e
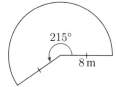
215°
8 m

f

9.2 cm
100°

6 Find the radius of a sector with angle $67°$ and area 16.2 cm^2.

7 Find the perimeter of a sector with angle $136°$ and area 28.8 cm^2.

8 A running track consists of two straight segments joined by semi-circular ends, as shown. The total perimeter of the track is 1600 metres.

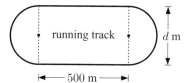
running track
d m
500 m

   a Determine the diameter of the semi-circular ends.

   b Jason takes 4 minutes and 25 seconds to complete a single lap of the track. Calculate Jason's average speed in m s^{-1}.

9 X and Y are the centres of the circles containing the two arcs AB shown.

Find:

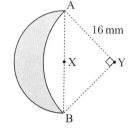
A
16 mm
X
Y
B

   a the length AX

   b the perimeter of the shaded crescent

   c the area of the crescent.

10

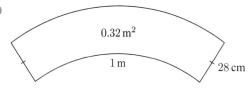
0.32 m^2
1 m
28 cm

Belinda has made a lampshade with area 0.32 m^2. Its shorter arc has length 1 m, and its slant height is 28 cm.

Suppose the material is cut as the difference between two sectors with common angle $\theta°$, and radii r and R.

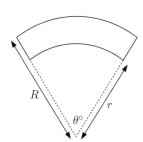
R
$\theta°$
r

   a Show that the area of the lampshade is given by
$$A = \frac{0.28\theta}{360} \pi(2r + 0.28) \text{ m}^2.$$

   b Use the smaller sector to show that $\theta = \dfrac{180}{\pi r}$.

   c Find r and θ.

   d Hence find the length of the longer arc.

B | SURFACE AREA

SOLIDS WITH PLANE FACES

The **surface area** of a three-dimensional figure with plane faces is the sum of the areas of the faces.

A *plane* face is one which is flat.

The surface area is therefore the same as the area of the **net** required to make the figure.

Example 2   ◀) **Self Tutor**

The pyramid shown is 10.8 cm high. Find its surface area.

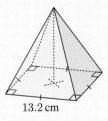

The net of the pyramid includes one square with side length 13.2 cm, and four isosceles triangles with base 13.2 cm.

Let the height of the triangles be h cm.

Now $h^2 = 10.8^2 + 6.6^2$ {Pythagoras}

$\therefore\ h = \sqrt{10.8^2 + 6.6^2} \approx 12.66$

$\therefore$ the surface area

$\approx 13.2^2 + 4 \times (\frac{1}{2} \times 13.2 \times 12.66)$ cm^2

≈ 508 cm^2

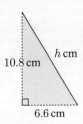

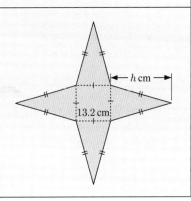

EXERCISE 6B.1

1   Find the surface area of each rectangular prism:

a

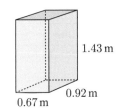
8.3 cm

b

1.43 m
0.92 m
0.67 m

c

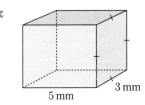
5 mm
3 mm

2   Find the surface area of each triangular prism:

a

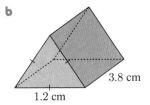
5 cm
6 cm
4 cm

b

3.8 cm
1.2 cm

c

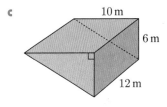
10 m
6 m
12 m

3 Draw each solid and hence find its surface area:

   a an ice cube with side length 2.5 cm

   b a block of cheese measuring 14 cm by 8 cm by 3 cm

   c a wooden wedge with length 6.2 cm and a cross-section which is a right angled triangle with legs 10.6 cm and 2.8 cm.

4 Find the surface area of each pyramid:

   a

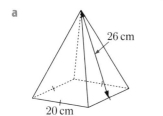

   b

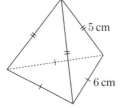

   c

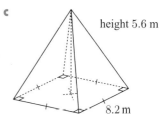

5

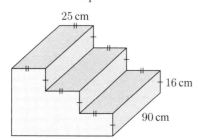

A harpsichord case has the dimensions shown.

   a Find the total area of the top and bottom surfaces.

   b Find the area of each side of the case.

   c If the timber costs €128 per square metre, find the value of the timber used to construct this case.

6 The walls and ceiling of this room need to be painted with two coats of paint. The door is 0.8 m by 2.2 m and the window is 183 cm by 91 cm. The door also has to be stained on *both* sides with two coats of stain. Use the following table to calculate the total cost of the stain and paint:

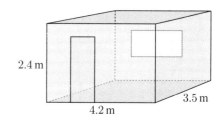

Type of paint	Size	Area covered	Cost per tin
wall paint	4 litres	16 m^2	$32.45
	2 litres	8 m^2	$20.80
wood stain	2 litres	10 m^2	$23.60
(for doors)	1 litre	5 m^2	$15.40

7 Find the surface area of:

   a this set of steps

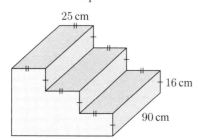

   b the sides and base of this swimming pool.

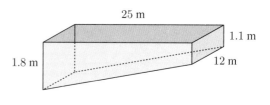

8 The **Taylor Prism** is a regular hexagonal prism made of clay with a historical record written on its sides. It was found by archaeologist **Colonel Taylor** in 1830. If the ancient Assyrians had written on all the surfaces, what total surface area would the writing have covered?

Hint: A regular hexagon can be divided into six equilateral triangles.

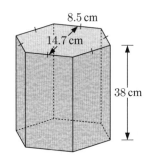

9 Write a formula for the surface area of:

a a rectangular prism with side lengths x cm, $(x + 2)$ cm, and $2x$ cm

b a square-based pyramid for which every edge has length x cm.

SOLIDS WITH CURVED SURFACES

These objects have curved surfaces, but their surface areas can still be calculated using formulae.

Cylinder	**Sphere**	**Cone**
$A = $ **curved surface** $+$ **2 circular ends** $= 2\pi r h + 2\pi r^2$	$A = 4\pi r^2$	$A = $ **curved surface** $+$ **circular base** $= \pi r s + \pi r^2$

...

Example 3	◀) Self Tutor

Find, to 1 decimal place, the outer surface area of:

a hollow top and bottom

b

c

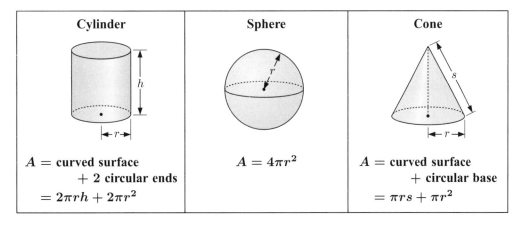

a The cylinder is hollow top and bottom, so we only have the curved surface.

$A = 2\pi r h$

$\quad = 2 \times \pi \times 6 \times 15$

$\quad \approx 565.5 \text{ cm}^2$

b $A = 4\pi r^2$

$\quad = 4 \times \pi \times 8^2$

$\quad \approx 804.2 \text{ cm}^2$

c $A = \pi r s + \pi r^2$

$\quad = \pi \times 5 \times 12 + \pi \times 5^2$

$\quad \approx 267.0 \text{ cm}^2$

EXERCISE 6B.2

1 Find, to 1 decimal place, the outer surface area of:

a

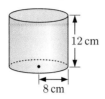

12 cm

8 cm

b

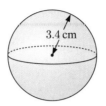

3.4 cm

c hollow

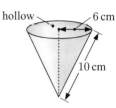

6 cm

10 cm

d

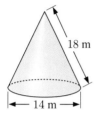

18 m

14 m

e hollow top only

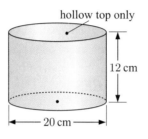

12 cm

20 cm

f

4.5 km

2 Find the total surface area of the solid hemisphere shown.

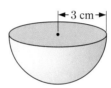

3 cm

3 Find the surface area of:

  a a cylinder with height 36 cm and radius 8 cm

  b a sphere with diameter 4.6 m

  c a cone with radius 38 mm and slant height 86 mm

  d a cone with radius 1.2 cm and height 1.6 cm.

4 A new wharf has 24 cylindrical concrete pylons, each with diameter 0.6 m and length 10 m. The pylons will be coated with a salt resistant material.

  a Find the total surface area of one pylon.

  b Coating the pylons with the material costs $45.50 per m^2. Find the cost of coating one pylon.

  c Find the total cost of coating the 24 pylons, to the nearest dollar.

10 m

0.6 m

5

s m

5 m

2 m

A conical tent has base radius 2 m and height 5 m.

  a Find the slant height s, to 2 decimal places.

  b Find the area of canvas necessary to make the tent, including the base.

  c If canvas costs $18 per m^2, find the cost of the canvas.

6 A cylindrical tank of base diameter 8 m and height 6 m requires a non-porous lining on its circular base and curved walls. The lining costs $23.20 per m^2 for the base, and $18.50 per m^2 for the sides.

    a Find the area of the base.
    b Find the cost of lining the base.

    c Find the area of the curved wall.
    d Find the cost of lining the curved wall.

    e Find the total cost of the lining, to the nearest $10.

Example 4   ◀⟩ **Self Tutor**

The length of a hollow pipe is three times its radius.

    a Write an expression for its outer surface area in terms of its radius r.

    b If the outer surface area is 301.6 m^2, find the radius of the pipe.

a Let the radius be r m, so the length is $3r$ m.

$$\text{Surface area} = 2\pi rh$$
$$= 2\pi r \times 3r$$
$$= 6\pi r^2 \text{ m}^2$$

b The surface area is 301.6 m^2

$$\therefore \ 6\pi r^2 = 301.6$$
$$\therefore \ r^2 = \frac{301.6}{6\pi}$$
$$\therefore \ r = \sqrt{\frac{301.6}{6\pi}} \quad \{\text{as } r > 0\}$$
$$\therefore \ r \approx 4.00$$

The radius of the pipe is 4 m.

---

7 The height of a hollow cylinder is the same as its diameter.

    a Write an expression for the outer surface area of the cylinder in terms of its radius r.

    b Find the height of the cylinder if its surface area is 91.6 m^2.

hollow top and bottom

8 The slant height of a hollow cone is three times its radius.

    a Write an expression for the outer surface area of the cone in terms of its radius r.

    b Given that the surface area is 21.2 cm^2, find the cone's:

        i slant height   **ii** height.

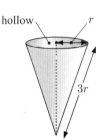

hollow

9 Write a formula for the surface area of:

    a a cylinder with radius x cm and height $2x$ cm

    b a hemisphere with radius r cm

    c a cone with radius x cm and height $2x$ cm.

10 Find:

    a the radius of a sphere with surface area 64π cm^2

    b the height of a solid cylinder with radius 6.3 cm and surface area 1243 cm^2

    c the radius of a cone with slant height 143 mm and surface area 60 000 mm^2.

11 Find, correct to 1 decimal place, the surface area of each solid:

a
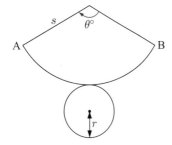
1.2 m

2.8 m

b
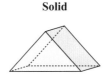
2 m

6 m

12 m

c
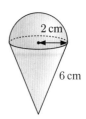
2 cm

6 cm

12 The planet Neptune is roughly spherical and has surface area $\approx 7.618 \times 10^9$ km². Estimate the radius of Neptune.

13

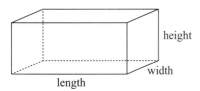

s $\theta°$

A   B

r

For the net of a cone alongside, notice that the length of arc AB must equal the circumference of the base circle.

a Write the arc length AB in terms of s and θ.

b Hence write θ in terms of r and s.

c Show that the surface area of the cone is given by $A = \pi r s + \pi r^2$.

C   VOLUME

The **volume** of a solid is the amount of space it occupies.

SOLIDS OF UNIFORM CROSS-SECTION

In the triangular prism alongside, any vertical slice parallel to the front triangular face will be the same size and shape as that face. Solids like this are called *solids of uniform cross-section*. The cross-section in this case is a triangle.

Another example is a cylinder which has a circular cross-section.

Solid   **Cross-section**

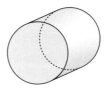

For any solid of uniform cross-section:

$$\text{Volume} = \text{area of cross-section} \times \text{length}$$

In particular, we can define formulae for the volume of:

- rectangular prisms

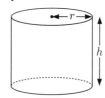
height

width

length

Volume = length × width × height

- cylinders

r

h

Volume = $\pi r^2 h$

Example 5   ◀» **Self Tutor**

Find the volume of:

a

45 mm

|← 36 mm →|

b

10 cm

12 cm

30 cm

a $V = \pi r^2 h$

$= \pi \times 18^2 \times 45$ mm^3

$\approx 45\,800$ mm^3

b

10 cm h cm

6 cm

Let the prism have height h cm.

$h^2 + 6^2 = 10^2$ {Pythagoras}

$\therefore\ h^2 + 36 = 100$

$\therefore\ h^2 = 64$

$\therefore\ h = 8$ {as $h > 0$}

Volume = area of cross-section $\times$ length

$= (\frac{1}{2} \times 12 \times 8) \times 30$ cm^3

$= 1440$ cm^3

EXERCISE 6C.1

1   Find the volume of:

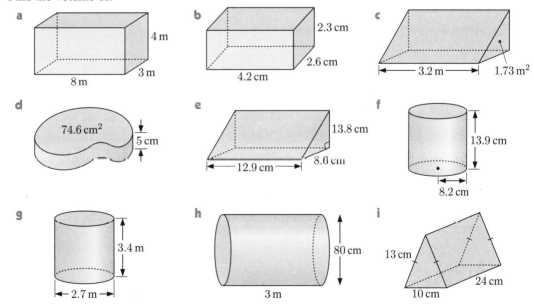

a

4 m

8 m   3 m

b

2.3 cm

2.6 cm

4.2 cm

c

3.2 m   1.73 m^2

d

74.6 cm^2 5 cm

e

13.8 cm

12.9 cm   8.0 cm

f

13.9 cm

8.2 cm

g

3.4 m

← 2.7 m →

h

80 cm

3 m

i

13 cm

10 cm   24 cm

2   A circular cake tin has radius 20 cm and height 7 cm. When cake mix was added to the tin, its depth was 2 cm. After the cake was cooked it rose to 1.5 cm below the top of the tin.

a   Sketch these two situations.

b   Find the volume of: **i**   the cake mix   **ii**   the cooked cake.

c   What was the percentage increase in the volume of the cake while it cooked?

3 Find the volume of:

a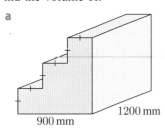

b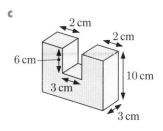

c

4 The Water Supply department uses huge concrete pipes to drain stormwater.

  a Find the external radius of a pipe.

  b Find the internal radius of a pipe.

  c Find the volume of concrete necessary to make one pipe.

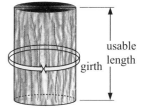

5 A rectangular garage floor 9.2 m by 6.5 m is to be concreted to a depth of 120 mm.

  a What volume of concrete is required?

  b Concrete costs \$135 per m³, and is only supplied in multiples of 0.2 m³. How much will the concrete cost?

6 A concrete path 1 m wide and 10 cm deep is placed around a circular lighthouse of diameter 12 m.

  a Draw an overhead view of the situation.

  b Find the surface area of the concrete.

  c Find the volume of concrete required for the path.

7 In the timber industry, treefellers need to calculate the volume of usable timber in a tree. They use the following approximation for the tree's volume:

$V \approx 0.06 \times g^2 \times l$ where V = volume (in m³)

g = approximate girth (in m)

and l = usable length (in m).

  a Estimate the volume of usable timber in a tree with an average girth of 3.8 m and usable length 9.9 m.

  b For a cylinder with circumference g, and height l, show that $V = \frac{1}{4\pi} g^2 \times l$.

  c Compare the volumes predicted by these two formulae, and explain the difference between them.

8 1000 km of black plastic cylindrical water piping with internal diameter 13 mm and walls of thickness 2 mm is required for a major irrigation project. The piping is made from bulk plastic which weighs 0.86 tonnes per cubic metre. How many tonnes of black plastic are required?

9 I am currently building a new rectangular garden which is 8.6 m by 2.4 m, and 15 cm deep. I have decided to purchase some soil from the local garden supplier, and will load it into my trailer which measures 2.2 m × 1.8 m × 60 cm. I will fill the trailer to within 20 cm from the top.

  a How many trailer loads of soil will I need?

  b Each load of soil costs $87.30. What will the total cost of the soil be?

  c I decide to put bark on top of the soil in the garden. Each load covers 11 m² of garden bed.

   i How many loads of bark will I need?

   ii Each load of bark costs $47.95. What is the total cost of the bark?

  d Calculate the total cost of establishing the garden.

10

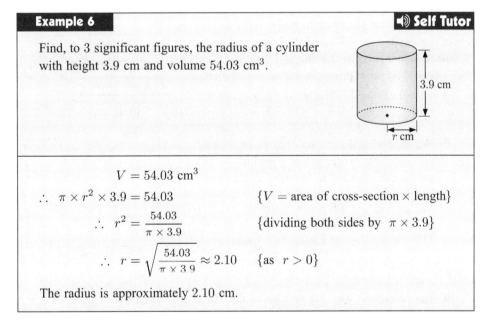

125 cm

150 cm

200 cm

A scout's tent is 150 cm wide and 200 cm long. It has the shape of an isosceles triangular prism as shown.

  a Find the height of each vertical support post.

  b Find the volume of the tent.

  c Find the total area of the canvas in the tent, including the ends and floor.

Example 6   ◀)) **Self Tutor**

Find, to 3 significant figures, the radius of a cylinder with height 3.9 cm and volume 54.03 cm³.

3.9 cm

r cm

$$V = 54.03 \text{ cm}^3$$

$$\therefore \ \pi \times r^2 \times 3.9 = 54.03 \qquad \{V = \text{area of cross-section} \times \text{length}\}$$

$$\therefore \ r^2 = \frac{54.03}{\pi \times 3.9} \qquad \{\text{dividing both sides by } \pi \times 3.9\}$$

$$\therefore \ r = \sqrt{\frac{54.03}{\pi \times 3.9}} \approx 2.10 \qquad \{\text{as } r > 0\}$$

The radius is approximately 2.10 cm.

---

11 Find:

  a the height of a rectangular prism with base 5 cm by 3 cm and volume 40 cm³

  b the side length of a cube of butter with volume 34.01 cm³

  c the radius of a steel cylinder with height 4.6 cm and volume 43.75 cm³.

12

5 cm

6 cm

8 cm

A gold bar has the trapezoidal cross-section shown. Its volume is 480 cm³.

Find the length of the bar.

TAPERED SOLIDS

For pyramids and cones, the cross-section is not uniform. Rather, the cross-sections are a set of similar shapes which get smaller and smaller as we approach the apex. We call these **tapered solids**.

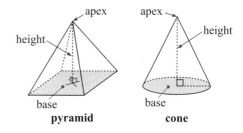

pyramid   cone

THE VOLUME OF TAPERED SOLIDS

Having seen formulae for the volume of solids of uniform cross-section, we now seek to establish formulae for tapered solids including pyramids and cones.

What to do:

1   **a**   Find the volume V_p of a rectangular prism whose base is a 10 cm $\times$ 10 cm square, and whose height is 15 cm.

b   Consider a pyramid with the same square base and same height as the rectangular prism in **a**. The pyramid can be approximated using a set of rectangular prisms with equal thickness, and each with a square base, as shown.

Suppose there are n prisms in our approximation.

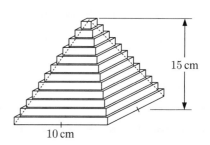

i   Explain why the height of each prism is $\dfrac{15}{n}$ cm.

ii   We suppose the base of each prism is the cross-section of the actual pyramid at the corresponding height. We start at the apex and move down.

We suppose the kth prism has base x_k cm $\times$ x_k cm.

Use the diagram alongside to explain why $x_k = \dfrac{10k}{n}$.

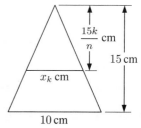

iii   Hence explain why the volume of the kth prism is equal to $\dfrac{V_p k^2}{n^3}$ cm^3, where V_p is the volume of the corresponding solid with uniform cross-section which you found in **a**.

c   Load the spreadsheet which will calculate the sum of the volumes of the n prisms, for values up to $n = 100\,000$.   SPREADSHEET

i   Check that the volume V_p of the corresponding solid with uniform cross-section is correct.

ii   Discuss with your class how the formulae in the spreadsheet work.

iii   Check that for $n = 1$, the approximation is simply the corresponding solid with uniform cross-section.

iv   Find the approximate volume of the pyramid manually for $n = 5$. Use the spreadsheet to check your answer.

v   Construct a table of values for the approximate volume of the pyramid. Use $n = 10$, 100, 1000, 10 000, and 100 000.

vi What do you think the actual volume of the pyramid is? What *fraction* of the corresponding solid with uniform cross-section is this?

2 Repeat **1** for a different sized square-based pyramid. Remember that you will need to change the appropriate "volume of corresponding solid of uniform cross-section" cell in the spreadsheet. Comment on your results.

3 **a** Find, in terms of π, the volume V_c of a cylinder with base radius 5 cm and height 10 cm.

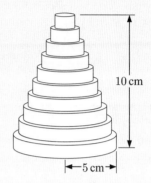

b Consider a cone with the same base and height as the cylinder in **a**. The cone can be approximated using a set of cylinders with equal thickness, as shown.

Suppose there are n cylinders in our approximation.

   i   Explain why the height of each cylinder is $\dfrac{10}{n}$ cm.

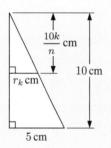

   ii We suppose the base of each cylinder is the cross-section of the actual cone at the corresponding height. We start at the apex and move down.
We suppose the kth cylinder has base radius r_k cm.

Use the diagram alongside to explain why $r_k = \dfrac{5k}{n}$.

   iii Hence explain why the volume of the kth cylinder is equal to $\dfrac{V_c k^2}{n^3}$ cm^3, where V_c is the volume of the corresponding solid with uniform cross-section which you found in **a**.

c Load the spreadsheet which will calculate the sum of the volumes of the n cylinders, for values up to $n = 100\,000$. Note that volumes are given in lots of π cm^3.

SPREADSHEET

   i   Check that the volume V_c of the corresponding solid with uniform cross-section is correct.

   ii Check that for $n = 1$, the approximation is simply the corresponding solid with uniform cross-section.

   iii Construct a table of values for the approximate volume of the cone. Use $n = 10$, 100, 1000, 10 000, and 100 000.

   iv What do you think the actual volume of the cone is? What *fraction* of the corresponding solid with uniform cross-section is this?

4 Repeat **3** for a different sized cone. Remember that you will need to change the appropriate "volume of corresponding solid of uniform cross-section" cell in the spreadsheet. Comment on your results.

From the **Investigation**, you should have established that the volume of any tapered solid is given by:

$$\textbf{Volume} = \tfrac{1}{3}(\textbf{area of base} \times \textbf{height})$$

It is a third of the volume of the solid of uniform cross-section with the same base and height.

SPHERES

In previous years you should have seen that the volume of a sphere with radius r is given by

$$\textbf{Volume} = \tfrac{4}{3}\pi r^3$$

Example 7   ◄)) **Self Tutor**

Find the volume of each solid:

a

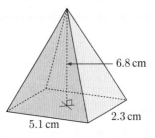

6.8 cm

5.1 cm   2.3 cm

b

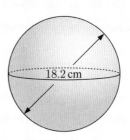

18.2 cm

a $V = \frac{1}{3}(\text{area of base} \times \text{height})$
  $= \frac{1}{3}(\text{length} \times \text{width} \times \text{height})$
  $= \frac{1}{3}(5.1 \times 2.3 \times 6.8) \text{ cm}^3$
  $\approx 26.6 \text{ cm}^3$

b $V = \frac{4}{3}\pi r^3$
  $= \frac{4}{3}\pi \left(\frac{18.2}{2}\right)^3$
  $\approx 3160 \text{ cm}^3$

EXERCISE 6C.2

1 Find the volume of:

a

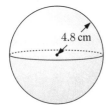

4.8 cm

b

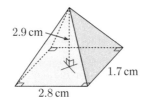

2.9 cm

2.8 cm

1.7 cm

c

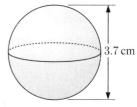

3.7 cm

d

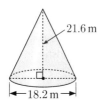

21.6 m

18.2 m

e

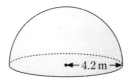

4.2 m

f

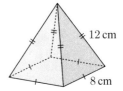

12 cm

8 cm

2 Find the volume of:

a

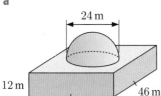

24 m

12 m   46 m

b

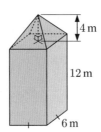

4 m

12 m

6 m

c

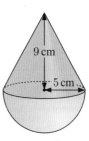

9 cm

5 cm

3 A ready mixed concrete tanker is to be constructed from steel as a cylinder with conical ends.

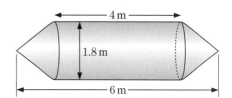

4 m

1.8 m

6 m

a Calculate the total volume of concrete that can be held in the tanker.

b How *long* would the tanker be if the ends were hemispheres instead of cones, but the cylindrical section remained the same?

c How much more or less concrete would fit in the tanker if the ends were hemispheres instead of cones?

d Show that the surface area of the tanker:

   i with conical ends is about 30 m^2 **ii** with hemispherical ends is about 33 m^2.

e Overall, which do you think is the better design for the tanker? Give reasons for your answer.

4 Find:

a the height of a glass cone with base radius 12.3 cm and volume 706 cm^3

b the radius of a spherical weather balloon with volume 73.62 m^3

c the base radius of a cone with height 6.2 cm and volume 203.9 cm^3.

5 A cylinder of resin has height equal to its diameter. Some of it is used to form a cone with the same height and diameter as the cylinder. Show that the remainder is the exact amount needed to form a sphere with the same diameter.

6 For a sphere of radius r, the volume of the **cap** of height h is

$$V = \frac{\pi h^2}{3}(3r - h).$$

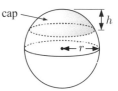

cap

h

r

a Find the volumes of these caps:

i

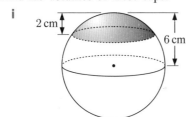

2 cm

6 cm

ii

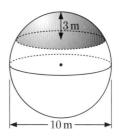

3 m

10 m

b Write an expression for the volume of the cap in the case that $h = r$. Compare this volume with the volume of the sphere. Explain your result.

ACTIVITY 1   DENSITY

The **density** of a substance is its mass per unit volume.

$$\text{density} = \frac{\text{mass}}{\text{volume}}$$

One **gram** is the mass of one cubic centimetre of pure water at $4°C$. The density of pure water at $4°C$ is therefore $\frac{1 \text{ g}}{1 \text{ cm}^3} = 1 \text{ g cm}^{-3}$.

Some densities of common substances are shown in the table:

Substance	Density (g cm^{-3})
pine wood	0.41
paper	0.80
oil	0.92
water	1.00
steel	8.05
copper	8.96
lead	11.34

What to do:

1 Find the density of:

   a a metal rod with mass 10 g and volume 2 cm^3

   b a cube of chocolate with side length 2 cm and mass 10.6 g

   c a glass marble with radius 4.5 mm and mass 1.03 g.

2 Rearrange the density formula to make: **a** mass the subject   **b** volume the subject.

3 Find the volume of 80 g of salt with density 2.16 g cm^{-3}.

4 Find the mass of a copper wire with radius 1 mm and length 250 m.

5 The gold bar shown has mass 13.60 kg. Find the density of gold.

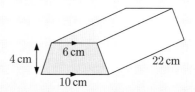

6 Jonathon has a steel ball bearing with radius 1.4 cm, and a lead sphere with radius 1.2 cm. Which sphere weighs more, and by what percentage?

7 Oil and water are *immiscible*, which means they do not mix. Does oil float on water, or water float on oil? Explain your answer.

8 **a** In general, as a substance is heated, it expands. What happens to the density of the substance?

   b Water is unusual in that its solid state is less dense than its liquid state. How do we observe this in the world around us?

9 Determine the total mass of stone required to build a square-based pyramid with all edges of length 200 m. The density of the stone is 2.25 tonnes per m^3.

10 The planet Uranus is approximately spherical with radius 2.536×10^7 m and mass 8.681×10^{25} kg.

   a Estimate the volume of Uranus.   **b** Hence find its density.

PROJECT   HOW BIG IS THE MOUNTAIN?

Choose an iconic mountain of the world. Your task is to estimate its volume.

To achieve this task, you will need:

- a topographic map of the mountain
- knowledge of Simpson's rule.

What to do:

1 **a** Use Simpson's rule to estimate the cross-sectional area of the mountain at each contour level.

   b Hence estimate the volume of the mountain added at each change in altitude level.

   c Use a solid of uniform cross-section to estimate the volume of the mountain from your lowest chosen contour down to sea level.

   d Sum your results to estimate the total volume of the mountain.

   e Discuss the assumptions you made in your calculations.

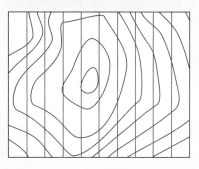

2 **a** Make regular slices across your contour map and use Simpson's rule to estimate the area of each slice.

   b Hence estimate the volume of the mountain for each interval between the slices.

   c Sum your results to give the total volume of the mountain.

   d Discuss the assumptions you made in your calculations.

3 **a** Overlay a fine grid on top of the topographical map. Use the contours to estimate the altitude at each vertex point of the grid. Hence estimate the average altitude of each grid square.

   b Hence estimate the volume of the mountain under each grid square.

   c Sum your results to give the total volume of the mountain.

   d Discuss the assumptions you have made in your calculations.

4 Compare the estimates you have obtained for the volume of the mountain.

   a What assumptions do you need to make in order to compare them fairly?

   b Which method do you think is the:

   i most elegant   **ii** most accurate   **iii** easiest to automate using software?

5 Can you suggest a more accurate method for estimating the volume of the mountain? Explain why you believe it is more accurate, and perform calculations.

6 Research the composition of your chosen mountain and use the information to estimate its mass.

7 If you measured the volume of a mountain down to the base plane around it rather than to sea level, what is the "biggest" mountain on Earth?

CAPACITY

The **capacity** of a container is the quantity of fluid it is capable of holding.

Notice that the term "capacity" belongs to the container rather than the fluid itself. The capacity of the container tells us what *volume* of fluid fits inside it. The units of volume and capacity are therefore linked:

1 mL of water occupies 1 cm³ of space.

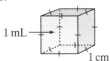

Volume		Capacity
1 cm³	≡	1 mL
1000 cm³	≡	1 L
1 m³	≡	1 kL
1 m³	≡	1000 L

≡ means "is equivalent to".

DISCUSSION

- In common language, are the terms *volume* and *capacity* used correctly?
- Which of the following statements are technically correct? Which are commonly accepted in language, even though they are not technically correct?
  ▸ The jug has capacity 600 mL.
  ▸ The jug can hold 600 mL of water.
  ▸ The volume of the jug is 600 cm³.
  ▸ The jug can hold 600 cm³ of water.
  ▸ I am going to the supermarket to buy a 2 L bottle of milk.
  ▸ I am going to the supermarket to buy 2 L of milk.

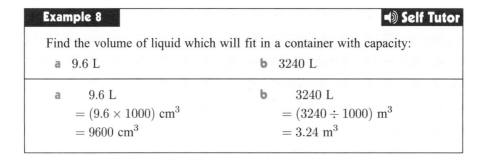

Example 8	◀) **Self Tutor**

Find the volume of liquid which will fit in a container with capacity:

a 9.6 L   **b** 3240 L

a   9.6 L
= (9.6 × 1000) cm³
= 9600 cm³

b   3240 L
= (3240 ÷ 1000) m³
= 3.24 m³

EXERCISE 6D

1 Find the volume of liquid which will fit in a container with capacity:

   a 800 mL   **b** 12 L   **c** 4.6 kL   **d** 3200 mL.

2 Find the capacity of a container needed to hold a fluid with volume:

   a 8.4 cm³   **b** 1800 cm³   **c** 1.8 m³   **d** 7154 m³.

3 Find, in m³, the volume of gas which will fit in a container with capacity 3.85×10^4 L.

Example 9   ◀)) **Self Tutor**

Find the capacity of a 2.6 m by 3.1 m by 1.45 m tank.

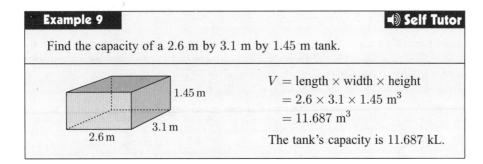

$V = \text{length} \times \text{width} \times \text{height}$
$= 2.6 \times 3.1 \times 1.45 \text{ m}^3$
$= 11.687 \text{ m}^3$

The tank's capacity is 11.687 kL.

4 Find the capacity (in kL) of the following tanks:

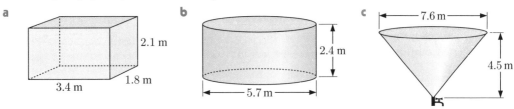

a

b

c

5 Find the volume of soup that will fit in this hemispherical pot. Give your answer in:

    a cm^3 b   L.

When talking about liquids, it is common to talk about their volume using the units of capacity.

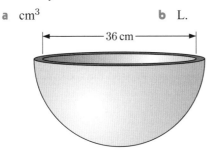

6 A dam wall is built at the narrow point of a river to create a small reservoir. When full, the reservoir has an average depth of 13 m, and has the shape shown in the diagram. Find the capacity of the reservoir.

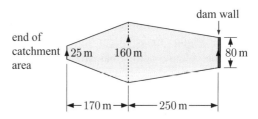

7 Jam is packed into cylindrical tins which have radius 4.5 cm and height 15 cm. The mixing vat is also cylindrical with cross-sectional area 1.2 m² and height 4.1 m.

    a Find the capacity of each tin.   b Find the capacity of the mixing vat.

    c How many tins of jam could be filled from one vat?

    d If the jam is sold at \$3.50 per tin, what is the value of one vat of jam?

8 Answer the **Opening Problem** on page **146**.

9

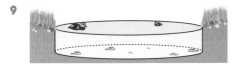

The circular pond in the park near my house has radius 2.4 m. It has just been filled with 10 kL of water. How deep is the pond?

Example 10   ◀⦆ **Self Tutor**

17.3 mm of rain falls on a flat rectangular shed roof which has length 10 m and width 6.5 m. All of the water goes into a cylindrical tank with base diameter 4 m. By how many millimetres does the water level in the tank rise?

For the roof: The dimensions of the roof are in m, so we convert 17.3 mm to metres.

$$17.3 \text{ mm} = (17.3 \div 1000) \text{ m} = 0.0173 \text{ m}$$

The volume of water collected by the roof = area of roof × depth
$$= 10 \times 6.5 \times 0.0173 \text{ m}^3$$
$$= 1.1245 \text{ m}^3$$

For the tank: The volume added to the tank
$$= \text{area of base} \times \text{height}$$
$$= \pi \times 2^2 \times h \text{ m}^3 = 4\pi \times h \text{ m}^3$$

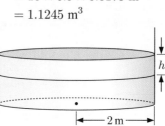

The volume added to the tank must equal the volume which falls on the roof, so

$4\pi \times h = 1.1245$

$\therefore \ h = \dfrac{1.1245}{4\pi}$ {dividing both sides by 4π}

$\therefore \ h \approx 0.0895$ m

$\therefore$ the water level rises by about 89.5 mm.

---

10 The base of a house has area 110 m². One night 12 mm of rain falls on the roof. All of the water goes into a tank which has base diameter 4 m.

   a Find the volume of water which fell on the roof.

   b How many kL of water entered the tank?

   c By how much did the water level in the tank rise?

11 The design department of a fish canning company wants to change the size of their cylindrical tins. The original tin is 15 cm high and 7.2 cm in diameter. The new tin is to have approximately the same volume, but its diameter will be 10 cm. How high must it be, to the nearest mm?

12 A conical wine glass has the dimensions shown.

   a Find the capacity of the glass.

   b Suppose the glass is 75% full.

      i How many mL of wine does it contain?

      ii If the wine is poured into a cylindrical glass of the same diameter, how high will it rise?

13 A fleet of trucks have containers with the shape illustrated. Wheat is transported in these containers, and its level must not exceed a mark 10 cm below the top. How many truck loads of wheat are necessary to fill a cylindrical silo with internal diameter 8 m and height 25 m?

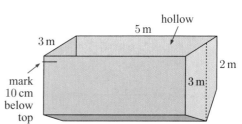

ACTIVITY 2   MINIMISING MATERIAL

Your boss asks you to design a rectangular box-shaped container which is open at the top and contains exactly 1 litre of fluid. The base measurements must be in the ratio $2 : 1$. She intends to manufacture millions of these containers, and wishes to keep manufacturing costs to a minimum. She therefore insists that the least amount of material is used.

What to do:

1 The base is to be in the ratio $2 : 1$, so we let the dimensions be x cm and $2x$ cm. The height is also unknown, so we let it be y cm. As the values of x and y vary, the container changes size.

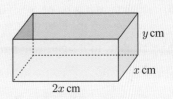

Explain why:

a the volume $V = 2x^2 y$ **b** $2x^2 y = 1000$ **c** $y = \dfrac{500}{x^2}$

2 Show that the surface area is given by $A = 2x^2 + 6xy$.

3 Construct a spreadsheet which calculates the surface area for $x = 1, 2, 3, 4, ...$

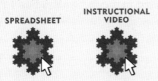

SPREADSHEET   INSTRUCTIONAL VIDEO

	A	B	C
1	**x values**	**y values**	**A values**
2	1	=500/A2^2	=2*A2^2+6*A2*B2
3	=A2+1		
4	↓	↓	↓
5		fill down	

4 Find the smallest value of A, and the value of x which produces it. Hence write down the dimensions of the box your boss desires.

REVIEW SET 6A

1 For the given sector, find to 3 significant figures:

    a the length of the arc

    b the perimeter of the sector

    c the area of the sector.

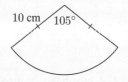

2 Find the radius of a sector with angle $80°$ and area 24π cm^2.

3 Find, to 1 decimal place, the outer surface area of:

a 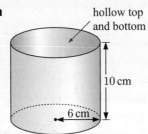 hollow top and bottom

b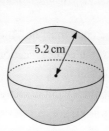

c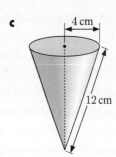

4 A tool shed with the dimensions illustrated is to be painted with two coats of zinc-alum. Each litre of zinc-alum covers 5 m² and costs $8.25. It must be purchased in whole litres.

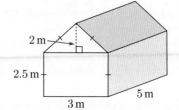

  a Find the area to be painted, including the roof.

  b Find the total cost of the zinc-alum.

5 A fish farm has *six* netted cylindrical cages open at the top. The cylinders have depth 17 m and diameter 7.5 m. Find the total area of netting in the cages.

6 Calculate, to 3 significant figures, the volume of:

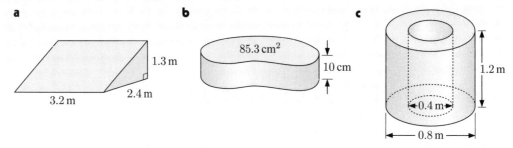

a   **b**   **c**

7 Tom has just had a load of sand delivered. The sand is piled in a cone with radius 1.6 m and height 1.2 m. Find the volume of the sand.

8 A manufacturer of spikes has 245 L of molten iron. If each spike contains 15 mL of iron, how many spikes can be made?

9 A plastic beach ball has radius 27 cm. Find its volume.

10 The capacity of a petrol tank is 65 L. State the volume of petrol required to fill the tank in:

  a cm³   **b** m³.

11 Find the capacity of:

a   **b**

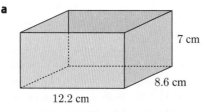   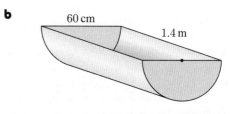

12 A rectangular shed has a roof of length 12 m and width 5.5 m. Rainfall from the roof runs into a cylindrical tank with base diameter 4.35 m. If 15.4 mm of rain falls, how many millimetres does the water level in the tank rise?

13 A feed silo is made out of sheet steel using a hemisphere, a cylinder, and a cone.

  a Explain why the height of the cone must be 70 cm.

  b Hence find the *slant height* of the conical section.

  c Calculate the total amount of steel used.

  d Show that the silo can hold about 5.2 cubic metres of grain.

  e Write the capacity of the silo in kL.

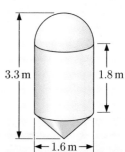

REVIEW SET 6B

1 For the given sector, find to 3 significant figures:

   a the angle $\theta°$

   b the area of the sector.

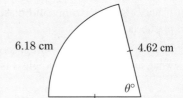

6.18 cm   4.62 cm

$\theta°$

2 For the given figure, find the:

   a perimeter   **b** area.

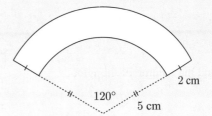

2 cm

120°

5 cm

3 Find the surface area of:

a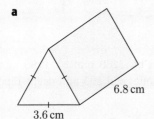

6.8 cm

3.6 cm

b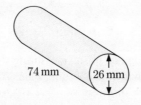

74 mm   26 mm

c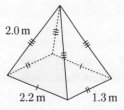

2.0 m

2.2 m   1.3 m

4 The hexagonal gazebo shown has wood panelling for the roof, floor, and part of five of the walls. Find the total surface area of wood panelling in the gazebo. Include the interior as well as the exterior.

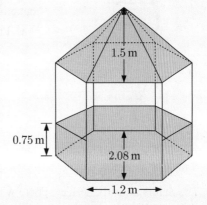

1.5 m

0.75 m

2.08 m

1.2 m

5 I am sending my sister some fragile objects inside a postal cylinder. The cylinder is 325 mm long and has diameter 40 mm. What area of bubble wrap do I need to line its inside walls?

6 Find the volume of:

a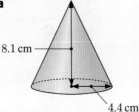

8.1 cm

4.4 cm

b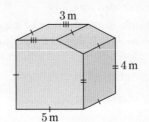

3 m

4 m

5 m

c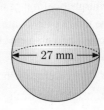

27 mm

7 Frank wants to have a large F outside his shop for advertising. He designs one with the dimensions shown.

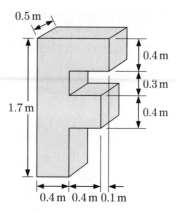

 a If the F is made from solid plastic, what volume of plastic is needed?

 b If the F is made from fibreglass as a hollow object, what surface area of fibreglass is needed?

8 Find the volume of the igloo:

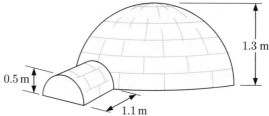

9 A kitchen bench is a rectangular prism measuring 3845 mm by 1260 mm by 1190 mm. It contains a rectangular sink which is 550 mm wide, 750 mm long, and 195 mm deep. Find the storage capacity of the bench in litres.

10

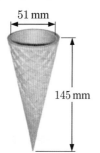

A gelateria sells gelato in cones with the dimensions shown. The cone is filled completely, with a hemispherical scoop on top.

 a Find the volume of gelato sold with each cone.

 b How many cones can be sold from 10 L of gelato?

11 A cylindrical drum for storing industrial waste has capacity 10 kL. If the height of the drum is 3 m, find its radius.

12 The Sun is a nearly perfect sphere with radius $\approx 6.955 \times 10^8$ m.
Find, in scientific notation, the Sun's:

 a surface area   **b** volume.

13 A solid metal spinning top is constructed by joining a hemispherical top to a cone-shaped base.
The radius of both the hemisphere and the base of the cone is 3 cm. The volume of the cone is half that of the hemisphere.
Calculate:

 a the volume of the hemispherical top

 b the height of the cone-shaped base

 c the outer surface area of the spinning top.

Chapter 7

Right angled triangle trigonometry

Contents:

OPENING PROBLEM

Things to think about:

a Both of the right angled triangles alongside contain a 30° angle. From the information we are given, can we determine:

   i the lengths PQ and QR

   ii the *ratio* of lengths $\dfrac{PQ}{QR}$?

b Both of the right angled triangles alongside contain a 35° angle. Can you explain why:

   i $\dfrac{AB}{BC} = \dfrac{PQ}{QR}$

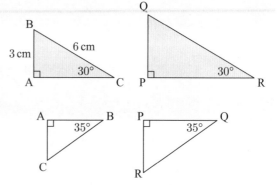

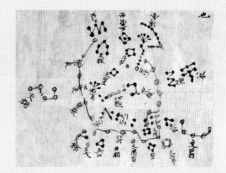

   ii any other right angled triangle containing a 35° angle will have corresponding sides in the same ratio?

Trigonometry is the study of the relationships between the side lengths and angles of triangles.

Trigonometry is extensively used in the real world, being essential for engineering, architecture, building, physics, astronomy, navigation, and many other industries.

THEORY OF KNOWLEDGE

The study of celestial objects such as the sun, moon, stars, and planets is called **astronomy**. It has been important to civilisations all over the world for thousands of years, not only because it allowed them to navigate at night, but because the celestial objects feature in so many of their myths and beliefs.

To create an accurate star map, astronomers measure the angles between objects in the sky. The oldest known star map was found in the Silk Road town of Dunhuang in 1907. It was made in the 7th century AD, presumably from the Imperial Observatory in either Chang'an (present day Xi'an) or Luoyang. A possible author of the map was the mathematician and astronomer **Li Chunfeng** (602 - 670). The map shows 1339 stars in 257 star groups recorded with great precision on 12 charts, each covering approximately 30 degree sections of the night sky.[1]

   1 How much of what we *believe* comes from what we *observe*? Is it necessary to *understand* something, in order to *believe* it? How much of what we *study* is a quest to *understand* what we *observe*, and *prove* what we *believe*?

   2 How much of what we want to know is a common desire of people and cultures all over the world?

3 How did ancient people calculate with such accuracy before computer technology?

[1] "The Dunhuang Chinese Sky: A comprehensive study of the oldest known star atlas", J-M Bonnet-Bidaud, F. Praderie, S. Whitfield, *J. Astronomical History and Heritage*, 12(1), 39-59 (2009).

In this Chapter we will study the trigonometry of right angled triangles. To help us, we will label the sides of a right angled triangle in the following way:

- The **hypotenuse (HYP)** of a right angled triangle is the side which is opposite the right angle. It is the longest side of the triangle.

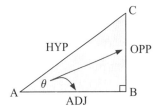

- For the angle marked θ:
  - ▸ [BC] is the side **opposite (OPP)** angle θ
  - ▸ [AB] is the side **adjacent (ADJ)** to angle θ.

- For the angle marked ϕ:
  - ▸ [AB] is the side **opposite (OPP)** angle ϕ
  - ▸ [BC] is the side **adjacent (ADJ)** to angle ϕ.

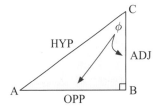

θ and ϕ are the Greek letters "theta" and "phi".

THE TRIGONOMETRIC RATIOS

INVESTIGATION   THE TRIGONOMETRIC RATIOS

These right angled triangles all contain a 37° angle.

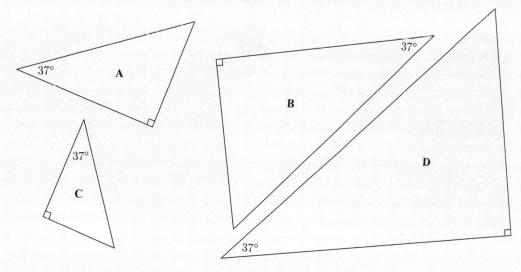

What to do:

1   Explain why the triangles are all *similar*.

2   For each triangle, measure to the nearest millimetre the length of the side opposite and adjacent to the 37° angle, and the hypotenuse.

Use your measurements to complete this table:

Triangle	OPP	ADJ	HYP	$\dfrac{OPP}{HYP}$	$\dfrac{ADJ}{HYP}$	$\dfrac{OPP}{ADJ}$
A						
B						
C						
D						

3   Explain why the ratios $\dfrac{\text{OPP}}{\text{HYP}}$, $\dfrac{\text{ADJ}}{\text{HYP}}$, and $\dfrac{\text{OPP}}{\text{ADJ}}$ are constant.

For any fixed angle θ, the ratio $\dfrac{\text{OPP}}{\text{HYP}}$, $\dfrac{\text{ADJ}}{\text{HYP}}$, and $\dfrac{\text{OPP}}{\text{ADJ}}$ are constant.

These ratios are called the **sine**, **cosine**, and **tangent** of the angle θ. Together, they are called the **trigonometric ratios**.

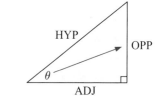

$$\sin\theta = \frac{\textbf{OPP}}{\textbf{HYP}} \qquad\qquad \cos\theta = \frac{\textbf{ADJ}}{\textbf{HYP}} \qquad\qquad \tan\theta = \frac{\textbf{OPP}}{\textbf{ADJ}}$$

Notice that $\dfrac{\sin\theta}{\cos\theta} = \dfrac{\frac{\text{OPP}}{\text{HYP}}}{\frac{\text{ADJ}}{\text{HYP}}} = \dfrac{\text{OPP}}{\text{ADJ}} = \tan\theta$

So, $$\tan\theta = \frac{\sin\theta}{\cos\theta}$$

In the **Investigation**, you should have found the trigonometric ratios for $\theta = 37°$ are $\sin 37° \approx 0.602$, $\cos 37° \approx 0.799$, and $\tan 37° \approx 0.754$.

Trigonometric ratios for any angle can be found using a calculator. You should first check that your calculator is in DEGREE mode.

GRAPHICS CALCULATOR INSTRUCTIONS

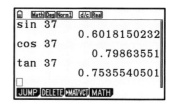

Example 1   ◀》 **Self Tutor**

For the following triangle, find:

   a $\sin\theta$ **b** $\cos\theta$ **c** $\tan\theta$

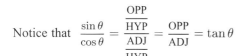

  a $\sin\theta = \dfrac{\text{OPP}}{\text{HYP}} = \dfrac{15}{17}$ **b** $\cos\theta = \dfrac{\text{ADJ}}{\text{HYP}} = \dfrac{8}{17}$ **c** $\tan\theta = \dfrac{\text{OPP}}{\text{ADJ}} = \dfrac{15}{8}$

EXERCISE 7A

1   For each of the following triangles, find:

    i $\sin\theta$ **ii** $\cos\theta$ **iii** $\tan\theta$

a 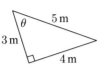   **b** 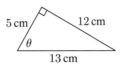   **c**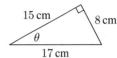

d 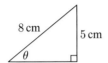   **e** 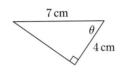   **f**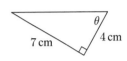

2   Use your calculator to find, correct to 3 decimal places:

    a $\sin 20°$ **b** $\sin 76°$ **c** $\cos 27°$

    d $\cos 43°$ **e** $\tan 32°$ **f** $\tan 70°$

3   The right angled triangle alongside contains an angle of 56°.

    a   Use a ruler to measure the length of each side, to the nearest millimetre.

    b   Hence estimate, to 2 decimal places:

        i $\sin 56°$ **ii** $\cos 56°$

        iii $\tan 56°$

    c   Check your answers using a calculator.

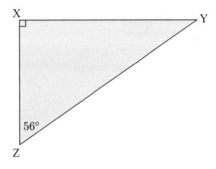

4

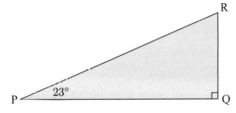

This right angled triangle contains a 23° angle.

    a   Which side is longer: [PQ] or [QR]?

    b   Hence decide whether $\cos 23°$ or $\sin 23°$ is larger. Check your answer using a calculator.

    c   Is $\tan 23°$ greater than 1, or less than 1? Check your answer using a calculator.

5   Consider the right angled isosceles triangle ABC alongside.

    a   Explain why $A\widehat{B}C - 45°$.

    b   Use Pythagoras' theorem to find AB.

    c   Hence find:

        i $\sin 45°$ **ii** $\cos 45°$ **iii** $\tan 45°$.

    d   Check your answers using a calculator.

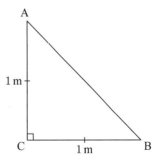

6   Explain why it is impossible for the sine or cosine of an angle to be greater than 1.

7 Consider the right angled triangle shown.

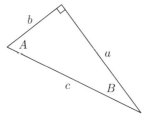

  a Write expressions for:

   i $\sin A$ **ii** $\cos A$ **iii** $\tan A$

   iv $\sin B$ **v** $\cos B$ **vi** $\tan B$

  b State the relationship between A and B.

  c Hence state the relationship between:

   i $\sin \theta$ and $\cos(90° - \theta)$

   ii $\cos \theta$ and $\sin(90° - \theta)$

   iii $\tan \theta$ and $\tan(90° - \theta)$

B   FINDING SIDE LENGTHS

If we are given the angles of a right angled triangle and the length of one side, we can use trigonometric ratios to find the other side lengths.

Example 2   🔊 **Self Tutor**

Find, correct to 3 significant figures, the unknown length in the following triangles:

a

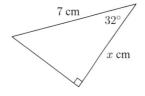

b

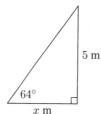

Make sure your calculator is set to **degrees** mode.

---

a

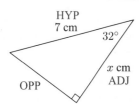

HYP
7 cm
32°
x cm
ADJ
OPP

The relevant sides are ADJ and HYP, so we use the *cosine* ratio.

$$\cos 32° = \frac{x}{7} \qquad \left\{ \cos \theta = \frac{\text{ADJ}}{\text{HYP}} \right\}$$

$$\therefore \ 7 \times \cos 32° = x \qquad \{\text{multiplying both sides by } 7\}$$

$$\therefore \ x \approx 5.94 \qquad \{\text{using technology}\}$$

So, the side is about 5.94 cm long.

b

HYP   OPP
5 m
64°
x m
ADJ

The relevant sides are ADJ and OPP, so we use the *tangent* ratio.

$$\tan 64° = \frac{5}{x} \qquad \left\{ \tan \theta = \frac{\text{OPP}}{\text{ADJ}} \right\}$$

$$\therefore \ x \times \tan 64° = 5 \qquad \{\text{multiplying both sides by } x\}$$

$$\therefore \ x = \frac{5}{\tan 64°} \qquad \{\text{dividing both sides by } \tan 64°\}$$

$$\therefore \ x \approx 2.44 \qquad \{\text{using technology}\}$$

So, the side is about 2.44 m long.

EXERCISE 7B

1 Construct a trigonometric equation connecting the given angle and sides:

a
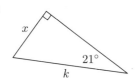

b
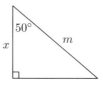

c
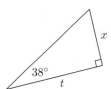

d
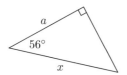

e
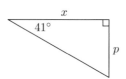

f
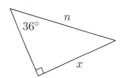

2 Find, correct to 3 significant figures, the unknown length:

a
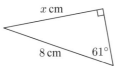

b
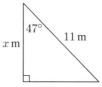

c
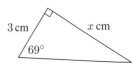

d
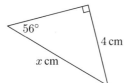

e
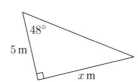

f
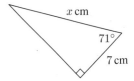

g
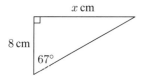

h

i
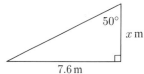

j
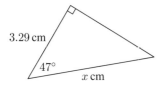

k
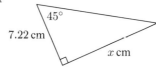

l
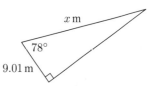

3 Consider the triangle alongside.
   a Find x.
   b Find y using:
      i Pythagoras' theorem
      ii trigonometry.

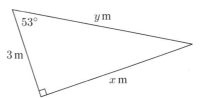

4 Find the unknowns, correct to 2 decimal places:

a
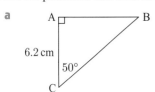

b
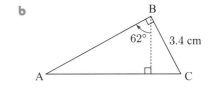

c

5 Find the perimeter and area of triangle ABC:

a
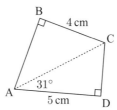

b
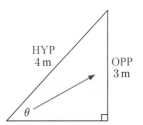

6 Use the information on the diagram to find:

a   the length AC

b   the length AB

c   the perimeter of quadrilateral ABCD

d   the area of quadrilateral ABCD.

C   FINDING ANGLES

If we know the lengths of two sides of a right angled triangle, we can use trigonometry to find its angles.

In the triangle alongside, $\sin \theta = \dfrac{\text{OPP}}{\text{HYP}} = \dfrac{3}{4}$.

To find θ, we need to find the angle whose sine is $\frac{3}{4}$.

We say that θ is the **inverse sine** of $\frac{3}{4}$, and write $\theta = \sin^{-1}\left(\frac{3}{4}\right)$.

We can evaluate inverse sines using a calculator.

We find that $\theta \approx 48.6°$.

$\sin^{-1} x$ is the angle with a sine of x.

GRAPHICS
CALCULATOR
INSTRUCTIONS

```
NORMAL FLOAT AUTO REAL DEGREE MP
sin⁻¹(3/4)
                      48.59037789
```

We define **inverse cosine** and **inverse tangent** in a similar way.

Example 3   ◀⑴ **Self Tutor**

Find, correct to 3 significant figures, the measure of the angle marked θ:

a   **b**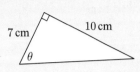

a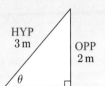

$\sin \theta = \frac{2}{3}$ $\{ \sin \theta = \dfrac{\text{OPP}}{\text{HYP}} \}$

$\therefore \quad \theta = \sin^{-1}(\frac{2}{3})$

$\therefore \quad \theta \approx 41.8°$ {using technology}

b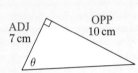

$\tan \theta = \frac{10}{7}$ $\{ \tan \theta = \dfrac{\text{OPP}}{\text{ADJ}} \}$

$\therefore \quad \theta = \tan^{-1}(\frac{10}{7})$

$\therefore \quad \theta \approx 55.0°$ {using technology}

EXERCISE 7C

1 Find, correct to 3 significant figures, the measure of the angle marked θ:

a 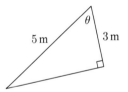   **b** 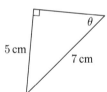   **c**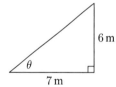

d 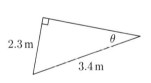   **e**   **f**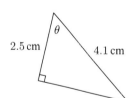

g 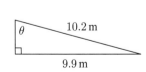   **h** 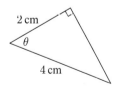   **i**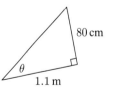

2 Consider the triangle alongside.

   a Find θ, correct to 1 decimal place.

   b Find ϕ using:

      i the angles in a triangle theorem

      ii trigonometry.

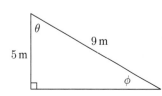

3 Find, correct to 1 decimal place, all unknown angles:

a
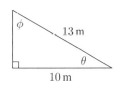

b
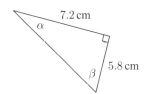

c
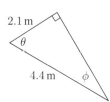

4 Try to find θ in the following diagrams. What conclusions can you draw?

a
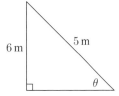

b
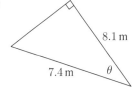

c
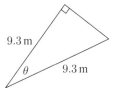

5 Find all unknown sides and angles in these figures:

a
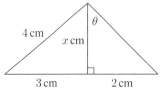

b
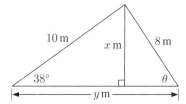

D   RIGHT ANGLES IN GEOMETRIC FIGURES

Many geometric figures contain right angles which we can use to help solve problems:

- In an **isosceles triangle** and an **equilateral triangle**, the altitude bisects the base at right angles.

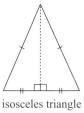

isosceles triangle   equilateral triangle

- The corners of a **rectangle** and a **square** are right angles. We can construct a diagonal to form a right angled triangle.

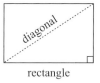
rectangle

square

- In a **square** and a **rhombus**, the diagonals bisect each other at right angles.

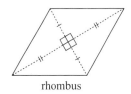

square   rhombus

- In a **kite**, the diagonals intersect at right angles.

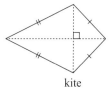
kite

- A **tangent** to a circle and a radius at the point of contact meet at right angles.
  We can form a right angled triangle with another point on the tangent.

- The angle in a **semi-circle** is always a right angle.

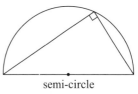

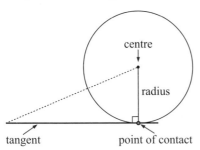

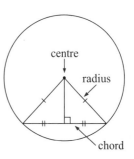

- The line drawn from the centre of a circle at right angles to a **chord**, bisects the chord.

Example 4 ◀) Self Tutor

Find the unknowns:

a

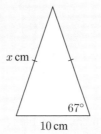

b

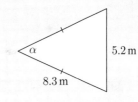

a

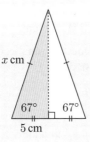

In the shaded right angled triangle,

$$\cos 67° = \frac{5}{x}$$

$$\therefore \ x = \frac{5}{\cos 67°} \approx 12.8$$

b

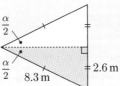

In the shaded right angled triangle,

$$\sin \frac{\alpha}{2} = \frac{2.6}{8.3}$$

$$\therefore \ \frac{\alpha}{2} = \sin^{-1}\left(\frac{2.6}{8.3}\right)$$

$$\therefore \ \alpha = 2\sin^{-1}\left(\frac{2.6}{8.3}\right) \approx 36.5°$$

EXERCISE 7D

1 Find the unknown, correct to 3 significant figures:

a

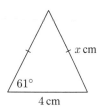

b

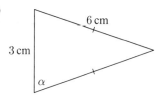

c

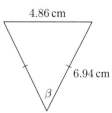

d

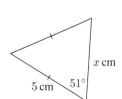

e

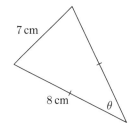

f

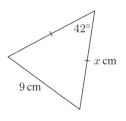

2 A rectangle is 9.2 m by 3.8 m. What angle does its diagonal make with its longer side?

3 The diagonal and the longer side of a rectangle make an angle of 43.2°. If the longer side is 12.6 cm, find the length of the shorter side.

4 Find the area of the rectangle:

a

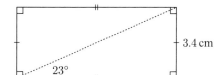

b

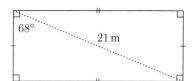

Example 5	◀) **Self Tutor**

A rhombus has diagonals of length 10 cm and 6 cm. Find the smaller angle of the rhombus.

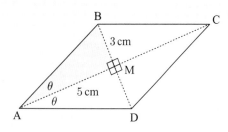

The diagonals bisect each other at right angles, so AM = 5 cm and BM = 3 cm.

In $\triangle$ABM, θ will be the smallest angle as it is opposite the shortest side.

$$\tan\theta = \tfrac{3}{5}$$
$$\therefore \ \theta = \tan^{-1}\left(\tfrac{3}{5}\right)$$
$$\therefore \ \theta \approx 30.964°$$

The required angle is 2θ as the diagonals bisect the angles at each vertex.
So, the angle is about 61.9°.

---

5 A rhombus has diagonals of length 12 cm and 7 cm. Find the larger angle of the rhombus.

6 The smaller angle of a rhombus measures 21.8° and the shorter diagonal has length 13.8 cm. Find the lengths of the sides of the rhombus.

7 Find θ in the given kite.

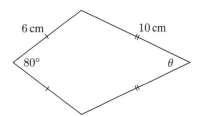

Example 6	◀ **Self Tutor**

Find x:

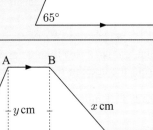

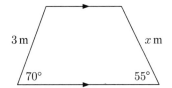

We draw perpendiculars [AM] and [BN] to [DC], creating right angled triangles and the rectangle ABNM.

In $\triangle$ADM, $\sin 65° = \dfrac{y}{10}$

$\qquad\qquad \therefore \ y = 10\sin 65°$

In $\triangle$BCN, $\sin 48° = \dfrac{y}{x}$

$\qquad\qquad\qquad = \dfrac{10\sin 65°}{x}$

$\qquad\qquad \therefore \ x = \dfrac{10\sin 65°}{\sin 48°} \approx 12.2$

---

8 Find the unknown value:

a

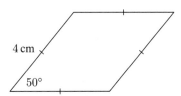

b

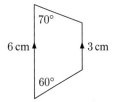

9 Find the area of the figure:

a

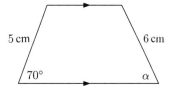

b

10 A rhombus has sides of length 8 metres, and the longer diagonal has length 13 metres.

    a Draw a diagram and label it with the given information.

    b Find the length of the shorter diagonal of the rhombus.

    c Find the measure of the smaller angle in the rhombus.

11 Find the radius of the circle:

a

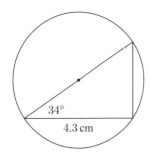

b

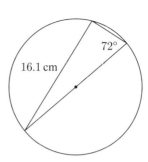

Example 7   ◀ঠ **Self Tutor**

A circle has radius 6.5 cm. A chord of the circle subtends an angle of 112° at its centre. Find the length of the chord.

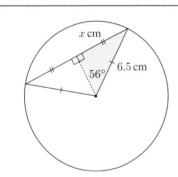

We complete an isosceles triangle and draw the line from the apex to the base.

For the shaded triangle, $\sin 56° = \dfrac{x}{6.5}$

$$\therefore \quad 6.5 \times \sin 56° = x$$
$$\therefore \quad x \approx 5.389$$
$$\therefore \quad 2x \approx 10.78$$

∴   the chord is about 10.8 cm long.

---

12 Find the value of the unknown:

a

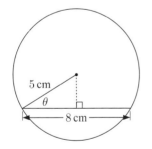

b

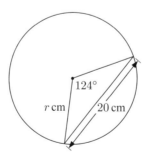

c

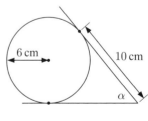

13 A circle has diameter 11.4 cm. A chord of the circle subtends an angle of 89° at its centre. Find the length of the chord.

14 A chord of a circle is 13.2 cm long and the circle's radius is 9.4 cm. Find the angle subtended by the chord at the centre of the circle.

15 Point P is 10 cm from the centre of a circle of radius 4 cm. Tangents are drawn from P to the circle. Find the angle between the tangents.

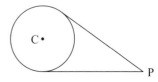

E PROBLEM SOLVING WITH TRIGONOMETRY

In this Section we consider practical applications of trigonometry. It allows us to find heights and distances which are very difficult or even impossible to measure directly.

ANGLES OF ELEVATION AND DEPRESSION

The angle between the horizontal and your line of sight to an object is called:

- the **angle of elevation** if you are looking upwards
- the **angle of depression** if you are looking downwards.

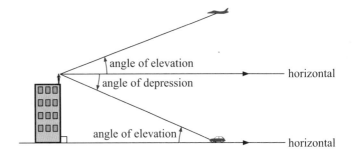

Example 8   ◄» **Self Tutor**

A tree casts a shadow of 12.4 m when the angle of elevation to the sun is $52°$. Find the height of the tree.

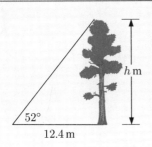

Let the tree's height be h m.

For the $52°$ angle, OPP $= h$ m, ADJ $= 12.4$ m

$$\therefore \ \tan 52° = \frac{h}{12.4}$$

$$\therefore \ 12.4 \times \tan 52° = h$$

$$\therefore \ h \approx 15.9$$

$\therefore$ the tree is about 15.9 m high.

EXERCISE 7E

1 A flagpole casts a shadow of 9.32 m when the angle of elevation to the sun is $63°$. Find the height of the flagpole.

2 A steep hill is inclined at $18°$ to the horizontal. It runs down to the beach so its base is at sea level.

   a If I walk 150 m up the hill, what is my height above sea level?

   b If I climb to a point 80 m above sea level, how far have I walked?

3

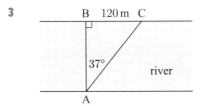

A surveyor has placed two posts B and C 120 m apart on one side of a river. He crosses the river using a bridge, then moves to the point A which is directly opposite B. He finds that the angle of sight between the posts is $37°$. How wide is the river?

4 A train must climb a constant gradient of 5.5 m for every 200 m of track. Find the angle of incline.

5 **a** Find the angle of elevation to the top of a 56 m high building from point A which is 113 m from its base.

   b What is the angle of depression from the top of the building to A?

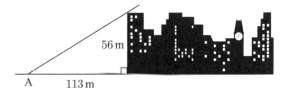

6 The angle of depression from the top of a 20 m high vertical cliff to a boat B is $8°$.

   How far is the boat from the base of the cliff?

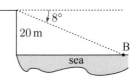

Example 9   ◀) Self Tutor

A builder has designed the roof structure illustrated. Find the pitch of this roof.

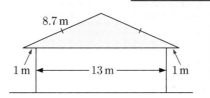

The *pitch* of a roof is the angle that the roof makes with the horizontal.

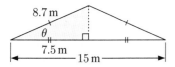

By constructing an altitude of the isosceles triangle, we form two right angled triangles.

$$\cos \theta = \frac{7.5}{8.7} \qquad \{\cos \theta = \frac{ADJ}{HYP}\}$$

$$\therefore \quad \theta = \cos^{-1}\left(\frac{7.5}{8.7}\right)$$

$$\therefore \quad \theta \approx 30.5°$$

The pitch of the roof is approximately $30.5°$.

---

7 Find θ, the pitch of the roof.

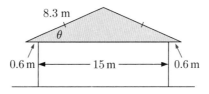

8

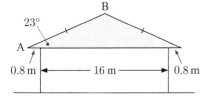

The pitch of the given roof is $23°$. Find the length of the timber beam [AB].

9 A rectangular field is 20 metres longer than it is wide. When Patrick walks from one corner to the opposite corner, he makes an angle of $55°$ with the shorter side of the field. Find the length of this shorter side.

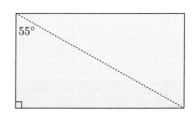

10   A stormwater drain has the shape illustrated. Determine the angle β where the left hand side meets with the bottom of the drain.

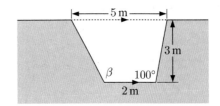

11   From an observer O who is 200 m from a building, the angles of elevation to the bottom and top of a flagpole are 36° and 38° respectively. Find the height of the flagpole.

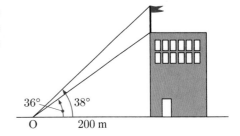

12   The angle of depression from the top of a 15 m high cliff to a boat at sea is 2.7°. How much closer to the cliff must the boat move for the angle of depression to become 4°?

13   A helicopter flies horizontally at 100 km h^{-1}. An observer notices that it takes 20 seconds for the helicopter to fly from directly overhead to being at an angle of elevation of 60°. Find the height of the helicopter above the ground.

14   [AC] is a straight shore line 5 km long. B is a boat out at sea. Find the shortest distance from the boat to the shore.

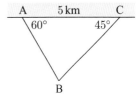

15

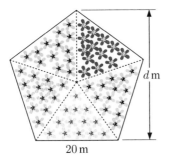

A new feature at the botanical gardens will be a regular pentagonal flower bed with sides of length 20 m.

Find the width of land d m required for the flower bed.

16   A circular clock has dots on its boundary which indicate the numbers 1 to 12. The dots representing 10 and 2 are 24 cm apart. Find the radius of the clock.

Example 10   ◀》 **Self Tutor**

A rectangular prism has the dimensions shown.
Find the measure of $A\widehat{B}C$.

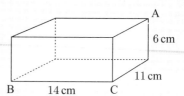

Consider the end of the prism containing points A and C.
Let $AC = x$ cm.

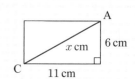

Using Pythagoras, $x^2 = 6^2 + 11^2$

$\therefore\ x^2 = 157$

$\therefore\ x = \sqrt{157}$ {as $x > 0$}

$\triangle ABC$ is right angled at C.

Let $A\widehat{B}C = \theta$

$\therefore\ \tan\theta = \frac{\sqrt{157}}{14}$ $\{\tan\theta = \frac{\text{OPP}}{\text{ADJ}}\}$

$\therefore\ \theta = \tan^{-1}\left(\frac{\sqrt{157}}{14}\right)$

$\therefore\ \theta \approx 41.8°$

So, $A\widehat{B}C \approx 41.8°$.

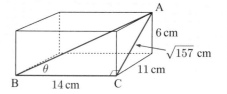

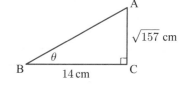

17 The cube shown has sides of length 13 cm. Find:

   a BD   **b** $F\widehat{D}B$.

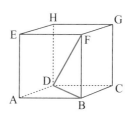

18

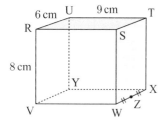

In the rectangular prism shown, Z is the midpoint of [WX].
Find:

   a VX   **b** $R\widehat{X}V$

   c YZ   **d** $Y\widehat{Z}U$.

19 An open cone has a vertical angle measuring $40°$ and a base radius of
30 cm. Find:

   a the height of the cone

   b the capacity of the cone in litres.

20

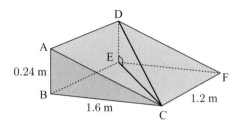

A ramp is built as the triangular prism shown.

a Find the length:

    i CE   **ii** CD.

b Find DĈE.

21 Elizabeth is terrified of spiders. When she walks into a room, she notices one in the opposite corner S.

a If Elizabeth is 1.6 m tall, how far is the spider from her head?

b The spider can see up to an angle of 42° from the direction it is facing. This spider is facing a fly at F. Can it see Elizabeth?

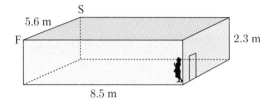

22 Rico is flying his kite with the aid of a southerly wind. He has let out 34 m of string, and the kite is at an angle of elevation of 37°. His friend Edward stands to the west, 65 m away.

a How far is Edward from the kite?

b What is the angle of elevation from Edward to the kite?

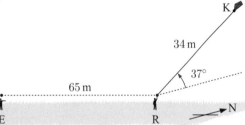

23 Find the angle between the slant edge [AX] and the base diagonal [AC].

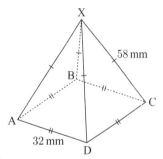

24 Find the volume of each solid:

a

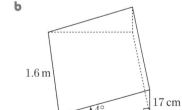

b

c

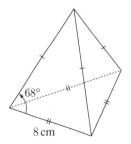

25 A **parallax** is the angle through which an object appears to move when viewed from different positions.

In 1838, the Prussian astronomer **Friedrich Wilhelm Bessel** (1784 - 1846) used the telescopes at the Königsberg Observatory to measure the parallax of the star 61 Cygni to be approximately 0.314 arc seconds, where one arc second is $\frac{1}{3600}$ of a degree. He did this by comparing the apparent positions of 61 Cygni during the year, relative to a fixed backdrop of distant stars.

Friedrich Bessel

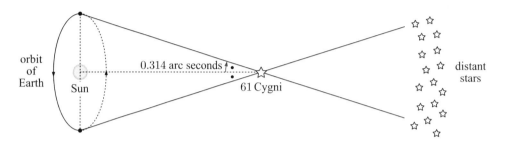

a Given that the radius of the Earth's orbit is $\approx 1.49 \times 10^{11}$ m and that 1 light-year $\approx 9.461 \times 10^{15}$ m, explain Bessel's calculation that 61 Cygni is about 10.3 light-years away.

b Modern estimates place 61 Cygni at about 11.4 light-years away. Calculate a more accurate value for the parallax of 61 Cygni.

> 1 parsec or "parallactic second" is the distance to a star with a parallax of 1 arc second measured across the Earth's orbit.
> 1 parsec ≈ 3.26 light-years.

F   TRUE BEARINGS

True bearings are used to describe the direction of one object from another. The direction is described by comparing it with the **true north direction**.

> True bearings are measured **clockwise** from true north.
> They are always written with 3 digits, plus decimals if necessary.

Suppose you are in town A and you want to go to town B. If you start facing true north, you need to turn $48°$ clockwise in order to face town B. We say that the **bearing of B from A** is $048°$.

Now suppose you are in town B and want to go to town A. If you start facing true north, you need to turn $228°$ clockwise in order to face town A. The bearing of A from B is $228°$.

Notice that the bearing of B from A and the bearing of A from B differ by $180°$.

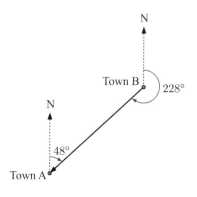

EXERCISE 7F

1 Draw a diagram showing that the bearing of B from A is:

    a 075°   **b** 205°   **c** 110°   **d** 325°

2 Find the bearing of Q from P in each diagram:

a 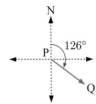   **b** 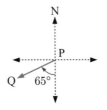   **c**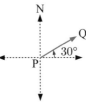

True bearings are measured clockwise from north.

d   **e** 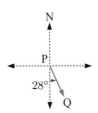   **f**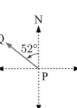

3 Find the bearing of A from B if the bearing of B from A is:

    a 136°   **b** 018°   **c** 291°   **d** 206°

4 In the diagram given, find the bearing of:

    a B from A   **b** B from C

    c A from B   **d** A from C.

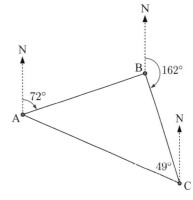

Example 11
◀)) Self Tutor

When Samantha goes jogging, she finishes 2 km south and 3 km west of where she started. Find Samantha's bearing from her starting point.

Suppose Samantha starts at S and finishes at F.

$\tan \theta = \frac{3}{2}$

$\therefore \quad \theta = \tan^{-1}\left(\frac{3}{2}\right) \approx 56.3°$

So, the bearing $\approx 180° + 56.3°$

$\qquad\qquad\quad \approx 236°$

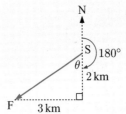

5 When Walter drives to his sports club, he finishes 10 km east and 7 km south of where he started. Find Walter's bearing from his starting point.

6 Julia is swimming in the ocean. A current takes her 200 m north and 100 m west of where she started.

  a How far is Julia from her starting point?

  b Find Julia's bearing from her starting point.

7 When Kenneth cycles in the hills, he finishes 30 km west and 24 km south of where he started.

  a Find Kenneth's distance from his starting point.

  b In which direction is the starting point from where Kenneth is now?

8 Paul runs 1.5 km on the bearing 127°.

  a Draw a diagram of the situation.

  b How far east is Paul from his starting point?

  c How far south is Paul from his starting point?

9 Tiffany kayaks 4 km on the bearing 323°. How far west is Tiffany from her starting point?

10 A train travels on the bearing 072° until it is 12 km east of its starting point. How far did the train travel on this bearing?

Example 12 · Self Tutor

A courier departs from his depot A and drives on a 136° course for 2.4 km to an intersection B. He turns right at the intersection, and drives on a 226° course for 3.1 km to his destination C. Find:

  a the distance of C from A

  b the bearing of C from A.

$A\hat{B}N = 180° - 136° = 44°$ {cointerior angles}

$\therefore \;\; A\hat{B}C = 360° - 44° - 226°$ {angles at a point}

$\qquad = 90°$

a $AC^2 = 2.4^2 + 3.1^2$ {Pythagoras}

$\quad \therefore \;\; AC = \sqrt{2.4^2 + 3.1^2}$ {as AC > 0}

$\qquad \approx 3.92$ km

So, C is about 3.92 km from A.

b To find the bearing of C from A, we first need to find θ.

Now $\tan\theta = \dfrac{3.1}{2.4}$

$\quad \therefore \;\; \theta = \tan^{-1}\left(\dfrac{3.1}{2.4}\right)$

$\quad \therefore \;\; \theta \approx 52.3°$

The bearing of C from A is $136° + 52.3° \approx 188°$.

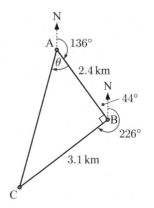

11   An orienteer runs 720 m in the direction 236° to a checkpoint, and then 460 m in the direction 146° to the finish. Find the:

    a   direct distance from the starting point to the finishing point

    b   bearing of the finishing point from the starting point.

12   A cruise ship sails from port P in the direction 112° for 13.6 km, and then in the direction 202° for 72 km. Find the distance and bearing of the cruise ship from P.

13   Yachts A and B depart from the same point. Yacht A sails 11 km on the bearing 034°. Yacht B sails 14 km on the bearing 124°. Find the distance and bearing of yacht B from yacht A.

G   THE ANGLE BETWEEN A LINE AND A PLANE

When the sun shines on the *gnomon* of a sundial, it casts a shadow onto the dial beneath it.

If the sun is directly overhead, its rays are *perpendicular* to the dial. The shadow formed is the **projection** of the gnomon onto the dial.

The **angle between a line and a plane** is the angle between the line and its **projection** on the plane.

Example 13   ◀ **Self Tutor**

Name the angle between the following line segments and the base plane TUVW:

    a   [PU]   **b**   [QX]

    a   The projection of [PU] onto the base plane is [TU].

        ∴   the required angle is $P\hat{U}T$.

    b   The projection of [QX] onto the base plane is [UX].

        ∴   the required angle is $Q\hat{X}U$.

EXERCISE 7G

1 Name the projection of each line segment onto the base plane of the given figure:

   a **i** [AH]
        ii [BE]
       iii [AG]
       iv [BH]

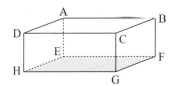

   b **i** [RX]
        ii [NX]

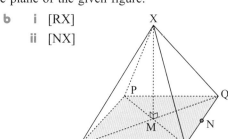

2 Name the angle between the following line segments and the base plane of the figure:

   a **i** [AF]
        ii [BM]
       iii [AD]
       iv [BN]

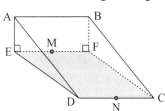

   b **i** [AB]
        ii [BN]
       iii [AE]

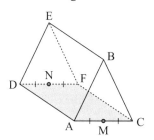

Example 14   **◄)) Self Tutor**

The diagram shows a cube with side length 12 cm. M is the midpoint of [GH].

Find the angle between the following line segments and the base plane EFGH:

   a [AH]   **b** [BM]

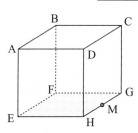

  a The projection of [AH] onto the base plane is [EH].

     ∴ the required angle is $A\widehat{H}E$.

$$\tan\theta = \tfrac{12}{12} \qquad \{\tan\theta = \tfrac{\text{OPP}}{\text{ADJ}}\}$$

     ∴ $\theta = \tan^{-1} 1$

     ∴ $\theta = 45°$

    The angle is $45°$.

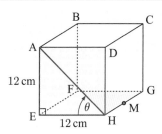

  b The projection of [BM] onto the base plane is [FM].

     ∴ the required angle is $B\widehat{M}F$.

    Let FM $= x$ cm.

    Using Pythagoras in △FGM,

$$x^2 = 12^2 + 6^2$$

     ∴ $x^2 = 180$

     ∴ $x = \sqrt{180}$ $\{$as $x > 0\}$

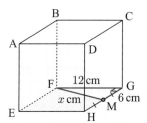

Let $\widehat{\text{BMF}} = \alpha$

$\therefore \tan \alpha = \frac{12}{\sqrt{180}}$ $\{ \tan \alpha = \frac{\text{OPP}}{\text{ADJ}} \}$

$\therefore \alpha = \tan^{-1}\left(\frac{12}{\sqrt{180}} \right)$

$\therefore \alpha \approx 41.81°$

The angle is about $41.8°$.

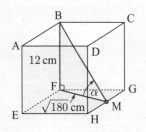

3 Find the angle between the following line segments and the base plane of the figure:

a **i** [CF]
   ii [AG]
   iii [BX]
   iv [DX]

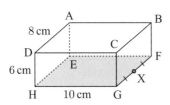

b **i** [PR]
   ii [QU]
   iii [PU]
   iv [QM]

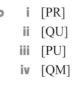
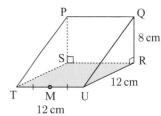

c **i** [QR]
   ii [QU]
   iii [QN]

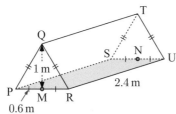

d **i** [AX]
   ii [XY]

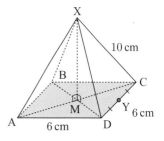

RESEARCH   SUNDIALS

1 Who invented sundials?

2 The gnomon of a sundial is the tilted arm that extends above the dial.

a At what time of day will the shadow of the gnomon be its mathematical projection on the dial?

b Why does the longitude of a sundial matter?

c How does the shadow help us tell the time at other times of the day?

3 Visit www.shadowspro.com to investigate sundials further. What other types of sundials are there? How do they differ?

4 In the 2018 ITV documentary *The Queen's Green Planet*, host Sir David Attenborough commented to Queen Elizabeth II of England that her sundial in the Buckingham Palace garden had been "neatly planted in the shade". The Queen asked her head gardener "Hadn't we thought of that? It wasn't in the shade originally, I'm sure. Maybe we could move it." But it is Sir David who responded "Depends if you want to tell the time or not!"

Jokes aside, the conversation highlights a very real problem that people faced for centuries: When the sky is overcast, one could neither use a sundial to tell the time, nor the stars to navigate.

What other inventions were made to help with timekeeping and navigation?

RESEARCH   ASTROLABES

The **astrolabe** was invented around 200 BC. The Greek astonomer Hipparchus is often credited with its invention.

An astrolabe is an astronomical model of the celestial sphere. It was used primarily to take astronomical measurements such as the altitudes of astronomical bodies, but philosophers, astrologers, and sailors found many other uses for it.

The astrolabe provided accurate measurements of the entire sky, such as the position of the sun, moon, and other heavenly bodies, and accurate times for sunrises, sunsets, and phases of the moon.

On land, we may be concerned about where we need to go, but at sea we also need to know where we are now. The astrolabe could be used to determine latitude and longitude, and measure altitude.

1 How was an astrolabe made?

2 How exactly does an astrolabe work?

REVIEW SET 7A

1

For the triangle alongside, find:

  a the length of the hypotenuse

  b $\sin\theta$ **c** $\cos\theta$ **d** $\tan\theta$.

2 Use your calculator to find, correct to 3 decimal places, the value of:

  a $\cos 59°$ **b** $\sin 8°$ **c** $\tan 76°$

3 Find x:

  a 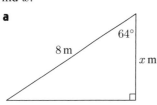   **b** 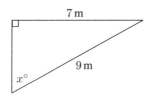   **c**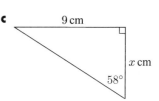

4 For the triangle PQR shown, find the:

  a perimeter

  b area.

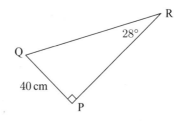

5 Find the measure of all unknown sides and angles in triangle CDE:

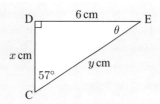

6 Find θ, the pitch of the roof.

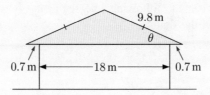

7 Find, correct to 2 significant figures, the value of x:

a

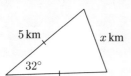

b

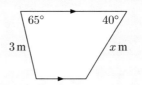

c

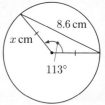

8 From a point 20 m horizontally from the base of a cylindrical lighthouse, the angle of elevation to the top of the lighthouse is $34°$. Find the height of the lighthouse.

9 Find the bearing of Q from P in each diagram:

a

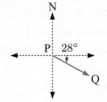

b

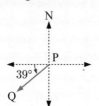

c

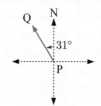

10 After a short flight, a helicopter is 12 km south and 5 km west of its helipad. Find the helicopter's distance and bearing from the helipad.

11 Two identical buildings stand parallel on opposite sides of a road. Find the angle of depression from A to B.

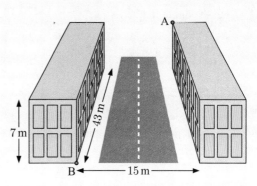

12 An open cone has a vertical angle measuring 35° and a height of 18 cm. Find the capacity of the cone in litres.

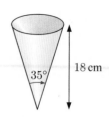

13 Find the angle between the following line segments and the base plane of the figure:

    a [AC]   **b** [AD]

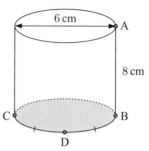

REVIEW SET 7B

1 Find $\sin\theta$, $\cos\theta$, and $\tan\theta$ for this triangle:

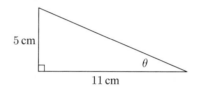

2

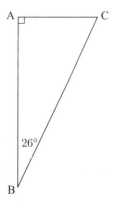

The right angled triangle alongside contains an angle of 26°.

    a Use a ruler to measure the length of each side, to the nearest millimetre.

    b Hence estimate the value, to 2 decimal places, of:

        i $\sin 26°$ **ii** $\cos 26°$ **iii** $\tan 26°$.

    c Check your answers using a calculator.

3 Find the angle marked θ:

    a   **b**   **c**

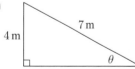
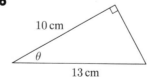
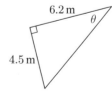

4 Find the lengths of the unknown sides:

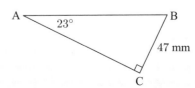

5 Find the measure of all unknown sides and angles in
triangle KLM:

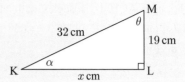

6 A rhombus has diagonals of length 15 cm and 8 cm. Find the larger angle of the rhombus.

7 Find the radius of the circle:

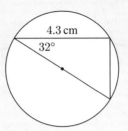

8 From a given point, the angle of elevation to the top of
a tall building is 20°. After walking 80 m towards the
building, the angle of elevation is now 23°. How tall is
the building?

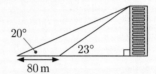

9 For the rectangular prism shown, find:

    a $A\widehat{H}G$ **b** $D\widehat{F}H$.

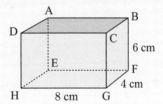

10 Aaron ran 3 km on the bearing 213°, then 2.5 km on the bearing 303°. Find Aaron's distance
and bearing from his starting point.

11 Find the volume of this pyramid:

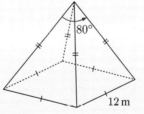

12 Find the angle between the following line segments
and the base plane of the given figure:

    a [BH]   **b** [CM]   **c** [XM]

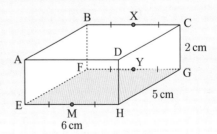

13 Triangle ACH is isosceles with altitude 25 cm and
base angles $\widehat{HAC} = \widehat{HCA} = 65°$.

   a Find the length:

     i AH   **ii** AC.

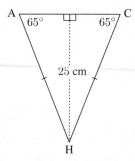

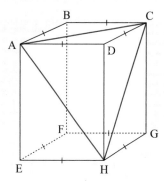

   b Triangle ACH lies within the square-based
rectangular prism shown. Find the volume of
this prism.

Chapter 8

Non-right angled triangle trigonometry

Contents:

OPENING PROBLEM

Robert works for the City Council. He has been asked to find the area of its central park, so he has arrived with a measuring wheel to measure some lengths.

Robert has just realised that while the park is a quadrilateral, it is not a rectangle.

Things to think about:

a Does Robert need to measure angles in order to find the area of the park? If not, what lengths does he need to measure? Are the four side lengths of the quadrilateral sufficient?

b Will Robert be able to find the angles at the corners of the park using length measurements alone?

In **Chapter 7** we defined trigonometric ratios for acute angles using right angled triangles. We now broaden our definitions to include other angles. This will allow us to calculate side lengths and angles of non-right angled triangles, and prepare us for further study of trigonometry.

A   THE UNIT CIRCLE

The **unit circle** is the circle with centre $(0, 0)$ and radius 1 unit.

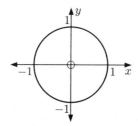

Applying the distance formula to a general point (x, y) on the circle, we find the equation of the unit circle is $x^2 + y^2 = 1$.

ANGLE MEASUREMENT

Suppose P lies anywhere on the unit circle, and A is $(1, 0)$. Let θ be the angle measured anticlockwise from [OA] on the positive x-axis.

θ is **positive** for anticlockwise rotations and **negative** for clockwise rotations.

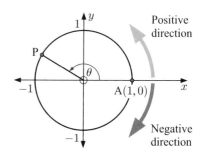

DEFINITION OF SINE AND COSINE

Consider a point $P(a, b)$ which lies on the unit circle in the first quadrant. [OP] makes an angle θ with the x-axis as shown.

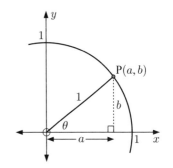

Using right angled triangle trigonometry:

$$\cos \theta = \frac{\text{ADJ}}{\text{HYP}} = \frac{a}{1} = a$$

$$\sin \theta = \frac{\text{OPP}}{\text{HYP}} = \frac{b}{1} = b$$

More generally, we define:

If P is any point on the unit circle such that [OP] makes an angle θ measured anticlockwise from the positive x-axis:

- **$\cos \theta$** is the x-coordinate of P
- **$\sin \theta$** is the y-coordinate of P

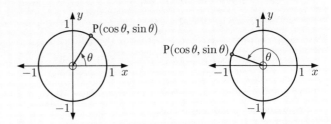

For all points on the unit circle, $-1 \leqslant x \leqslant 1$, $-1 \leqslant y \leqslant 1$, and $x^2 + y^2 = 1$. We therefore conclude:

For any angle θ:

- $-1 \leqslant \cos \theta \leqslant 1$ and $-1 \leqslant \sin \theta \leqslant 1$
- $\cos^2 \theta + \sin^2 \theta = 1$

SUPPLEMENTARY ANGLES

Two angles are **supplementary** if their sum is $180°$.

Consider an acute angle θ, and its supplement which is the obtuse angle $(180° - \theta)$.

The point P′ corresponding to angle $(180° - \theta)$ is the reflection of $P(\cos \theta, \sin \theta)$ in the y-axis.

$\therefore$ the coordinates of P′ are $(-\cos \theta, \sin \theta)$.

But P′ has coordinates $(\cos(180° - \theta), \sin(180° - \theta))$.

We conclude that for any angle θ:

$$\cos(180° - \theta) = -\cos \theta$$
$$\sin(180° - \theta) = \sin \theta$$

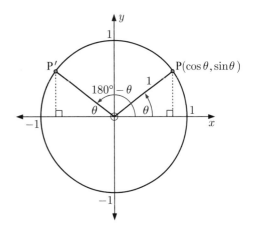

EXERCISE 8A

1 Copy and complete the following table, giving answers correct to four decimal places:

θ	$\cos\theta$	$\sin\theta$	$\cos(180° - \theta)$	$\sin(180° - \theta)$
12°				
25°				
38°				
56°				
70°				
85°				

Make sure your calculator is in degrees mode.

For each value of θ, check that:

- $\cos^2\theta + \sin^2\theta = 1$
- $\cos(180° - \theta) = -\cos\theta$
- $\sin(180° - \theta) = \sin\theta$

2 Use your calculator to find the coordinates of P and Q, rounded to 3 decimal places.

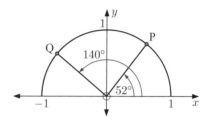

3 Find the obtuse angle which has the same sine as:

   a 45°　　　　**b** 50°　　　　**c** 18°　　　　**d** 71°

4 Find the acute angle which has the same sine as:

   a 103°　　　　**b** 119°　　　　**c** 126°　　　　**d** 155°

5 Find the obtuse angle whose cosine is the negative of:

   a $\cos 3°$　　　　**b** $\cos 22°$　　　　**c** $\cos 47°$　　　　**d** $\cos 63°$

6 Find the acute angle whose cosine is the negative of:

   a $\cos 95°$　　　　**b** $\cos 102°$　　　　**c** $\cos 146°$　　　　**d** $\cos 162°$

B　　　　THE AREA OF A TRIANGLE

We have seen in previous years that the area of any triangle can be calculated using:

$$\textbf{Area} = \tfrac{1}{2} \textbf{ base} \times \textbf{height}$$

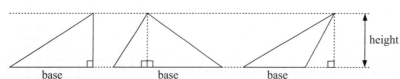

DEMO

However, if we do not know the perpendicular height of a triangle, we can use trigonometry to calculate the area.

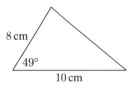

To do this we need to know two sides of the triangle and the **included angle** between them. For example, in the triangle alongside the angle 49° is *included* between the sides of length 8 cm and 10 cm.

CONVENTION FOR LABELLING TRIANGLES

For triangle ABC, the angles at vertices A, B, and C are labelled A, B, and C respectively. The sides opposite these angles are labelled a, b, and c respectively.

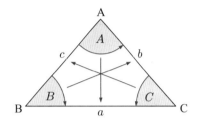

CALCULATING THE AREA OF A TRIANGLE

Any triangle that is not right angled must be either acute or obtuse. We will consider both cases:

Acute case:

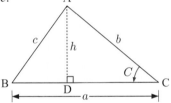

Obtuse case:

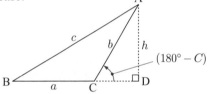

In both triangles the altitude h is constructed from A to D on [BC] (extended if necessary).

Acute case: $\sin C = \dfrac{h}{b}$

$\therefore \ h = b \sin C$

Obtuse case: $\sin(180° - C) = \dfrac{h}{b}$

$\therefore \ h = b \sin(180° - C)$

But $\sin(180° - C) = \sin C$

$\therefore \ h = b \sin C$

So, since   area $= \frac{1}{2}ah$,   we now have   **Area $= \frac{1}{2}ab \sin C$.**

Using different altitudes we can show that the area is also $\frac{1}{2}bc \sin A$ or $\frac{1}{2}ac \sin B$.

Given the lengths of two sides of a triangle, and the size of the included angle between them, the area of the triangle is

half of the product of two sides and the sine of the included angle.

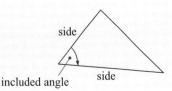

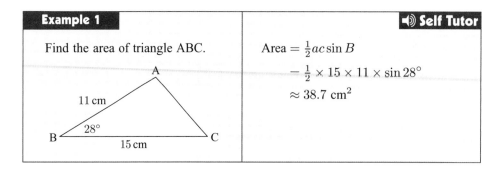

Example 1   ◀)) **Self Tutor**

Find the area of triangle ABC.

$$\text{Area} = \tfrac{1}{2}ac\sin B$$
$$= \tfrac{1}{2} \times 15 \times 11 \times \sin 28°$$
$$\approx 38.7 \text{ cm}^2$$

EXERCISE 8B

1 Find the area of:

a
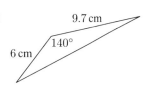

b
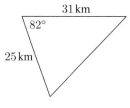

c
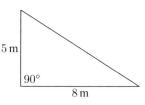

d
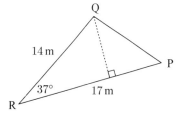

e
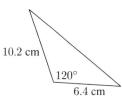

f
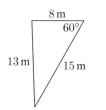

2 Triangle ABC has area 150 cm². Find the value of x.

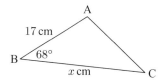

3 Calculate the area of:
  a an isosceles triangle with equal sides of length 21 cm and an included angle of 49°
  b an equilateral triangle with sides of length 57 cm.

4 A parallelogram has two adjacent sides with lengths 4 cm and 6 cm respectively. If the included angle measures 52°, find the area of the parallelogram.

5 A rhombus has sides of length 12 cm and an angle of 72°. Find its area.

6

  a Find the area of triangle PQR to 3 decimal places.
  b Hence find the length of the altitude from Q to [RP].

7 Find the area of a regular hexagon with sides of length 12 cm.

8 A rhombus has area 50 cm² and an internal angle of size 63°. Find the length of its sides.

9 A regular pentagonal garden plot has centre of symmetry O and an area of 338 m². Find the distance OA.

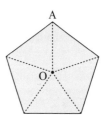

Example 2 ◀⦚ **Self Tutor**

A triangle has two sides with lengths 10 cm and 11 cm, and an area of 50 cm². Determine the possible measures of the included angle. Give your answers accurate to 1 decimal place.

If the included angle is θ, then $\frac{1}{2} \times 10 \times 11 \times \sin\theta = 50$

$$\therefore \; \sin\theta = \frac{50}{55}$$

Now $\sin^{-1}\left(\frac{50}{55}\right) \approx 65.4°$

$\therefore \quad \theta \approx 65.4°$ or $180° - 65.4°$

$\therefore \quad \theta \approx 65.4°$ or $114.6°$

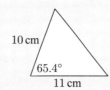 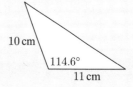

The two different possible angles are 65.4° and 114.6°.

---

10 Find the possible values of the included angle of a triangle with:

  a sides of length 5 cm and 8 cm, and area 15 cm²

  b sides of length 45 km and 53 km, and area 800 km².

11 The Australian 50 cent coin has the shape of a regular dodecagon, which is a polygon with 12 sides.

Eight of these 50 cent coins will fit exactly on an Australian $5 note as shown. What fraction of the $5 note is *not* covered?

12 Find the shaded area:

a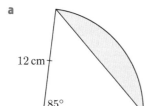

b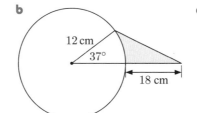

c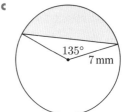

13 ADB is an arc of the circle with centre C and radius
7.3 cm. AEB is an arc of the circle with centre F and
radius 8.7 cm.

Find the shaded area.

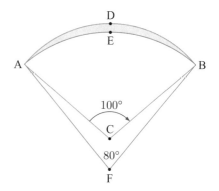

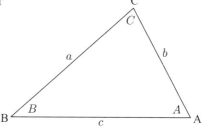

THE COSINE RULE

The **cosine rule** relates the three sides of a triangle and one of
the angles.

In any $\triangle ABC$:
$$a^2 = b^2 + c^2 - 2bc \cos A$$
$$or \quad b^2 = a^2 + c^2 - 2ac \cos B$$
$$or \quad c^2 = a^2 + b^2 - 2ab \cos C$$

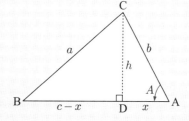

Proof: First, consider an acute angled triangle ABC.

Draw the altitude from C to [AB].

Let $AD = x$ and let $CD = h$.

Applying Pythagoras in $\triangle BCD$,

$$a^2 = h^2 + (c - x)^2$$
$$\therefore \quad a^2 = h^2 + c^2 - 2cx + x^2$$

Applying Pythagoras in $\triangle ADC$ gives $h^2 + x^2 = b^2$
$$\therefore \quad h^2 = b^2 - x^2$$
$$\therefore \quad a^2 = b^2 + c^2 - 2cx$$

In $\triangle ADC$, $\cos A = \dfrac{x}{b}$

$$\therefore \quad x = b \cos A$$
$$\therefore \quad a^2 = b^2 + c^2 - 2bc \cos A$$

The other variations of the
cosine rule can be
developed by rearranging
the vertices of $\triangle ABC$.

Now suppose triangle ABC has an obtuse angle at A. It still has two acute angles at B and C for which the proof on the previous page is valid. However, we need to consider the obtuse angle at A separately.

Draw the altitude from C to [AB] extended.

Let $AD = x$ and let $CD = h$.

Applying Pythagoras in $\triangle BCD$, $a^2 = h^2 + (c + x)^2$

$$\therefore \; a^2 = h^2 + c^2 + 2cx + x^2$$

Applying Pythagoras in $\triangle ADC$ gives $h^2 = b^2 - x^2$

$$\therefore \; a^2 = b^2 + c^2 + 2cx$$

In $\triangle ADC$, $\cos(180° - A) = \dfrac{x}{b}$

$$\therefore \; -\cos A = \dfrac{x}{b}$$

$$\therefore \; x = -b\cos A$$

$$\therefore \; a^2 = b^2 + c^2 - 2bc\cos A$$

Note that if $A = 90°$ then $\cos A = 0$, and $a^2 = b^2 + c^2 - 2bc\cos A$ reduces to $a^2 = b^2 + c^2$, which is the Pythagorean Rule.

There are two situations in which the cosine rule can be used.

- If we are given **two sides** and an **included angle**, the cosine rule can be used to find the length of the third side.

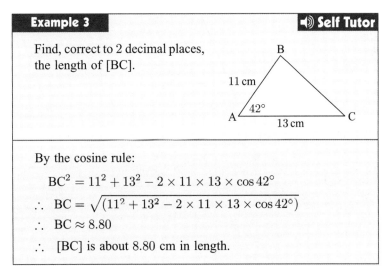

Example 3   ◀》 **Self Tutor**

Find, correct to 2 decimal places, the length of [BC].

By the cosine rule:

$$BC^2 = 11^2 + 13^2 - 2 \times 11 \times 13 \times \cos 42°$$

$$\therefore \; BC = \sqrt{(11^2 + 13^2 - 2 \times 11 \times 13 \times \cos 42°)}$$

$$\therefore \; BC \approx 8.80$$

$$\therefore \; \text{[BC] is about 8.80 cm in length.}$$

- If we are given **all three sides** of a triangle, the cosine rule can be used to find any of the angles. To do this, we rearrange the original cosine rule formulae:

$$\cos A = \dfrac{b^2 + c^2 - a^2}{2bc} \qquad \cos B = \dfrac{a^2 + c^2 - b^2}{2ac} \qquad \cos C = \dfrac{a^2 + b^2 - c^2}{2ab}$$

We then use the inverse cosine function $\cos^{-1}$ to evaluate the angle.

Example 4   ◀» **Self Tutor**

In triangle ABC, AB = 7 cm, BC = 5 cm, and CA = 8 cm.

a Find the measure of $B\widehat{C}A$.   b Find the area of triangle ABC.

a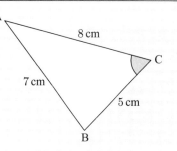

By the cosine rule:

$$\cos C = \frac{(5^2 + 8^2 - 7^2)}{(2 \times 5 \times 8)}$$

$$\therefore \quad C = \cos^{-1}\left(\frac{5^2 + 8^2 - 7^2}{2 \times 5 \times 8}\right)$$

$$\therefore \quad C = \cos^{-1}\left(\tfrac{1}{2}\right)$$

$$\therefore \quad C = 60°$$ So, $B\widehat{C}A$ measures 60°.

b The area of $\triangle ABC = \tfrac{1}{2} \times 8 \times 5 \times \sin 60°$

$$\approx 17.3 \text{ cm}^2$$

EXERCISE 8C

1 Find the length of the remaining side in each triangle:

a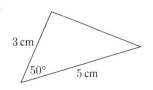

b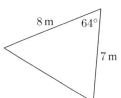

c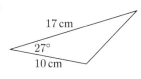

d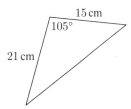

e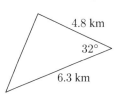

f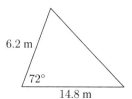

2 Find the measure of the angle marked θ:

a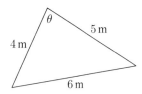

b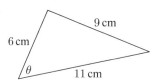

c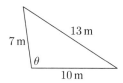

3 Find the measure of all angles of:

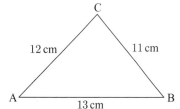

4 a Find the measure of obtuse $P\widehat{Q}R$.

b Hence find the area of $\triangle PQR$.

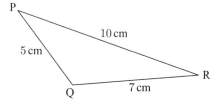

5 **a** Find the smallest angle of a triangle with sides 11 cm, 13 cm, and 17 cm.

   b Find the largest angle of a triangle with sides 4 cm, 7 cm, and 9 cm.

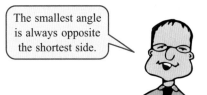

The smallest angle is always opposite the shortest side.

6 **a** Find $\cos\theta$ but not θ.

   b Hence, find the value of x.

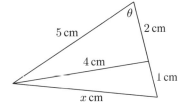

7 A triangular sail is to be cut from a section of cloth. Two of the sides must have lengths 4 m and 6 m as illustrated. The total area for the sail must be 11.6 m², the maximum allowed for the boat to race in its class.

   a Find the angle θ between the two sides of given length.

   b Find the length of the third side of the sail.

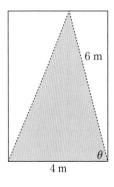

8

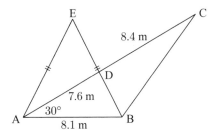

Consider the figure shown.

   a Find the lengths of [DB] and [BC].

   b Calculate the measures of $A\widehat{B}E$ and $D\widehat{B}C$.

   c Find the area of $\triangle BCD$.

9 **a** Show that $x^2 - 6x - 13 = 0$.

   b Hence find the exact value of x.

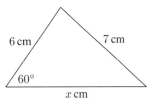

10 Find the value of x:

   a

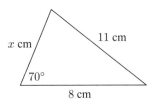

   b

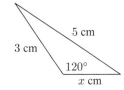

   c

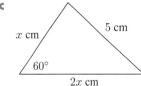

11   Find the possible values for x.

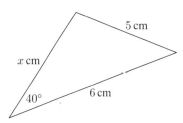

12

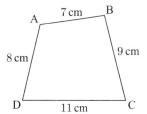

In quadrilateral ABCD, the diagonal [AC] has length 12 cm. Find the length of the other diagonal [BD].

13   Find the angle θ:

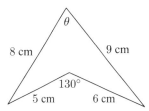

14   ABC is an equilateral triangle with sides 10 cm long. P is a point within the triangle which is 5 cm from A and 6 cm from B. How far is P from C?

D   THE SINE RULE

The **sine rule** is a set of equations which connects the lengths of the sides of any triangle with the sines of the angles of the triangle. The triangle does not have to be right angled for the sine rule to be used.

INVESTIGATION 1   THE SINE RULE

You will need: Paper, scissors, ruler, protractor

What to do:

1   Cut out a large triangle. Label the sides a, b, and c, and the opposite angles A, B, and C.

2   Use your ruler to measure the length of each side.

3   Use your protractor to measure the size of each angle.

4   Copy and complete this table:

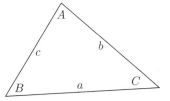

a	b	c	A	B	C	$\dfrac{\sin A}{a}$	$\dfrac{\sin B}{b}$	$\dfrac{\sin C}{c}$

5   Comment on your results.

In any triangle ABC with sides a, b, and c units in length, and opposite angles A, B, and C respectively,

$$\frac{\sin A}{a} = \frac{\sin B}{b} = \frac{\sin C}{c} \quad or \quad \frac{a}{\sin A} = \frac{b}{\sin B} = \frac{c}{\sin C}.$$

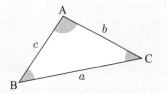

Proof: The area of any triangle ABC is given by $\frac{1}{2}bc\sin A = \frac{1}{2}ac\sin B = \frac{1}{2}ab\sin C.$

Dividing each expression by $\frac{1}{2}abc$ gives $\dfrac{\sin A}{a} = \dfrac{\sin B}{b} = \dfrac{\sin C}{c}.$

FINDING SIDE LENGTHS

If we are given two angles and one side of a triangle we can use the sine rule to find another side length.

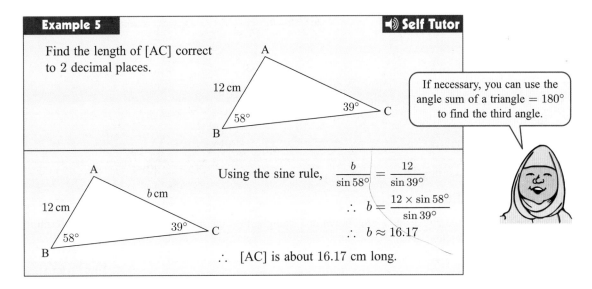

Example 5

Find the length of [AC] correct to 2 decimal places.

If necessary, you can use the angle sum of a triangle $= 180°$ to find the third angle.

Using the sine rule, $\dfrac{b}{\sin 58°} = \dfrac{12}{\sin 39°}$

$\therefore \ b = \dfrac{12 \times \sin 58°}{\sin 39°}$

$\therefore \ b \approx 16.17$

$\therefore$ [AC] is about 16.17 cm long.

EXERCISE 8D.1

1   Find the value of x:

a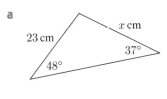

b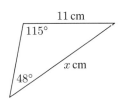

c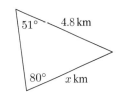

d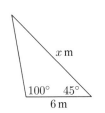

e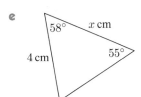

f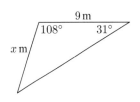

2 Consider triangle ABC.

    a Given $A = 63°$, $B = 49°$, and $b = 18$ cm, find a.

    b Given $A = 82°$, $C = 25°$, and $c = 34$ cm, find b.

    c Given $B = 21°$, $C = 48°$, and $a = 6.4$ cm, find c.

3 Find *all* unknown sides and angles of:

  a

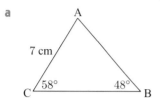

  b

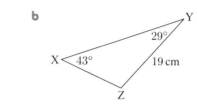

4 Find x and y in the given figure.

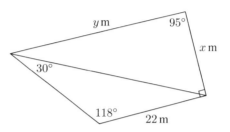

5 Find the exact value of x, giving your answer in the form $a + b\sqrt{2}$ where $a, b \in \mathbb{Q}$.

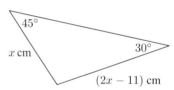

FINDING ANGLES

If two sides and a non-included angle are known in a triangle, the sine rule can often be used to determine the size of the other angles.

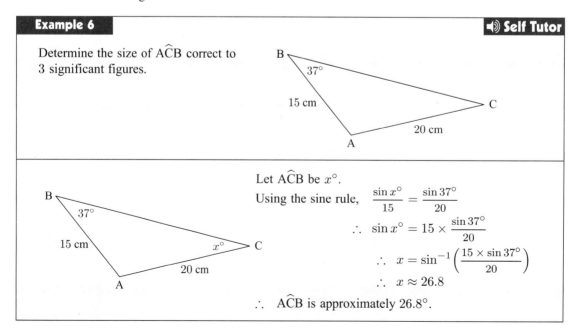

Example 6

🔊 **Self Tutor**

Determine the size of $\widehat{ACB}$ correct to 3 significant figures.

Let $\widehat{ACB}$ be $x°$.

Using the sine rule, $\dfrac{\sin x°}{15} = \dfrac{\sin 37°}{20}$

$$\therefore \quad \sin x° = 15 \times \frac{\sin 37°}{20}$$

$$\therefore \quad x = \sin^{-1}\left(\frac{15 \times \sin 37°}{20}\right)$$

$$\therefore \quad x \approx 26.8$$

$\therefore$ $\widehat{ACB}$ is approximately $26.8°$.

In some cases the sine rule may not give us a unique answer. We call this an **ambiguous case**, and will discuss it further in **Section F**. The problems in this Section all have unique answers.

EXERCISE 8D.2

1 Find the value of x:

a

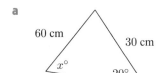

b

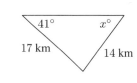

c

2 Consider triangle ABC.

a Given $a = 8$ cm, $b = 11$ cm, and $\widehat{ABC} = 45°$, find $\widehat{BAC}$.

b Given $a = 32$ cm, $b = 23$ cm, and $\widehat{BAC} = 42°$, find $\widehat{ABC}$.

c Given $c = 30$ m, $b = 36$ m, and $\widehat{ABC} = 37°$, find $\widehat{ACB}$.

3 Unprepared for class, Mr Whiffen asks his students to find the value of x in the diagram shown.

a Show that Mr Whiffen's question cannot be solved.

b Explain what this means about the triangle Mr Whiffen created.

4 In triangle ABC, $\widehat{ABC} = 30°$, AC = 9 cm, and AB = 7 cm.

a Find the measure of:

i $\widehat{ACB}$ **ii** $\widehat{BAC}$

b Hence, find the area of the triangle.

E   # PROBLEM SOLVING WITH TRIGONOMETRY

If we are given a problem involving a triangle, we must first decide which rule is best to use.

If the triangle is right angled then the trigonometric ratios or Pythagoras' theorem can be used. For some problems we can add an extra line or two to the diagram to create a right angled triangle.

However, if we do not have a right angled triangle then we usually have to choose between the sine and cosine rules. In these cases the following checklist may be helpful:

> Use the **cosine rule** when given:
>
> • three sides
>
> • two sides and an included angle.
>
> Use the **sine rule** when given:
>
> • one side and two angles
>
> • two sides and a non-included angle.

However, because an ambiguous case may exist when using the sine rule to find an angle, the cosine rule should be used in these cases.

Example 7   ◀⑨ **Self Tutor**

The angles of elevation to the top of a mountain are measured from two beacons A and B at sea.

The measurements are shown on the diagram.

If the beacons are 1473 m apart, how high is the mountain?

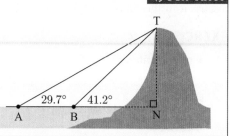

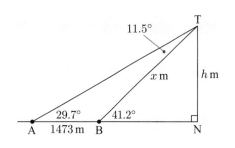

Let BT be x m and NT be h m.

$A\widehat{T}B = 41.2° - 29.7°$ {exterior angle of $\triangle$BNT}

$\qquad = 11.5°$

We find x in $\triangle$ABT using the sine rule:

$$\frac{x}{\sin 29.7°} = \frac{1473}{\sin 11.5°}$$

$$\therefore \quad x = \frac{1473}{\sin 11.5°} \times \sin 29.7°$$

$$\approx 3660.62$$

Now, in $\triangle$BNT, $\sin 41.2° = \dfrac{h}{x} \approx \dfrac{h}{3660.62}$

$$\therefore \quad h \approx \sin 41.2° \times 3660.62$$

$$\approx 2410$$

The mountain is about 2410 m high.

EXERCISE 8E

1 Rodrigo wishes to determine the height of a flagpole. He takes a sighting to the top of the flagpole from point P. He then moves 20 metres further away from the flagpole to point Q, and takes a second sighting. The information is shown in the diagram alongside. How high is the flagpole?

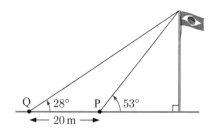

2

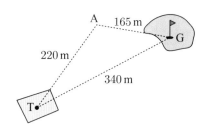

To get from P to R, a park ranger has to walk along a path to Q and then to R.

What is the distance in a straight line from P to R?

3 A golfer played his tee shot a distance of 220 m to point A. He then played a 165 m six iron to the green. If the distance from tee to green is 340 m, determine the angle the golfer was off line with his tee shot.

4 An orienteer runs for $4\frac{1}{2}$ km, then turns through an angle of $32°$ and runs for another 6 km. How far is she from her starting point?

5 A helicopter A observes two ships B and C. B is 23.8 km from the helicopter and C is 31.9 km from it. The angle of view $B\widehat{A}C$ from the helicopter to B and C, is $83.6°$. How far are the ships apart?

6 Hikers Ritva and Esko leave point P at the same time. Ritva walks 4 km on the bearing $040°$, then a further 6 km on the bearing $155°$ to get to their campsite.
Esko hikes to the camp site directly from P.

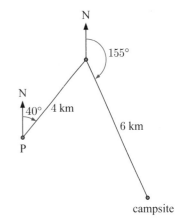

   a How far does Esko hike?

   b In which direction does Esko hike?

   c Ritva hikes at 5 km h^{-1} and Esko hikes at 3 km h^{-1}.

     i Who will arrive at the camp site first?

     ii How long will this person need to wait before the other person arrives?

   d On what bearing should the hikers walk from the camp site to return directly to P?

7 A football goal is 5 metres wide. When a player is 26 metres from one goal post and 23 metres from the other, he shoots for goal. What is the angle of view of the goal that the player sees?

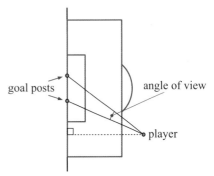

8 A tower 42 metres high stands on top of a hill. From a point some distance from the base of the hill, the angle of elevation to the top of the tower is $13.2°$, and the angle of elevation to the bottom of the tower is $8.3°$. Find the height of the hill.

9 From the foot of a building I have to look $22°$ upwards to sight the top of a tree. From the top of the building, 150 metres above ground level, I have to look down at an angle of $50°$ below the horizontal to sight the tree top.

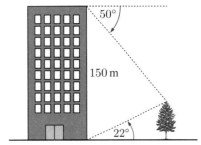

   a How high is the tree?

   b How far from the building is this tree?

10 Two yachts are sailing close to a dangerous reef. The captain of the *Porpoise* notices a lighthouse 2.4 km away on the bearing $223°$. The captain of the *Queen Maria* measures the lighthouse as 2.1 km away. He also observes the *Porpoise* to the right of the lighthouse, with an angle of $53°$ between them.

   a Display this information on a diagram.   **b** Find the distance between the yachts.

   c Find the bearing of the *Queen Maria* from the *Porpoise*.

11 Two observation posts A and B are 12 km apart. A third observation post C is located 15 km from A such that $C\widehat{B}A$ is $67°$. Find the measure of $C\widehat{A}B$.

12 Thabo and Palesa start at point A. They each walk in a straight line at an angle of $120°$ to one another. Thabo walks at 6 km h^{-1} and Palesa walks at 8 km h^{-1}. How far apart are they after 45 minutes?

13 Stan and Olga are considering buying a sheep farm. A surveyor has supplied them with the given accurate sketch. Find the area of the property, giving your answer in:

    a km^2 **b** hectares.

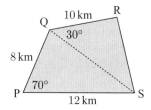

14

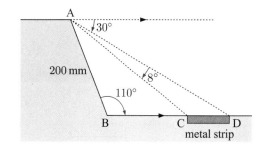

The cross-section design of the kerbing for a driverless-bus roadway is shown opposite. The metal strip is inlaid into the concrete and is used to control the direction and speed of the bus. Find the width of the metal strip.

15 Robert from the City Council has made some measurements of the park in the **Opening Problem**. They are summarised in the diagram.

Find the area of the park and the angle at each corner.

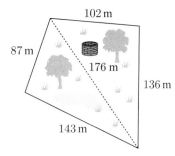

16

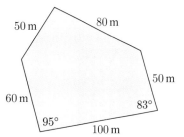

A surveyor has produced this plan of a property. Find its area.

17 Sam and Markus are standing on level ground 100 metres apart. A large tree is due north of Markus and on the bearing $065°$ from Sam. The top of the tree appears at an angle of elevation of $25°$ to Sam and $15°$ to Markus. Find the height of the tree.

F   THE AMBIGUOUS CASE OF THE SINE RULE

Finding angles using the sine rule is complicated because there may be two possible answers. For example, if $\sin\theta = \frac{1}{2}$ then θ could be $30°$ or $150°$. We call this situation an **ambiguous case**.

You can click on the icon to obtain a demonstration of the ambiguous case, or else you can work through the following **Investigation**.

DEMO

INVESTIGATION 2   THE AMBIGUOUS CASE

You will need a blank sheet of paper, a ruler, a protractor, and a compass for the tasks that follow. In each task you will be required to construct triangles from given information.

What to do:

1 Draw AB = 10 cm. Construct an angle of $30°$ at point A. Using B as the centre, draw an arc of a circle with radius 6 cm. Let C denote the point where the arc intersects the ray from A. How many different possible points C are there, and therefore how many different triangles ABC may be constructed?

2 Repeat the procedure from **1** three times, starting with AB = 10 cm and constructing an angle of $30°$ at point A. When you draw the arc with centre B, use the radius:

   a 5 cm   **b** 3 cm   **c** 12 cm

3 Using your results from **1** and **2**, discuss the possible number of triangles you can obtain given two sides and a non-included angle.

You should have discovered that when you are given two sides and a non-included angle, you could get two triangles, one triangle, or it may be impossible to draw any triangles at all.

Now consider the calculations involved in each of the cases in the **Investigation**.

Case 1:   Given: $c = 10$ cm, $a = 6$ cm, $A = 30°$

$$\frac{\sin C}{c} = \frac{\sin A}{a}$$

$$\therefore \ \sin C = \frac{c \sin A}{a}$$

$$\therefore \ \sin C = \frac{10 \times \sin 30°}{6} \approx 0.8333$$

$$\therefore \ C \approx 56.44° \ \text{ or } \ 180° - 56.44° = 123.56°$$

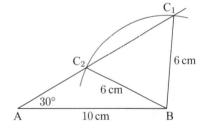

Case 2:   Given: $c = 10$ cm, $a = 5$ cm, $A = 30°$

$$\frac{\sin C}{c} = \frac{\sin A}{a}$$

$$\therefore \ \sin C = \frac{c \sin A}{a}$$

$$\therefore \ \sin C = \frac{10 \times \sin 30°}{5} = 1$$

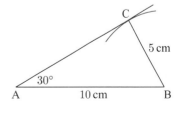

There is only one possible solution for C in the range from $0°$ to $180°$, and that is $C = 90°$. Only one triangle is therefore possible. Complete the solution of the triangle yourself.

Case 3:   Given: $c = 10$ cm, $a = 3$ cm, $A = 30°$

$$\frac{\sin C}{c} = \frac{\sin A}{a}$$

$$\therefore \quad \sin C = \frac{c \sin A}{a}$$

$$\therefore \quad \sin C = \frac{10 \times \sin 30°}{3} \approx 1.6667$$

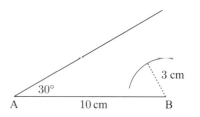

There is no angle that has a sine value > 1, so no triangles can be drawn to match the information given.

Case 4:   Given: $c = 10$ cm, $a = 12$ cm, $A = 30°$

$$\frac{\sin C}{c} = \frac{\sin A}{a}$$

$$\therefore \quad \sin C = \frac{c \sin A}{a}$$

$$\therefore \quad \sin C = \frac{10 \times \sin 30°}{12} \approx 0.4167$$

$$\therefore \quad C \approx 24.62° \quad or$$
$$\qquad 180° - 24.62° = 155.38°$$

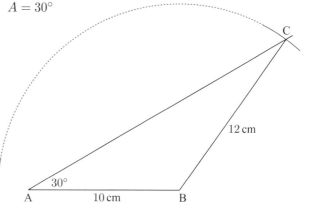

However, in this case only one of these two angles is valid. Since $A = 30°$, C cannot possibly equal $155.38°$ because $30° + 155.38° > 180°$.

Therefore, there is only one possible solution, $C \approx 24.62°$.

Conclusion: Each situation using the sine rule with two sides and a non-included angle must be examined very carefully.

Example 8   ◀) **Self Tutor**

Find the measure of angle C in triangle ABC if $AC = 7$ cm, $AB = 11$ cm, and angle B measures $25°$.

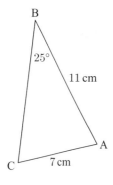

$$\frac{\sin C}{c} = \frac{\sin B}{b} \qquad \text{\{sine rule\}}$$

$$\therefore \quad \frac{\sin C}{11} = \frac{\sin 25°}{7}$$

$$\therefore \quad \sin C = \frac{11 \times \sin 25°}{7}$$

$$\therefore \quad C = \sin^{-1}\left(\frac{11 \times \sin 25°}{7}\right) \quad \text{or its supplement}$$
$$\qquad\qquad\qquad\qquad\qquad\qquad\qquad\quad \text{\{as } C \text{ may be obtuse\}}$$

$$\therefore \quad C \approx 41.6° \quad \text{or} \quad 180° - 41.6°$$
$$\therefore \quad C \approx 41.6° \quad \text{or} \quad 138.4°$$

$\therefore$ C measures $41.6°$ if angle C is acute, or $138.4°$ if angle C is obtuse.

In this case there is insufficient information to determine the actual shape of the triangle. There are two possible triangles.

Example 9   ◀)) **Self Tutor**

Find the measure of angle L in triangle KLM given that angle K measures $56°$, $LM = 16.8$ m, and $KM = 13.5$ m.

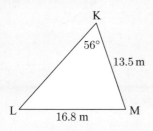

$$\frac{\sin L}{13.5} = \frac{\sin 56°}{16.8} \quad \text{\{sine rule\}}$$

$$\therefore \quad \sin L = \frac{13.5 \times \sin 56°}{16.8}$$

$$\therefore \quad L = \sin^{-1}\left(\frac{13.5 \times \sin 56°}{16.8}\right) \quad \text{or its supplement}$$

$$\therefore \quad L \approx 41.8° \quad \text{or} \quad 180° - 41.8°$$

$$\therefore \quad L \approx 41.8° \quad \text{or} \quad 138.2°$$

We reject $L \approx 138.2°$, since $138.2° + 56° > 180°$ which is impossible in a triangle.

$\therefore \quad L \approx 41.8°$, a unique solution in this case.

EXERCISE 8F

1 Triangle ABC has angle $B = 40°$ and side lengths $b = 8$ cm and $c = 11$ cm. Find the two possible measures of angle C.

2 Consider triangle ABC.

   a Given $a = 8.4$ cm, $b = 10.3$ cm, and $A\widehat{B}C = 63°$, find the measure of $B\widehat{A}C$.

   b Given $b = 22.1$ cm, $c = 16.5$ cm, and $A\widehat{C}B = 38°$, find the measure of $A\widehat{B}C$.

   c Given $a = 3.1$ km, $c = 4.3$ km, and $B\widehat{A}C = 18°$, find the measure of $A\widehat{C}B$.

3 In triangle PQR, $P\widehat{R}Q = 50°$, $PR = 11$ m, and $PQ = 9$ m.

   a Show that there are two possible measures of $P\widehat{Q}R$.

   b Sketch triangle PQR for each case.

   c For each case, find:

      i the measure of $Q\widehat{P}R$ **ii** the area of the triangle

      iii the perimeter of the triangle.

THEORY OF KNOWLEDGE

Trigonometry appears to be one of the most useful disciplines of mathematics. Its study has been driven by the need to solve real world problems throughout history.

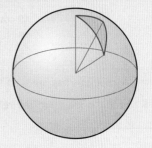

The study of trigonometry began when Greek, Babylonian, and Arabic astronomers needed to calculate the positions of stars and planets. These early mathematicians considered the trigonometry of spherical triangles, which are triangles on the surface of a sphere formed by three great arcs.

Trigonometric functions were developed by Hipparchus around 140 BC, and then by Ptolemy and Menelaus around 100 AD.

Around 500 AD, Hindu mathematicians published a table called the *Aryabhata*. It was a table of lengths of half chords, which are the lengths $AM = r \sin \theta$ in the diagram. This is trigonometry of triangles in a plane, as we study in schools today.

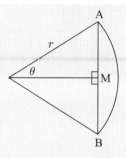

1 How does society and culture affect mathematical knowledge?

2 Should congruence and similarity, or the work of Pythagoras, be considered part of modern trigonometry?

3 A man walks south from the North Pole and turns 90° left when he reaches the equator. He walks for a while and then turns 90° left to walk back to the North Pole.

   a Has the man walked in a triangle?

   b Is the angle sum of a triangle always equal to 180°?

4 Is a spherical triangle more or less complicated than a triangle in a plane?

5 How does the research of the ancient astronomers relate to modern problems of satellites, telecommunications, and GPS navigation?

6 Why did a "flat Earth" theory persist for so long, despite ancient astronomers knowing the Earth was round? What lessons can be learned from this in protecting and promoting knowledge?

REVIEW SET 8A

1 Find the acute angle which has the same sine as:

   a 120°   **b** 165°

2 Find the obtuse angle whose cosine is the negative of:

   a $\cos 19°$ **b** $\cos 84°$

3 Find the area of:

   a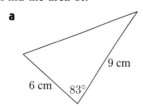   **b**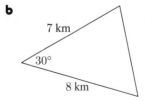   **c**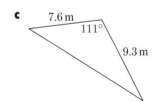

4 A rhombus has sides of length 5 cm and an angle of 65°. Find its area.

5 Find the length of the remaining side in each triangle:

   a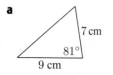   **b**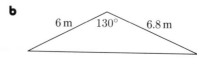

6 Find the unknown in:

a
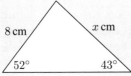

b
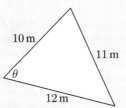

c
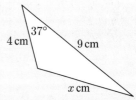

7 You are given enough details of a triangle so that you could use either the cosine rule or the sine rule to find an angle. Which rule should you use? Explain your answer.

8 Find the area of quadrilateral ABCD:

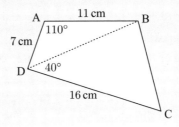

9 Find the area of this triangle.

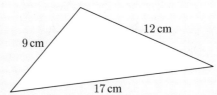

10 Kady was asked to draw the illustrated triangle exactly.

  a Use the cosine rule to find x.

  b What should Kady's response be?

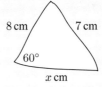

11 Triangle LMO has $\widehat{\text{LMO}} = 120°$, $LM = 3$ cm, $LO = 21$ cm, and $MO = x$ cm.

  a Show that $x^2 + 3x - 432 = 0$.

  b Find x correct to 3 significant figures.

  c Find the perimeter of triangle LMO.

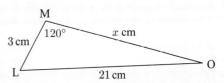

12 From point A, the angle of elevation to the top of a tall tree is $42°$. On walking 30 m towards the tree, the angle of elevation is now $60°$. How tall is the tree?

13 Find x and y in this figure.

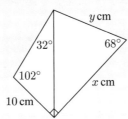

14

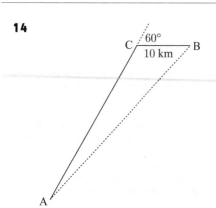

A boat was supposed to be sailing directly from A to B. However, it travelled in a straight line to C before the captain realised he was off course. He turned the boat through an angle of 60°, then travelled another 10 km to B. The trip would have been 4 km shorter if the boat had gone straight from A to B. How far did the boat travel?

15 In triangle ABC, $\widehat{ACB} = 42°$, $AB = 5$ cm, and $AC = 7$ cm.

    a Find the two possible measures of $\widehat{ABC}$.

    b Find the area of triangle ABC in each case.

REVIEW SET 8B

1 Find the obtuse angle which has the same sine as:

    a 31°   **b** 62°

2 Find the acute angle whose cosine is the negative of:

    a $\cos 122°$ **b** $\cos 175°$

3 Find the value of x:

    a

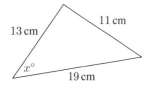

    b

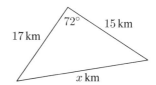

4 A triangle has two sides with lengths 11.3 cm and 19.2 cm, and an area of 80 cm². Find the possible measures of the included angle.

5 Find the measure of the angle marked θ:

    a

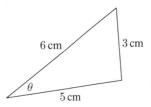

    b

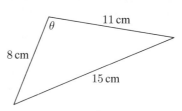

6 Find any unknown sides and angles in:

    a

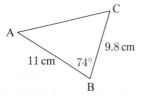

    b

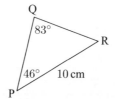

    c

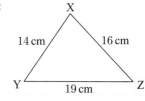

7 Find x in each triangle:

a

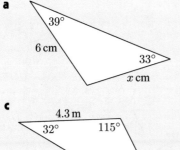

b

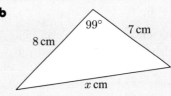

c   **d**

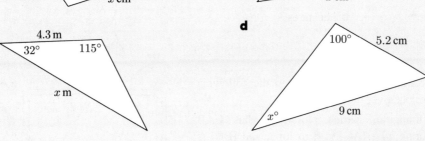

8 Paul "puts" a shot put from the front of a throwing circle with diameter 2.135 m. It only just lands inside the 40° throwing boundaries.

The official measurement goes from the shot to the nearest point of the throwing circle, and reads 17.64 m.

How far did Paul actually put the shot?

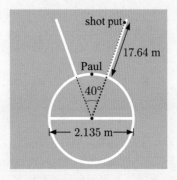

9

A vertical tree is growing on the side of a hill with gradient 10° to the horizontal. From a point 50 m downhill from the tree, the angle of elevation to the top of the tree is 18°. Find the height of the tree.

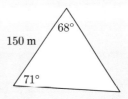

10 Find the perimeter and area of this triangle.

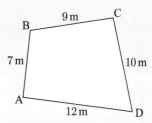

11 Peter, Sue, and Alix are sea-kayaking. Peter is 430 m from Sue on the bearing 113°. Alix is on the bearing 210° and is 310 m from Sue. Find the distance and bearing of Peter from Alix.

12 In quadrilateral ABCD, $\widehat{ABC} = 105°$. Find the measure of the other three angles.

13 Find the measure of angle Q in triangle PQR given that $Q\widehat{P}R = 47°$, $QR = 11$ m, and $PR = 9.6$ m.

14 Anke and Lucas are considering buying a block of land. The land agent supplies them with the given accurate sketch. Find the area of the property, giving your answer in:

    a m^2 **b**   hectares.

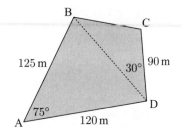

15 Soil contractor Frank was given the following dimensions over the telephone:

The triangular garden plot ABC has $C\widehat{A}B$ measuring $44°$, [AC] is 8 m long, and [BC] is 6 m long. Frank needs to supply soil for the plot to a depth of 10 cm.

    a Explain why Frank needs extra information from his client.

    b What is the maximum volume of soil that could be needed if his client is unable to supply the necessary information?

16   **a** Consider the regular hexagon shown. Find:

        i the length AB

        ii the area of the hexagon.

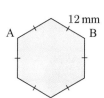

    b Find the volume of this metal nut.

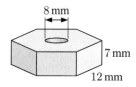

Chapter **9**

Points in space

Contents:

OPENING PROBLEM

The map of a park is shown alongside.

To help us describe the location of objects in the park, we can place a 2-dimensional coordinate grid over the map, so that the origin is at the park's entrance, and each grid unit represents 10 metres.

Ayla is currently at the location marked with an **✗**. A bird is sitting in a tree, 10 metres above the ground. It is directly above Ayla.

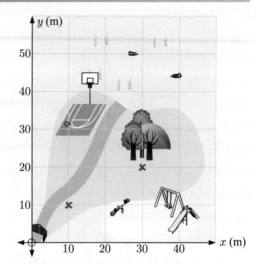

Things to think about:

  a How can we use coordinates to describe Ayla's location?

  b How can we extend our coordinate system to describe the location of the bird?

  c The bird spies a worm in the garden at **✗**.

   i How far is the bird from the worm?

   ii If the bird flies in a straight line to the worm, at what angle to the ground will it fly?

A   POINTS IN SPACE

In 3-dimensional coordinate geometry, we specify an origin O, and three mutually perpendicular axes called the X-axis, the Y-axis, and the Z-axis.

3-D POINT PLOTTER

Any point in space can then be specified using an ordered triple in the form (x, y, z).

We generally suppose that the Y and Z-axes are in the plane of the page, and the X-axis is coming out of the page as shown.

The point $(3, 4, 2)$ is found by starting at the origin O$(0, 0, 0)$, moving 3 units along the X-axis, 4 units in the Y-direction, and then 2 units in the Z-direction.

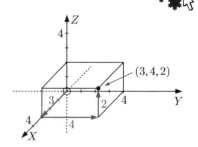

We see that $(3, 4, 2)$ is located on the corner of a rectangular prism opposite O.

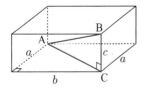

Now consider the rectangular prism illustrated, in which A is opposite B.

$$AC^2 = a^2 + b^2 \qquad \text{\{Pythagoras\}}$$
$$\text{and} \quad AB^2 = AC^2 + c^2 \qquad \text{\{Pythagoras\}}$$
$$\therefore \quad AB^2 = a^2 + b^2 + c^2$$
$$\therefore \quad AB = \sqrt{a^2 + b^2 + c^2} \qquad \{AB > 0\}$$

Suppose A is (x_1, y_1, z_1) and B is (x_2, y_2, z_2).

- The **distance** $AB = \sqrt{(x_2 - x_1)^2 + (y_2 - y_1)^2 + (z_2 - z_1)^2}$.

- The **midpoint** of [AB] is $\left(\dfrac{x_1 + x_2}{2}, \dfrac{y_1 + y_2}{2}, \dfrac{z_1 + z_2}{2} \right)$.

Example 1   ◀)) **Self Tutor**

Consider $A(4, -3, 1)$ and $B(-2, 4, -1)$. Find:

  a the distance AB   **b** the midpoint of [AB].

---

  a $AB = \sqrt{(-2 - 4)^2 + (4 - -3)^2 + (-1 - 1)^2}$

   $ = \sqrt{(-6)^2 + 7^2 + (-2)^2}$

   $ = \sqrt{36 + 49 + 4}$

   $ = \sqrt{89}$ units

  b The midpoint is $\left(\dfrac{4 + -2}{2}, \dfrac{-3 + 4}{2}, \dfrac{1 + -1}{2} \right)$,

   which is $(1, \frac{1}{2}, 0)$.

EXERCISE 9A

1 On separate axes, plot the points:

PRINTABLE 3-D
PLOTTER PAPER

  a $(5, 0, 0)$ **b** $(0, -1, 0)$ **c** $(0, 0, 2)$ **d** $(4, 3, 0)$

  e $(2, 0, -1)$ **f** $(0, 4, -3)$ **g** $(3, 1, 1)$ **h** $(2, 4, 2)$

  i $(3, -2, 5)$ **j** $(-3, 3, 3)$ **k** $(-4, 3, -2)$ **l** $(-1, -4, -2)$

2 For each pair of points, find:

  i the distance AB   **ii** the midpoint of [AB].

  a $A(0, 0, 0)$ and $B(6, -4, 2)$ **b** $A(4, 1, 0)$ and $B(0, 1, -2)$

  c $A(1, -1, 2)$ and $B(5, -3, 0)$ **d** $A(-2, 0, 5)$ and $B(-6, 7, 3)$

  e $A(-1, 5, 2)$ and $B(4, 1, -1)$ **f** $A(2, 6, -3)$ and $B(-5, 3, 2)$

3 Determine whether triangle ABC is scalene, isosceles, or equilateral:

  a A is $(2, 1, -3)$, B is $(-5, 5, 3)$, and C is $(-2, 3, 6)$

  b A is $(3, -1, 5)$, B is $(-1, -4, 0)$, and C is $(2, 7, -3)$

4 Suppose A is $(3, 1, -2)$, B is $(-6, 7, 13)$, and C is $(5, 9, -4)$. Show that triangle ABC is right angled.

5 Consider the points $P(1, 4, -1)$, $Q(6, -8, 7)$, and $R(-5, -2, -9)$. Let M be the midpoint of [PQ], and N be the midpoint of [QR].

  a Find the coordinates of M and N.

  b Show that [MN] is half the length of [PR].

6 The distance from $P(2, 4, -3)$ to $Q(k, -1, -2)$ is 7 units. Find the possible values of k.

B · MEASUREMENT

We can use the measurement formulae studied in **Chapter 6** to find the surface area and volume of solids in 3-dimensional space.

Example 2   ◀ッ **Self Tutor**

A square-based pyramid has base coordinates
$O(0, 0, 0)$, $A(4, 0, 0)$, $B(4, 4, 0)$, and $C(0, 4, 0)$.
The apex of the pyramid is $D(2, 2, 5)$.

  a Verify that the apex lies directly above the centre of the base.

  b Find the volume of the pyramid.

  c Suppose M is the midpoint of [BC].

    i Find the coordinates of M.

    ii Find the exact length of [MD].

    iii Hence find the surface area of the pyramid.

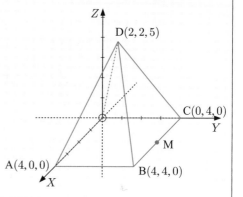

a To find the centre of the base, we locate the midpoints of the diagonals.

The midpoint of [OB] is $\left(\dfrac{0+4}{2}, \dfrac{0+4}{2}, \dfrac{0+0}{2}\right)$ which is $(2, 2, 0)$.

The midpoint of [AC] is $\left(\dfrac{4+0}{2}, \dfrac{0+4}{2}, \dfrac{0+0}{2}\right)$ which is $(2, 2, 0)$.

∴ the centre of the base is $(2, 2, 0)$.

∴ the apex $(2, 2, 5)$ lies directly above the centre of the base.

b Volume $= \frac{1}{3}$(area of base $\times$ height)

$= \frac{1}{3} \times 4 \times 4 \times 5$

$= \frac{80}{3}$ units^3

c **i** M is $\left(\dfrac{4+0}{2}, \dfrac{4+4}{2}, \dfrac{0+0}{2}\right)$ which is $(2, 4, 0)$.

  ii $MD = \sqrt{(2-2)^2 + (2-4)^2 + (5-0)^2}$

$= \sqrt{0^2 + (-2)^2 + 5^2}$

$= \sqrt{29}$ units

  iii Area of triangle BCD $= \frac{1}{2} \times 4 \times \sqrt{29}$

$= 2\sqrt{29}$ units^2

∴ surface area of pyramid

$=$ area of base $+$ area of 4 triangular faces

$= (4 \times 4 + 4 \times 2\sqrt{29})$ units^2

≈ 59.1 units^2

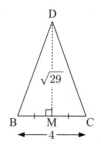

EXERCISE 9B

1 Find the volume of each rectangular prism:

a
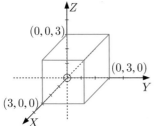

b
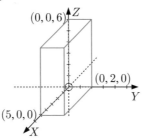

c
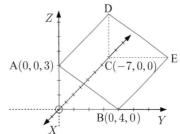

2 Consider the triangular-based prism alongside.

a State the coordinates of D and E.

b Find the volume of the prism.

c Find the length of [AB].

d Hence find the surface area of the prism.

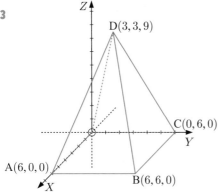

3

A square-based pyramid has base coordinates O(0, 0, 0), A(6, 0, 0), B(6, 6, 0), and C(0, 6, 0). The apex of the pyramid is D(3, 3, 9).

a Verify that the apex lies directly above the centre of the base.

b Find the volume of the pyramid.

c Suppose M is the midpoint of [AB].

   i Find the coordinates of M.

   ii Find the length of [MD].

   iii Hence find the surface area of the pyramid.

4 Find the volume and surface area of a rectangular-based pyramid with base coordinates O(0, 0, 0), A(10, 0, 0), B(10, 18, 0), and C(0, 18, 0), and apex (5, 9, 12).

5 The base of a cone lies in the X-Y plane, and is centred at the origin.

The point (4, 5, 0) lies on the edge of the base, and the apex of the cone is (0, 0, 6).

a Find the base radius of the cone.

b Find the exact volume of the cone.

c Find the slant height of the cone.

d Hence find the surface area of the cone.

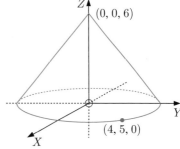

6 The point (−4, −6, 10) lies on the surface of a sphere with centre (2, 3, −1).

a Find the radius of the sphere.   **b** Hence find the volume of the sphere.

7 A sphere has diameter [PQ], where P is (−1, 1, 2), and Q is (−5, 7, −8).

a Locate the centre of the sphere.   **b** Find the radius of the sphere.

c Hence find the volume and surface area of the sphere.

8 The map for a park is shown alongside, where each grid unit represents 10 m.

A large tent is to be constructed on the park for a festival. It will be a rectangular-based pyramid with base ABCD indicated on the map. The apex of the tent is 15 m above the centre of the base.

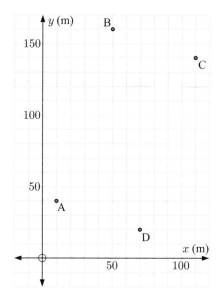

 a Suppose ground level has Z-coordinate 0. Find the 3-dimensional coordinates of:

  i each corner of the base

  ii the apex of the tent.

 b Find the volume of air inside the tent.

 c Find the amount of material needed for the tent. Do not include the floor.

C   TRIGONOMETRY

The trigonometry techniques we studied in **Chapter 7** can also be applied to figures in 3-dimensional space.

Example 3   ◀)) **Self Tutor**

Find the angle between the line segment [EC] and the base plane ABCO.

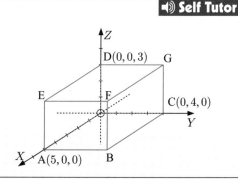

The required angle is $\widehat{ACE}$.

Now AE = 3 units

and AC $= \sqrt{(0-5)^2 + (4-0)^2 + (0-0)^2}$

$\qquad = \sqrt{(-5)^2 + 4^2}$

$\qquad = \sqrt{41}$ units

$\therefore \ \tan \theta = \frac{3}{\sqrt{41}}$

$\therefore \ \theta = \tan^{-1}\left(\frac{3}{\sqrt{41}}\right) \approx 25.1°$

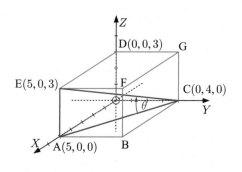

The angle is about $25.1°$.

EXERCISE 9C

1

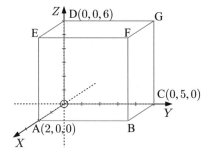

Find the angle between the following line segments and the base plane ABCO:

a [BE]   **b** [AG]

2

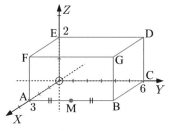

Find:

a the midpoint M of [AB]

b $A\widehat{D}O$

c $B\widehat{M}D$.

3 M is the midpoint of [QR].

a Find the coordinates of M.

b Find the measure of $Q\widehat{M}T$.

c Find the angle between the following line segments and the base plane:

    i [QS]   **ii** [TM]

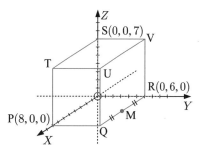

4

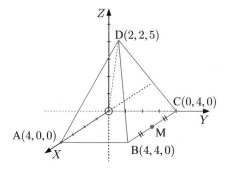

a State the coordinates of M.

b Find the angle between the following line segments and the base plane of the pyramid:

    i [DM]   **ii** [DA]

5 **a** State the coordinates of M.

b Find the angle between the following line segments and the base plane:

    i [AE]   **ii** [MB]

c Find the angle $A\widehat{B}M$.

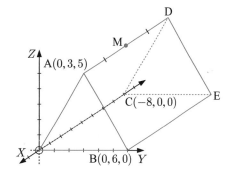

6 **a** Find the coordinates of M, the centre of the face ABCD.

b Calculate the angle:

I $\widehat{EDF}$ **II** $\widehat{AME}$.

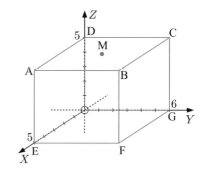

7 Answer the **Opening Problem** on page **228**.

8 The radar from an airport's control centre is shown alongside. The grid units are kilometres.

An aeroplane with altitude 500 m appears on the radar at $(-3, 4)$. It is approaching a runway 1 km east of the control centre.

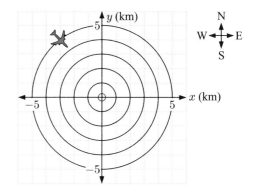

a Find the 3-dimensional coordinates of the plane.

b How far is the plane from the control centre?

c Find the true bearing of the runway from the plane.

d Find the angle of the plane's descent.

THEORY OF KNOWLEDGE   EUCLID'S POSTULATES

Euclid was one of the great mathematical thinkers of ancient times. He founded a school in Alexandria during the reign of Ptolemy I, which lasted from 323 BC until 284 BC.

Euclid's most famous mathematical writing is a set of 13 books called *Elements*. It is the first attempt to create a complete, systematic study of geometry as pure mathematics, and has been a major source of information for the study of geometric techniques, logic, and reasoning.

Elements is sometimes regarded as the most influential textbook ever written, consisting of definitions, postulates, theorems, constructions, and proofs. It was first printed in 1482 in Venice, making it one of the first mathematical works ever printed.

The foundation of Euclid's work is his set of postulates, which are the assumptions or **axioms** used to prove further results. Euclid's postulates are:

1. Any two points can be joined by a straight line.

2. Any straight line segment can be extended indefinitely in a straight line.

3. Given any straight line segment, a circle can be drawn having the segment as radius and one endpoint as centre.

4. All right angles are congruent.

5. **Parallel postulate**:   If two lines intersect a third in such a way that the sum of the inner angles on one side is less than two right angles, then the two lines inevitably must intersect each other on that side if extended far enough.

1 Can an axiom be proven? Is an axiom necessarily true?

2 Consider the first postulate.

   a What is a straight line? How do you know that a line is straight?

   b Is straightness more associated with shortest distance or with shortest time? Does light travel in a straight line?

VIDEO

   c Is straightness a matter of perception? Does it depend on the reference frame of the observer?

3 For hundreds of years, many people believed the world to be flat. It was then discovered the world was round, so that if you travelled for long enough in a particular direction, you would return to the same place, but at a different time.

   a How do we define direction?

   b Is a three-dimensional vector sufficient to describe a direction in space-time?

   c Can any straight line segment be extended indefinitely in a straight line?

4 Comment on the definition:

     A straight line is an infinite set of points in a particular direction.

5 **a** Which direction is south if you are standing at the:

     i north pole   **ii** south pole?

   b Are east and west directions, in the same sense that north and south are?

   c Assuming that all planets spin, will the Sun always rise in the east?

REVIEW SET 9A

1 On separate axes, plot the points:

   a $(3, 1, 0)$ **b** $(-4, 0, 2)$ **c** $(2, -3, -1)$

2 For each pair of points, find:

     i the distance PQ   **ii** the midpoint of [PQ].

   a $P(1, -2, 0)$, $Q(-3, -6, 2)$ **b** $P(-3, 1, 6)$, $Q(-2, -7, 1)$

3 Suppose A is $(-2, 5, 1)$, B is $(3, 5, -3)$, and C is $(0, -1, 2)$. Determine whether triangle ABC is scalene, isosceles, or equilateral.

4 The base of a hemisphere lies in the X-Y plane, and is centred at the origin. The point $(2, -5, 0)$ lies on the edge of the base.

   a Find the radius of the hemisphere.

   b Find the volume and surface area of the hemisphere.

5

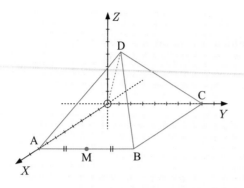

A square-based pyramid has base coordinates O(0, 0, 0), A(8, 0, 0), B(8, 8, 0), and C(0, 8, 0). The apex of the pyramid is D(4, 4, 6). M is the midpoint of [AB].

  a Find the volume of the pyramid.

  b Find the coordinates of M.

  c Find the length MD.

  d Hence find the surface area of the pyramid.

  e Find the measure of $\widehat{MDB}$.

6 The base of a cylinder lies in the X-Y plane, and is centred at the origin. The point $(-3, -4, 8)$ lies on the curved edge of the cylinder as shown.

Find the volume and surface area of the cylinder.

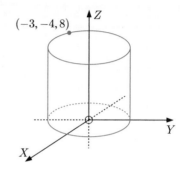

7

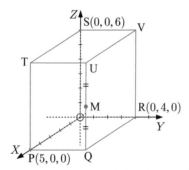

In this rectangular prism, M is the midpoint of [UQ].

  a Find the coordinates of M.

  b Find angle $\widehat{UMS}$.

  c Find the angle between the following line segments and the base plane:

   i [PV]   **ii** [OM]

8 An archaeological dig site has been divided up using grid lines at 1 metre intervals, to make it easier to describe locations on the site.

Fossils have been found at P, 2.5 m underground, and at Q, 2.9 m underground.

  a Suppose ground level has Z-coordinate 0. Find the 3-dimensional coordinates of each fossil.

  b Find the distance between the fossils.

  c Find the angle of depression from P to Q.

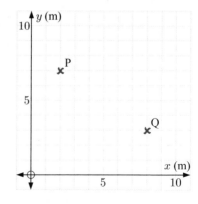

REVIEW SET 9B

1 For each pair of points, find:

    i the distance AB   **ii** the midpoint of [AB].

  a A$(-3, 0, 5)$, B$(-1, 6, 4)$ **b** A$(-7, 4, 6)$, B$(-2, 1, -1)$

2 Suppose P is $(-5, 0, 1)$, Q is $(-2, -2, 2)$, and R is $(-1, 5, -1)$.

  a Show that triangle PQR is right angled.

  b Find the measure of $P\widehat{Q}R$.

3 The distance from $(4, -2, 1)$ to $(1, 3, k)$ is 8 units. Find the possible values of k.

4 Consider the triangular-based prism shown.

  a Find the volume of the prism.

  b Find the length of [AB].

  c Hence find the surface area of the prism.

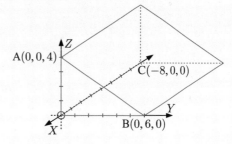

5 A sphere has diameter [PQ], where P is $(4, -2, 3)$ and Q is $(-6, 2, -5)$.

  a Find the coordinates of the centre of the sphere.

  b Find the radius of the sphere.

  c Hence find the volume and surface area of the sphere.

6 In the rectangular-based pyramid alongside, M is the midpoint of [BD].

  a Find the coordinates of M.

  b Find the angle between the following line segments and the base plane:

    i [DA]   **ii** [MC]

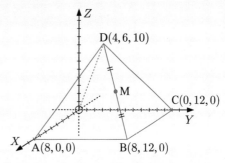

7 On the terrain map shown, the grid units are kilometres. The hiker is at a viewing platform H, 200 m above the base camp O.

  a State the 3-dimensional coordinates of the hiker.

  b How far is the hiker from the base camp?

  c From the viewing platform, the hiker can see the summit of a mountain at M. The mountain top is 500 m above base camp level.

    i Find the 3-dimensional coordinates of the mountain top.

  ii Find the distance between the hiker and the mountain top.

  iii Find the angle of elevation from the hiker to the mountain top.

8 The base of this cone lies in the X-Y plane, and is centred at C(2, 3, 0). The cone has apex A(2, 3, 5), and the point B(1, −1, 0) lies on the edge of the base.

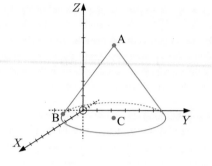

  a Find the surface area of the cone.

  b Find the measure of AB̂C.

Chapter 10

Probability

Contents:

OPENING PROBLEM

In the late 17th century, English mathematicians compiled and analysed mortality tables which showed the number of people who died at different ages. From these tables they could estimate the probability that a person would be alive at a future date. This led to the establishment of the first life insurance company in 1699.

Life insurance companies use statistics on **life expectancy** and **death rates** to calculate the premiums to charge people who insure with them.

The **life table** shown is from Australia. It shows the number of people out of 100 000 births who survive to different ages, and the expected years of remaining life at each age.

For example, we can see that out of 100 000 births, 98 052 males are expected to survive to the age of 20, and from that age the survivors are expected to live a further 54.35 years.

LIFE TABLE					
Male			**Female**		
Age	Number surviving	Expected remaining life	Age	Number surviving	Expected remaining life
0	100 000	73.03	0	100 000	79.46
5	98 809	68.90	5	99 307	75.15
10	98 698	63.97	10	99 125	70.22
15	98 555	59.06	15	98 956	65.27
20	98 052	54.35	20	98 758	60.40
25	97 325	49.74	25	98 516	55.54
30	96 688	45.05	30	98 278	50.67
35	96 080	40.32	35	98 002	45.80
40	95 366	35.60	40	97 615	40.97
45	94 323	30.95	45	96 997	36.22
50	92 709	26.45	50	95 945	31.59
55	89 891	22.20	55	94 285	27.10
60	85 198	18.27	60	91 774	22.76
65	78 123	14.69	65	87 923	18.64
70	67 798	11.52	70	81 924	14.81
75	53 942	8.82	75	72 656	11.36
80	37 532	6.56	80	58 966	8.38
85	20 998	4.79	85	40 842	5.97
90	8416	3.49	90	21 404	4.12
95	2098	2.68	95	7004	3.00
99	482	2.23	99	1953	2.36

Things to think about:

a Can you use the life table to estimate how many years you can expect to live?

b Can you estimate the chance that a new-born boy or girl will reach the age of 15?

c Can the table be used to estimate the chance that:
  i a 15 year old boy *will* reach age 75
  ii a 15 year old girl *will not* reach age 75?

d In general, do males or females live longer?

e An insurance company sells policies to people to insure them against death over a 30-year period. If the person dies during this period, the beneficiaries receive the agreed payout figure. Why are such policies cheaper to take out for a 20 year old than for a 50 year old?

f How many of your classmates would you expect to be alive and able to attend a 30 year class reunion?

g How do you think life tables would compare between countries?

In the real world, we cannot predict with certainty what will happen in the future. Understanding the **chance** or likelihood of something happening is extremely useful for us to make decisions.

In mathematics, the chance of an event occurring is assigned a number between 0 and 1 inclusive. We call this number a **probability**.

> An **impossible** event has 0% chance of happening, and is assigned the probability 0.
>
> A **certain** event has 100% chance of happening, and is assigned the probability 1.
>
> All other events can be assigned a probability between 0 and 1.

This number line shows how we could interpret different probabilities:

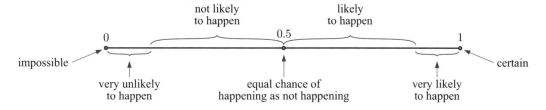

We can determine probabilities based on:

- the results of an experiment
- what we theoretically expect to happen.

Probability theory is applied in physical and biological sciences, economics, politics, sport, quality control, production planning, and many other areas.

A   EXPERIMENTAL PROBABILITY

In experiments involving chance we use the following terms to talk about what we are doing and the results we obtain:

- The **number of trials** is the total number of times the experiment is repeated.
- The **outcomes** are the different results possible for one trial of the experiment.
- The **frequency** of a particular outcome is the number of times that this outcome is observed.
- The **relative frequency** of an outcome is the frequency of that outcome expressed as a fraction or percentage of the total number of trials.

For example, when a small plastic cone was tossed into the air 279 times it fell on its *side* 183 times and on its *base* 96 times.

We say:

side   base

- the number of trials is 279
- the outcomes are *side* and *base*
- the frequencies of *side* and *base* are 183 and 96 respectively
- the relative frequencies of *side* and *base* are $\frac{183}{279} \approx 0.656$ and $\frac{96}{279} \approx 0.344$ respectively.

In the absence of any further data, the relative frequency of each event is our best estimate of the probability of that event occurring.

experimental probability = relative frequency

In this case: P(*side*) ≈ the experimental probability the cone will land on its side when tossed
                          ≈ 0.656
                 P(*base*) ≈ the experimental probability the cone will land on its base when tossed
                          ≈ 0.344

INVESTIGATION 1   DICE ROLLING EXPERIMENT

You will need:

At least one normal six-sided die with numbers 1 to 6 on its faces. Several dice would be useful to speed up the experiment.

What to do:

1   List the possible outcomes for the uppermost face when the die is rolled.

2   Discuss what you would expect the relative frequency of rolling a 2 to be when a die is rolled many times.

3   Roll a die 20 times, and count the number of times a 2 is rolled. Hence, calculate the relative frequency of rolling a 2.

4   Pool your results with another student, so in total you have data for 40 rolls. Calculate the relative frequency of rolling a 2 for 40 rolls.

5   Use the simulation to roll a die 60, 100, 200, 300, 500, and 1000 times. In each case, calculate the relative frequency of rolling a 2.

6   Plot a graph of relative frequency against the number of rolls. What do you notice?

7   What do you think will happen to the relative frequency of rolling a 2 as the number of rolls increases?

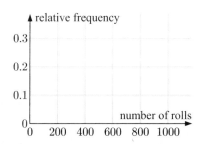

The larger the number of trials, the more confident we are that the estimated probability is accurate.

INVESTIGATION 2   TOSSING DRAWING PINS

If a drawing pin tossed in the air finishes we say it has finished on its *back*. If it

finishes   we say it has finished on its *side*.

If two drawing pins are tossed simultaneously, the possible results are:

two backs   *back and side*   *two sides*

What to do:

1 Obtain two drawing pins of the same shape and size. Toss the pair 80 times and record the outcomes in a table.

2 Obtain relative frequencies (experimental probabilities) for each of the three outcomes.

3 Pool your results with four other people using drawing pins with the same shape. Hence obtain experimental probabilities from 400 tosses.

4 Which gives the more reliable probability estimates, your results or the whole group's? Explain your answer.

In some situations, such as in the **Investigation** above, experimentation is the only way of obtaining probabilities.

EXERCISE 10A

1 When a batch of 145 paper clips was dropped onto 6 cm by 6 cm squared paper, it was observed that 113 fell completely inside squares and 32 landed on a grid line. Find, to 2 decimal places, the experimental probability of a clip falling:

    a inside a square   **b** on a line.

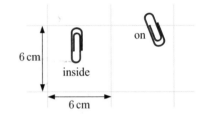

2

Length	Frequency
0 - 19	17
20 - 39	38
40 - 59	19
60+	4

Jose surveyed the length of TV commercials (in seconds). Find, to 3 decimal places, the experimental probability that the next TV commercial will last:

    a 20 to 39 seconds   **b** at least one minute

    c between 20 and 59 seconds (inclusive).

3 Betul records the number of phone calls she receives over a period of consecutive days.

    a For how many days did the survey last?

    b Estimate the probability that tomorrow Betul will receive:

        i no phone calls

        ii 5 or more phone calls

        iii less than 3 phone calls.

4 Pat does a lot of travelling in her car, and she keeps records on how often she fills her car with petrol. The table alongside shows the frequencies of the number of days between refills. Estimate the probability that:

    a there is a four day gap between refills

    b there is at least a four day gap between refills.

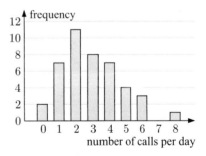

Days between refills	Frequency
1	37
2	81
3	48
4	17
5	6
6	1

Example 1   ◆)) **Self Tutor**

The table below shows the number of short-term visitors coming to Australia in the period April - June 2018, and the main reason for their visit.

Short-Term Visitors to Australia

Main reason for journey	April 2018	May 2018	June 2018
Convention/conference	8300	14 800	8800
Business	27 200	33 900	31 900
Visiting friends/relatives	77 500	52 700	59 900
Holiday	159 300	119 300	156 500
Employment	4200	4300	5500
Education	9800	7900	12 500
Other	35 200	28 000	33 200
Total	321 500	260 900	308 300

a Estimate the probability that a person who visits in June is on holiday.

b Estimate the probability that a person who came to Australia in the period April - June 2018 arrived in May.

c Lars arrived in Australia in April, May, or June 2018 to visit his brother. Estimate the probability that he arrived in April.

a P(on holiday in June) $\approx \dfrac{156\,500}{308\,300}$ ◀——— number on holiday in June
  ◀——— total number for June

≈ 0.508

b $321\,500 + 260\,900 + 308\,300 = 890\,700$ short-term visitors arrived during the three months.

$\therefore$ P(arrives in May) $\approx \dfrac{260\,900}{890\,700} \approx 0.293$

c $77\,500 + 52\,700 + 59\,900 = 190\,100$ people came to Australia to visit friends or relatives during this period.

$\therefore$ P(arrived in April) $\approx \dfrac{77\,500}{190\,100}$ ◀——— number visiting friends or relatives in April
  ◀——— total number visiting friends or relatives over April, May, and June

≈ 0.408

5 The table shows data from a survey conducted at five schools to study the rate of smoking among 15 year old students.

a Estimate the probability that a randomly chosen female 15 year old student at school **C** is a smoker.

b Estimate the probability that a randomly chosen 15 year old student at school **E** is *not* a smoker.

School	Number of 15 year olds		Number of smokers	
	Male	*Female*	*Male*	*Female*
A	45	51	10	11
B	36	42	9	6
C	52	49	13	13
D	28	33	9	10
E	40	39	7	4
Total	201	214	48	44

c If a 15 year old is chosen at random from the five schools, estimate the probability that he or she is a smoker.

6 This table describes the complaints received by a telecommunications ombudsman concerning internet services over a four year period.

Reason	2014/15	2015/16	2016/17	2017/18
Access	585	1127	2545	1612
Billing	1822	2102	3136	3582
Contracts	242	440	719	836
Credit control	3	44	118	136
Customer Service	12	282	1181	1940
Disconnection	n/a	n/a	n/a	248
Faults	86	79	120	384
Privacy	93	86	57	60
Provision	172	122	209	311
Total	3015	4282	8085	9109

Find the probability that a complaint received:

a in 2016/17 was about customer service

b at any time during the 4 year period was related to billing

c in 2017/18 did *not* relate to either billing or faults.

7 This table provides data on the daily maximum temperatures in Barcelona during summer.

Summer Temperatures in Barcelona	Month		
	June	July	Aug
Mean days max. $\geqslant 40°C$	0.3	1.2	0.7
Mean days max. $\geqslant 35°C$	3.0	5.8	5.3
Mean days max. $\geqslant 30°C$	9.4	12.3	12.0

a Estimate the probability that on an August day in Barcelona, the maximum temperature will be:

i 35°C or higher   ii less than 30°C.

b Estimate the probability that on any summer day in Barcelona, the temperature will be 30°C or higher.

c It is a 40°C summer day in Barcelona. Estimate the probability that the month is July.

B   TWO-WAY TABLES

Two-way tables are tables which compare two categorical variables.

For example, the teachers at a school were asked which mode of transport they used to travel to school. Their responses are summarised in the table below. The variables are *gender* and *mode of transport*.

	Car	Bicycle	Bus
Male	37	10	10
Female	30	5	13

13 female teachers catch the bus to school.

In the following Example we will see how these tables can be used to estimate probabilities. To help us, we extend the table to include totals for each row and column.

Example 2   ◀ঃ **Self Tutor**

People exiting a new ride at a theme park were asked whether they liked or disliked the ride. The results are shown in the two-way table alongside.

	Child	Adult
Liked the ride	55	28
Disliked the ride	17	30

Use this table to estimate the probability that a randomly selected person who went on the ride:

a liked the ride   b is a child *and* disliked the ride

c is an adult *or* disliked the ride.

We extend the table to include totals for each row and column.

	Child	Adult	Total
Liked the ride	55	28	83
Disliked the ride	17	30	47
Total	72	58	130

a 83 out of the 130 people surveyed liked the ride.

∴ P(liked the ride) $\approx \frac{83}{130} \approx 0.638$

b 17 of the 130 people surveyed are children who disliked the ride.

∴ P(child *and* disliked the ride) $\approx \frac{17}{130} \approx 0.131$

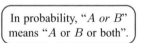

In probability, "*A or B*" means "*A or B* or both".

c $28 + 30 + 17 = 75$ of the 130 people are adults or people who disliked the ride.

∴ P(adults *or* disliked the ride) $\approx \frac{75}{130} \approx 0.577$

EXERCISE 10B

1 The types of ticket used to attend a basketball game were recorded as people entered the stadium. The results are shown alongside.

	Adult	Child
Season ticket holder	1824	779
Not a season ticket holder	3247	1660

a What was the total attendance for the match?

b One person is randomly selected to sit on the home team's bench. Find the probability that the person selected is:

i a child   ii not a season ticket holder   iii an adult season ticket holder.

2 A sample of adults in a suburb was surveyed about their current employment status and their level of education. The results are summarised in the table below.

	Employed	Unemployed
Attended university	225	7
Did not attend university	197	18

a Estimate the probability that the next randomly chosen adult:

i attended university   ii did not attend university and is currently employed

iii is unemployed   iv is unemployed or attended university.

b A randomly chosen adult is found to be unemployed. Estimate the probability that he or she attended university.

3 Students at a school were asked whether they played a sport.

- In the junior school, 131 students played a sport and 28 did not.
- In the middle school, 164 students played a sport and 81 did not.
- In the senior school, 141 students played a sport and 176 did not.

a Copy and complete this table.

	Junior	Middle	Senior	Total
Sport				
No sport				
Total				

b Find the probability that a randomly selected student:

   i plays sport   **ii** plays sport and is in the junior school

   iii does not play sport and is in middle school or higher.

4 A small hotel in London has kept a record of all room bookings made for the year. The results are summarised in the two-way table.

	Single	Double	Family
Peak season	225	420	98
Off-peak season	148	292	52

a Estimate the probability that the next randomly selected booking will be:

   i in the peak season   **ii** a single room in the off-peak season

   iii a single or a double room   **iv** during the peak season or a family room.

b A randomly selected booking is in the off-peak season. Estimate the probability that it is a family room.

c A randomly selected booking is *not* a single room. Estimate the probability that it is in the peak season.

C   SAMPLE SPACE AND EVENTS

The **sample space** U is the set of all possible outcomes of an experiment.

An **event** is a set of outcomes in the sample space that have a particular property.

You should notice that we are applying the set theory we studied in **Chapter 2**:

- the sample space is the **universal set** U
- the outcomes are the **elements** of the sample space
- events are **subsets** of the sample space.

We can therefore **list** the outcomes in the sample space and in events using **set notation**, and illustrate them with a **Venn diagram**.

COMPLEMENTARY EVENTS

Two events are **complementary** if exactly one of the events *must* occur.

If A is an event, then A' is the complementary event of A, or "not A".

Example 3   ◄) **Self Tutor**

A normal six-sided die is rolled once. Let A be the event that a prime number is rolled.

    a Use set notation to list the outcomes in:

        i the sample space U **ii** A **iii** A'.

    b Draw a Venn diagram to illustrate the sample space.

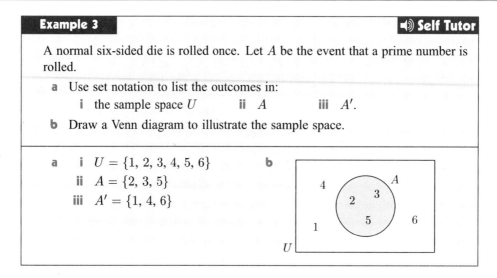

    a   **i** $U = \{1, 2, 3, 4, 5, 6\}$

        ii $A = \{2, 3, 5\}$

        iii $A' = \{1, 4, 6\}$

2-DIMENSIONAL GRIDS AND TREE DIAGRAMS

When an experiment involves more than one operation we can still list the sample space. However, it is often more efficient to illustrate the sample space on a **2-dimensional grid** or using a **tree diagram**.

Example 4   ◄) **Self Tutor**

Illustrate the possible outcomes when two coins are tossed using:

    a a 2-dimensional grid   **b** a tree diagram.

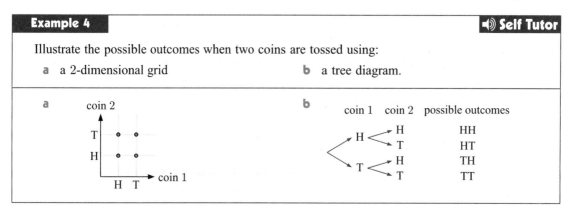

Notice in the Example that each outcome in the sample space $\{HH, HT, TH, TT\}$ is represented by:

- a point on the grid
- a "branch" on the tree diagram.

EXERCISE 10C

1 List using set notation, the sample space for:

    a twirling a square spinner labelled A, B, C, D

    b spinning a wheel with sectors labelled with the numbers 1 to 8

    c the sexes of a 2-child family.

2 One of Peter, Quentin, Ronan, Sam, and Thomas will be chosen as the volleyball team captain. Let E be the event that the captain's name will contain the letter "e".

    a State the complementary event E', in words.

    b List the outcomes in:

        i the sample space U **ii** the event E **iii** the complementary event E'.

    c Draw a Venn diagram to illustrate the sample space.

3 One ticket is drawn from a box containing tickets labelled with the numbers 1 to 16 inclusive.
  a Write down the sample space U.
  b List the outcomes in the following events:
    i A = the ticket's number is a multiple of 4
    ii B = the ticket's number is a perfect square.
  c Draw a Venn diagram to illustrate the sample space U and the events A and B.

4 Illustrate on a 2-dimensional grid the sample space for:
  a rolling a die and tossing a coin simultaneously
  b rolling two dice
  c rolling a die and spinning a spinner with sides A, B, C, D
  d twirling two square spinners, one labelled A, B, C, D and the other 1, 2, 3, 4.

5 Illustrate on a tree diagram the sample space for:
  a tossing a 5-cent and a 10-cent coin simultaneously
  b tossing a coin and twirling an equilateral triangular spinner labelled A, B, C
  c twirling two equilateral triangular spinners labelled 1, 2, 3, and X, Y, Z
  d drawing two tickets from a hat containing a large number of pink, blue, and white tickets.

Example 5   ◄⑴ Self Tutor

Use a tree diagram to illustrate the possible outcomes when this spinner is spun three times.

Highlight the outcomes corresponding to the event "obtaining blue twice".

Let B represent blue and W represent white.

1st spin	2nd spin	3rd spin	outcome
		B	BBB
	B	W	BBW
B		B	BWB
	W	W	BWW
	B	B	WBB
		W	WBW
W		B	WWB
	W	W	WWW

Tree diagrams can be used when more than two operations are involved.

---

6 From the whole numbers 1 to 7, Adam and Bill each select a number. Illustrate the sample space on a 2-dimensional grid. Circle the outcomes in the event "Adam and Bill's numbers are the same".

7 Suppose three coins are tossed simultaneously. Draw a tree diagram to illustrate the sample space. Highlight the outcomes corresponding to the event "getting at least 1 head".

INVESTIGATION 3   COIN TOSSING EXPERIMENTS

The coins of most currencies have two distinct faces. They are traditionally called "heads" and "tails". When we toss a coin in the air, we expect it will land on a head or tail with equal probability.

head   tail

What to do:

1 Suppose you are tossing *two* coins.

   a List the possible outcomes of the experiment.

   b How many of the possible outcomes correspond to the event:

      i no heads   **ii** 1 head   **iii** 2 heads?

   c Toss *two* coins 60 times. Record the number of heads in each trial in a table like this:

Result	Tally	Frequency	Relative frequency
2 heads			
1 head			
no heads			

   d Comment on the distribution of results in the table. How does the number of outcomes in each event affect its probability?

   e Click on the icon to access a coin tossing simulation.

      COIN TOSSING

      Set it to toss two coins 10 000 times.

      Run the simulation ten times, each time recording the relative frequency for the three events. Do your results agree with your previous conclusion?

2 Now suppose you are tossing *three* coins.

   a List the possible outcomes of the experiment.

   b How many of the possible outcomes correspond to the event:

      i no heads   **ii** 1 head   **iii** 2 heads   **iv** 3 heads?

   c Toss *three* coins 80 times. Record the number of heads in each trial in a table like this:

Result	Tally	Frequency	Relative frequency
3 heads			
2 heads			
1 head			
no heads			

   d Comment on the distribution of your results.

   e Run the simulation with three coins ten times with 10 000 trials in each. Do your results agree with your previous conclusion?

D   THEORETICAL PROBABILITY

The sample space when spinning the octagonal spinner shown is $\{1, 2, 3, 4, 5, 6, 7, 8\}$.

Since the spinner is symmetrical, we expect that each of the eight outcomes will be **equally likely** to occur. We say that the **theoretical probability** of any particular outcome occurring is 1 in 8, or $\frac{1}{8}$.

If a sample space has n outcomes which are **equally likely** to occur when the experiment is performed once, then each outcome has probability $\frac{1}{n}$ of occurring.

Consider the event of *spinning a prime number* with the spinner on the previous page. Of the 8 possible outcomes, the four outcomes 2, 3, 5, and 7 all correspond to this event. So, the probability of rolling a prime number is 4 in 8, or $\frac{4}{8}$.

When the outcomes of an experiment are equally likely, the probability that an event A occurs is:

$$P(A) = \frac{\textbf{number of outcomes corresponding to } A}{\textbf{number of outcomes in the sample space}} = \frac{n(A)}{n(U)}$$

Example 6 ◀◎ Self Tutor

A ticket is *randomly selected* from a basket containing 3 green, 4 yellow, and 5 blue tickets. Determine the probability of getting:

a   a green ticket

b   a green or yellow ticket

c   an orange ticket

d   a green, yellow, or blue ticket.

There are $3 + 4 + 5 = 12$ tickets which could be selected with equal chance.

a $P(G)$	b $P(G \text{ or } Y)$	c $P(O)$	d $P(G, Y, \text{ or } B)$
$= \frac{3}{12}$	$= \frac{3+4}{12}$	$= \frac{0}{12}$	$= \frac{3+4+5}{12}$
$= \frac{1}{4}$	$= \frac{7}{12}$	$= 0$	$= 1$

Example 7 ◀◎ Self Tutor

An ordinary six-sided die is rolled once. Determine the chance of:

a   getting a 6   b   not getting a 6   c   getting a 1 or 2   d   not getting a 1 or 2.

The sample space is $\{1, 2, 3, 4, 5, 6\}$.

a $P(6)$	b $P(\text{not a } 6)$	c $P(1 \text{ or } 2)$	d $P(\text{not a } 1 \text{ or } 2)$
$= \frac{1}{6}$	$= P(1, 2, 3, 4, \text{ or } 5)$	$= \frac{2}{6}$	$= P(3, 4, 5, \text{ or } 6)$
	$= \frac{5}{6}$	$= \frac{1}{3}$	$= \frac{4}{6}$
			$= \frac{2}{3}$

In **Example 7**,   notice that $P(6) + P(\text{not a } 6) = 1$

and that $P(1 \text{ or } 2) + P(\text{not a } 1 \text{ or } 2) = 1$.

This is no surprise as "6" and "not a 6" are complementary events. It is certain that exactly one of the events will occur, and impossible for both of them to occur at the same time.

Likewise, "1 or 2" and "not a 1 or 2" are complementary events.

In general, $P(A) + P(A') = 1$.

EXERCISE 10D

1 A marble is randomly selected from a box containing 5 green, 3 red, and 7 blue marbles. Determine the probability that the marble is:

   a red   **b** green   **c** blue

   d not red   **e** neither green nor blue   **f** green or red.

2 A carton of a dozen eggs contains eight brown eggs.
The rest are white.

   a How many white eggs are there in the carton?

   b Find the probability that an egg selected at random is:

      i brown   **ii** white.

3 A giant spinner has 36 sectors labelled 1 to 36. Determine the probability that when it is spun, the arrow will land on a sector labelled with:

   a a multiple of 4

   b a number between 6 and 9 inclusive

   c a number greater than 20

   d 9   **e** a multiple of 13

   f an odd number that is a multiple of 3

   g a multiple of both 4 and 6

   h a multiple of 4 or 6, or both.

4 What is the probability that a randomly chosen person has his or her next birthday:

   a on a Tuesday   **b** on a weekend   **c** in July   **d** in January or February?

5 **a** List the six different orders in which Antti, Kai, and Neda may sit in a row.

   b If the three of them sit randomly in a row, determine the probability that:

      i Antti sits in the middle   **ii** Antti sits at the left end

     iii Antti does not sit at the right end   **iv** Kai and Neda are seated together.

6 **a** List the 8 possible 3-child families according to the gender of the children. For example, GGB means "*the first is a girl, the second is a girl, the third is a boy*".

   b Assuming that each of these is equally likely to occur, determine the probability that a randomly selected 3-child family consists of:

      i all boys   **ii** all girls   **iii** boy then girl then girl

     iv two girls and a boy   **v** a girl for the eldest   **vi** at least one boy.

7 **a** List, in systematic order, the 24 different orders in which four people A, B, C, and D may sit in a row.

   b Determine the probability that when the four people sit at random in a row:

      i A sits on one of the end seats

     ii B sits on one of the two middle seats

    iii A and B are seated together

    iv A, B, and C are seated together, not necessarily in that order.

Example 8   ◀) **Self Tutor**

Use a 2-dimensional grid to illustrate the sample space for tossing a coin and rolling a die simultaneously. Hence determine the probability of:

a tossing a head   **b** tossing a tail and rolling a 5   **c** tossing a tail or rolling a 5.

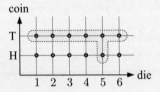

In probability, we take "a tail or a 5" to mean "a tail or a 5, or both".

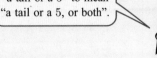

There are 12 outcomes in the sample space.

a $P(\text{head}) = \frac{6}{12} = \frac{1}{2}$ **b** $P(\text{tail and a 5}) = \frac{1}{12}$

c $P(\text{tail or a 5}) = \frac{7}{12}$ {the points in the shaded region}

8 A 5-cent and a 20-cent coin are tossed simultaneously.

  a Draw the grid to illustrate the sample space.

  b Hence determine the probability of tossing:

   i two heads   **ii** two tails   **iii** exactly one tail   **iv** at most one tail.

9 A coin and a pentagonal spinner with sectors 1, 2, 3, 4, and 5 are tossed and spun respectively.

  a Draw a grid to illustrate the sample space.

  b Hence determine the chance of getting:

   i a head and a 5   **ii** a tail and a prime number

   iii an even number   **iv** a head or a 4.

"A head or a 4" means "a head or a 4, or both".

10 The 36 different possible results from rolling two dice are illustrated on the 2-dimensional grid.

Use the grid to find the probability of rolling:

  a two 3s   **b** a 5 and a 6

  c a 5 or a 6 (or both)   **d** at least one 6

  e exactly one 6   **f** no sixes.

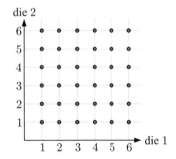

11 Two children A and B toss a coin to determine which of them will select a ticket from a bag. The bag contains two red tickets and one green ticket.

  a Which of these grids shows the sample space correctly? Discuss your answer.

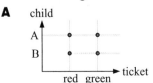
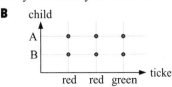

  b Use the appropriate grid to find the probability that child B will select a green ticket.

Example 9   ◀⟩ Self Tutor

Display the possible results when two dice are rolled and the scores are added together.
Hence find the probability that the sum of the dice is 7.

die 2

6	7	8	9	10	11	12
5	6	7	8	9	10	11
4	5	6	7	8	9	10
3	4	5	6	7	8	9
2	3	4	5	6	7	8
1	2	3	4	5	6	7

    1 2 3 4 5 6 ▶ die 1

Of the 36 possible combinations of scores from the two dice, six have the sum 7.

$\therefore$ the probability $= \frac{6}{36} = \frac{1}{6}$

---

12 **a** Display the possible results when two dice are rolled and the scores are added together.

    b Hence find the probability that the sum of the dice is:

      i 11   **ii** 6   **iii** 8 or 9

      iv less than 6   **v** greater than 8   **vi** no more than 8.

13 **a** Display the possible results when two dice are rolled and the difference between the numbers is found.

    b Hence find the probability that the resulting value is:

      i 0   **ii** 2   **iii** 1 or 2

      iv more than 3   **v** less than 3.

14 The spinners alongside are spun, and the scores are multiplied together.

    a Display the possible results.

    b Hence find the probability that the result is:

      i 6   **ii** less than 5   **iii** odd.

Example 10   ◀⟩ Self Tutor

In this Venn diagram, the universal set U is the children in a class. Each dot represents a student. The event B is that a student has blue eyes. Find the probability that a randomly selected child:

  a has blue eyes   **b** does not have blue eyes.

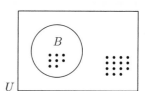

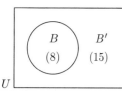

$n(U) = 23, \quad n(B) = 8$

a P(blue eyes) $= \dfrac{n(B)}{n(U)} = \dfrac{8}{23}$

b P(not blue eyes) $= \dfrac{n(B')}{n(U)} = \dfrac{15}{23}$

  or P(not blue) $= 1 -$ P(blue eyes) $= 1 - \dfrac{8}{23} = \dfrac{15}{23}$

15 In this Venn diagram, the universal set U is the sheep in a pen. Each dot represents a sheep. The event B is that a sheep has black wool.

Find the probability that a randomly selected sheep:

   a has black wool   **b** does not have black wool.

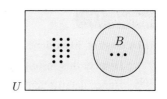

16 In this Venn diagram, the universal set U is the cars in a car park. The event R corresponds to cars that are red. Determine the probability that a randomly selected car:

   a is red   **b** is not red.

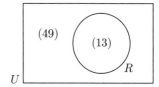

17 In a survey at an alpine resort, people were asked whether they liked skiing (S) or snowboarding (B). The results are shown in the Venn diagram. Find the probability that a randomly chosen person at the resort likes:

   a both activities   **b** neither activity

   c exactly one activity.

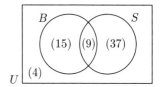

18 This Venn diagram shows the number of students in a particular class who study Geography (G) and History (H). Find the probability that a randomly selected student in the class studies:

   a both of these subjects

   b at least one of these subjects

   c only Geography.

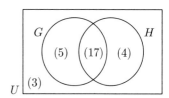

19 This Venn diagram shows the number of students in a group who play soccer (S), rugby (R), or archery (A). Find the probability that a randomly chosen student:

   a plays only rugby

   b plays both soccer and archery

   c does not play soccer or rugby.

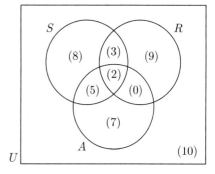

20 A group of 50 employees were surveyed regarding their interest in music, sport, and computers. The number of employees interested in each area is shown in the Venn diagram.

If an employee is selected at random, determine the probability that they are:

   a interested in music

   b interested in music, sport, and computers

   c not interested in computers.

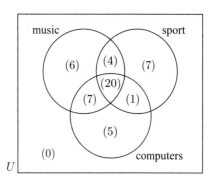

Example 11   ◀) **Self Tutor**

In a class of 30 students, 19 study Physics, 17 study Chemistry, and 15 study both of these subjects.

a Display this information on a Venn diagram.

b Hence determine the probability that a randomly selected student from this class studies:

   i both subjects   **ii** at least one of the subjects

  iii Physics but not Chemistry   **iv** exactly one of the subjects

   v neither subject.

a Let P represent the event "the student studies Physics"
and C represent the event "the student studies Chemistry".

$$n(P \cap C) = 15$$
$$\therefore \quad n(P \cap C') = 19 - 15 = 4$$
$$\text{and} \quad n(P' \cap C) = 17 - 15 = 2$$
$$\therefore \quad n(P' \cap C') = 30 - 15 - 4 - 2 = 9$$

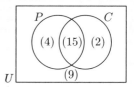

b **i** P(studies both)   **ii** P(studies at least one subject)   **iii** P(P but not C)

$$= \tfrac{15}{30} \qquad\qquad\qquad = \tfrac{4+15+2}{30} \qquad\qquad\qquad = \tfrac{4}{30}$$
$$= \tfrac{1}{2} \qquad\qquad\qquad\quad = \tfrac{7}{10} \qquad\qquad\qquad\qquad = \tfrac{2}{15}$$

  iv P(studies exactly one)   **v** P(studies neither)

$$= \tfrac{4+2}{30} \qquad\qquad\qquad\qquad = \tfrac{9}{30}$$
$$= \tfrac{1}{5} \qquad\qquad\qquad\qquad\quad = \tfrac{3}{10}$$

21 50 married men were asked whether they gave their wife flowers or chocolates for her last birthday. 31 gave chocolates, 12 gave flowers, and 5 gave both chocolates and flowers.

  a Display this information on a Venn diagram.

  b If one of the married men was chosen at random, determine the probability that he gave his wife:

    i chocolates or flowers

   ii chocolates but not flowers

  iii neither chocolates nor flowers.

22 In a class of 40 students, 19 play tennis, 20 play netball, and 8 play neither of these sports. A student is randomly chosen from the class. Determine the probability that the student:

  a plays tennis   **b** does not play netball

  c plays at least one of the sports   **d** plays exactly one of the sports

  e plays netball but not tennis.

23 The medical records for a class of 30 children showed that 24 had previously had measles, 12 had previously had measles and mumps, and 26 had previously had at least one of measles or mumps. If one child from the class is selected at random, determine the probability that he or she has had:

  a mumps   **b** mumps but not measles   **c** neither mumps nor measles.

24 In this Venn diagram, U is the set of all 60 members of a club.

The members indicate their liking for Chinese (C), Italian (I), and Thai (T) food.

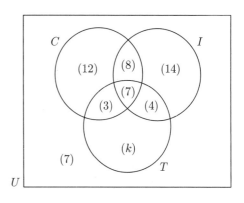

  a Find the value of k.

  b A randomly chosen member is asked about their preferences. Find the probability that the member likes:

    i only Italian
        ii Italian and Thai

    iii none of these foods
       iv at least one of these foods

    v all of these foods
        vi Chinese and Italian, but not Thai

    vii Thai or Italian
       viii exactly one of these foods.

25 As a group bonding project, 50 delegates at a European conference were asked what languages they had conversations in at lunch time. The data collected is summarised alongside.

  a Construct a Venn diagram to display the information.

  b Find the probability that a randomly selected delegate had a conversation in:

    i English
        ii French

    iii Spanish, but not in English

    iv French, but not in Spanish
     v French, and also one in English.

Languages	Delegates
English only	17
French only	7
Spanish only	12
English and French only	3
English and Spanish only	6
French and Spanish only	4
English, French, and Spanish	1

26 The Venn diagram opposite indicates the types of programs a group of 40 individuals watched on television last night.

M represents movies, S represents sports, and D represents dramas.

  a Given that 10 people watched a movie last night, calculate a and b.

  b Find the probability that one of these individuals, selected at random, watched:

    i sport
        ii drama and sport

    iii a movie but not sport

    iv drama but not a movie

    v drama or a movie.

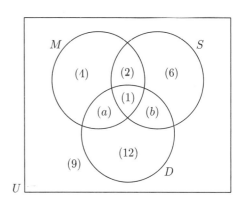

DISCUSSION

Three children have been tossing a coin in the air and recording the outcomes. They have done this 10 times and have recorded 10 tails. Before the next toss they make these statements:

Jackson: "It's got to be a head next time!"

Sally: "No, it always has an equal chance of being a head or a tail. The coin cannot remember what the outcomes have been."

Amy: "Actually, I think it will probably be a tail again, because I think the coin must be biased. It might be weighted so it is more likely to give a tail."

Discuss the statements of each child. Who do you think is correct?

E   THE ADDITION LAW OF PROBABILITY

We now more carefully consider **compound events** where there is more than one event in our sample space. This may be because the experiment has more than one process, or because we are interested in more than one property of the outcome.

Suppose there are two events A and B in a sample space U. Following set notation:

- The event that both A **and** B occur is written $A \cap B$, and read as "A intersection B".
- The event that A **or** B **or both** occur is written $A \cup B$, and read as "A union B".

INVESTIGATION 4   THE ADDITION LAW OF PROBABILITY

In this Investigation we look for a formula connecting the probabilities for $P(A \cap B)$ and $P(A \cup B)$.

What to do:

1   Suppose $U = \{x \mid x \text{ is a positive integer less than } 100\}$.

   Let $A = \{\text{multiples of } 7 \text{ in } U\}$ and $B = \{\text{multiples of } 5 \text{ in } U\}$.

   a   How many elements are there in:

      i A **ii** B **iii** $A \cap B$ **iv** $A \cup B$?

   b   Show that $n(A \cup B) = n(A) + n(B) - n(A \cap B)$.

2   By comparing regions of the Venn diagram, verify that $n(A \cup B) = n(A) + n(B) - n(A \cap B)$ for all sets A and B in a universal set U.

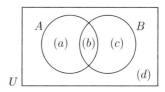

3

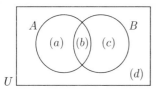

   a   From the Venn diagram, explain why

   $$P(A) = \frac{a+b}{a+b+c+d}.$$

   b   Use the Venn diagram to find:

      i $P(B)$ **ii** $P(A \cap B)$ **iii** $P(A \cup B)$ **iv** $P(A) + P(B) - P(A \cap B)$

   c   State the connection between $P(A \cup B)$ and $P(A) + P(B) - P(A \cap B)$.

From the **Investigation** you should have discovered the **addition law of probability**:

For two events A and B, $\quad\quad P(A \cup B) = P(A) + P(B) - P(A \cap B)$

which means: $\quad\quad$ P(**either** A **or** B **or** both) = P(A) + P(B) - P(**both** A **and** B).

Example 12   ◀) **Self Tutor**

If $P(A) = 0.6$, $P(A \cup B) = 0.7$, and $P(A \cap B) = 0.3$, find $P(B)$.

$$P(A \cup B) = P(A) + P(B) - P(A \cap B)$$
$$\therefore \ 0.7 = 0.6 + P(B) - 0.3$$
$$\therefore \ P(B) = 0.4$$

If A and B are disjoint **mutually exclusive** events then $P(A \cap B) = 0$ and so the addition law becomes $P(A \cup B) = P(A) + P(B)$.

Example 13   ◀) **Self Tutor**

A class of 30 students was given a History test. 7 students scored an A and 11 students scored a B.

A student is randomly selected. Let A be the event that the student scored an A, and B be the event that the student scored a B.

  a   Are A and B mutually exclusive?

  b   Find:

     i $P(A)$ **ii** $P(B)$ **iii** $P(A \cap B)$ **iv** $P(A \cup B)$

---

  a   It is impossible for a student to score both an A and a B for the test.

     $\therefore$ A and B are mutually exclusive.

  b   **i** $P(A) = \frac{7}{30}$ **ii** $P(B) = \frac{11}{30}$

     iii $P(A \cap B) = 0$ **iv** $P(A \cup B) = P(A) + P(B)$

         {A and B are mutually exclusive} $= \frac{7}{30} + \frac{11}{30}$

                                                      $= \frac{3}{5}$

EXERCISE 10E

1   If $P(A) = 0.2$, $P(B) = 0.4$, and $P(A \cap B) = 0.05$, find $P(A \cup B)$.

2   If $P(A) = 0.4$, $P(A \cup B) = 0.9$, and $P(A \cap B) = 0.1$, find $P(B)$.

3   If $P(X) = 0.6$, $P(Y) = 0.5$, and $P(X \cup Y) = 0.9$, find $P(X \cap Y)$.

4   Suppose $P(A) = 0.25$, $P(B) = 0.45$, and $P(A \cup B) = 0.7$.

     a   Find $P(A \cap B)$.   **b**   What can you say about A and B?

5 A and B are mutually exclusive events.
   If $P(B) = 0.45$ and $P(A \cup B) = 0.8$, find $P(A)$.

6 Tickets numbered 1 to 15 are placed in a hat, and one ticket is chosen at random. Let A be the event that the number drawn is greater than 11, and B be the event that the number drawn is less than 8.

   a Are A and B mutually exclusive?

   b Find: **i** $P(A)$ **ii** $P(B)$ **iii** $P(A \cup B)$.

7 A class consists of 25 students.

   11 students are fifteen years old (F).
   12 students are sixteen years old (S).
   8 students own a dog (D).
   7 students own a cat (C).
   4 students do not own any pets (N).

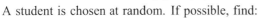

   A student is chosen at random. If possible, find:

   a $P(F)$ **b** $P(S)$ **c** $P(D)$ **d** $P(C)$ **e** $P(N)$

   f $P(F \cup S)$ **g** $P(F \cup D)$ **h** $P(C \cup N)$ **i** $P(C \cup D)$ **j** $P(D \cup N)$

8 Suppose A and B are mutually exclusive, and that A' and B' are mutually exclusive. Find $P(A \cup B)$.

F   INDEPENDENT EVENTS

Two events are **independent** if the occurrence of each event does not affect the occurrence of the other.

INVESTIGATION 5   INDEPENDENT EVENTS

In this Investigation we seek a rule for calculating $P(A \cap B)$ for two independent events A and B.

WORKSHEET

What to do:

1 Suppose a coin is tossed and a die is rolled at the same time.

   a Does the outcome of the coin toss affect the outcome of the die roll, or vice versa?

   b Draw a 2-dimensional grid to show the possible outcomes of the experiment.

   c Copy and complete this table of probabilities for different events A and B:

	A	B	$P(A)$	$P(B)$	$P(A \cap B)$
i	head	4			
ii	head	odd number			
iii	tail	number greater than 1			
iv	tail	number less than 3			

2 Consider randomly selecting a ball from each of the boxes alongside.

   a Does the outcome of the draw from either box affect the occurrence of the other?

X

Y

b Draw a 2-dimensional grid to show the possible outcomes of the experiment.

c Copy and complete this table of probabilities for different events A and B:

	A	B	$P(A)$	$P(B)$	$P(A \cap B)$
i	green from box X	red from box Y			
ii	green from box X	white from box Y			
iii	blue from box X	red from box Y			
iv	blue from box X	white from box Y			

3 For independent events A and B, what is the connection between $P(A \cap B)$, $P(A)$, and $P(B)$?

From the **Investigation** you should have concluded that:

If A and B are independent events, then **$P(A \cap B) = P(A) \times P(B)$.**

This rule can be extended for any number of independent events.

For example: If A, B, and C are all independent events, then
$$P(A \cap B \cap C) = P(A) \times P(B) \times P(C).$$

Example 14 ◀)) **Self Tutor**

A coin is tossed and a die is rolled simultaneously. Determine the probability of getting a head and a 3, without using a grid.

$P(\text{a head} \cap \text{a 3}) = P(H) \times P(3)$ {events are independent}
$\qquad = \frac{1}{2} \times \frac{1}{6}$
$\qquad = \frac{1}{12}$

EXERCISE 10F

1 Each of these spinners is spun once. Find the probability of spinning:

  a a green with spinner 1 and a blue with spinner 2

  b a red with both spinners.

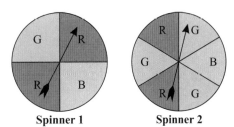

Spinner 1   Spinner 2

2 A coin is tossed 3 times. Determine the probability of getting the following sequences of results:

  a head, head, head

  b tail, head, tail.

3 A school has two photocopiers. On any given day, machine A has an 8% chance of malfunctioning and machine B has a 12% chance of malfunctioning. Determine the probability that on any given day, both machines will:

  a malfunction

  b work effectively.

4 A couple has 4 children, none of whom were adopted. Assuming boys and girls are born with equal likelihood, find the probability that the children:

   a were born in the order boy, girl, boy, girl

   b were *not* born in the order boy, girl, boy, girl.

5 Two marksmen fire at a target simultaneously. Jiri hits the target 70% of the time and Benita hits it 80% of the time. Determine the probability that:

   a they both hit the target   **b** they both miss the target

   c Jiri hits but Benita misses   **d** Benita hits but Jiri misses.

6

An archer hits the bullseye on average 2 out of every 5 shots. If 3 arrows are fired at the target, determine the probability that the bullseye is hit:

   a every time

   b the first two times, but not on the third shot

   c on no occasion.

Example 15   **◄)) Self Tutor**

Carl is not having much luck lately. His car will only start 80% of the time and his motorbike will only start 60% of the time, independently of one another.

   a Draw a tree diagram to illustrate this situation.

   b Use the tree diagram to determine the chance that on the next attempt:

      i both will start   **ii** Carl can only use his car.

   a Let C be the event that Carl's car starts, and M be the event that his motorbike starts.

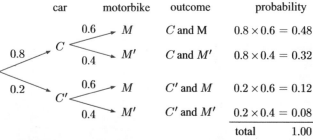

The probability of each outcome is obtained by **multiplying** the probabilities along its branch.

   b **i**   P(both start)   **ii**   P(car starts and motorbike does not)

            $= \text{P}(C \cap M)$ $= \text{P}(C \cap M')$

            $= 0.8 \times 0.6$ $= 0.8 \times 0.4$

            $= 0.48$ $= 0.32$

---

7 For a particular household, there is a 90% chance that at the end of the week the rubbish bin is full, and a 50% chance that the recycling bin is full, independently of one another.

   a Draw a tree diagram to illustrate this situation.

   b Find the probability that at the end of the week:

      i both bins are full   **ii** the recycling bin is full but the rubbish bin is not.

Example 16

🔊 **Self Tutor**

Liam rolls a six-sided die twice. Determine the probability that exactly one 4 is rolled.

Let A be the event that a 4 is rolled on the first roll, and B be the event that a 4 is rolled on the second roll.

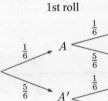

If more than one outcome corresponds to an event, **add** the probabilities of these outcomes.

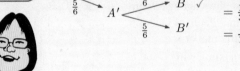

1st roll	2nd roll	P(one 4)

$$P(\text{one } 4)$$
$$= P(A \cap B') + P(A' \cap B)$$
$$= \tfrac{1}{6} \times \tfrac{5}{6} + \tfrac{5}{6} \times \tfrac{1}{6} \quad \{\text{branches marked } \checkmark\}$$
$$= \tfrac{5}{36} + \tfrac{5}{36}$$
$$= \tfrac{10}{36}$$
$$= \tfrac{5}{18}$$

8 Two baskets each contain 5 red apples and 2 green apples. Celia chooses an apple at random from each basket.

   a Draw a tree diagram to illustrate the possible outcomes.

   b Find the probability that Celia chooses:

   i two red apples
   ii one red and one green apple.

9 Suppose this spinner is spun twice.

   a Copy and complete the branches on the tree diagram:

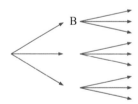

   b Find the probability that:
   i black appears on both spins
   ii yellow appears on both spins
   iii different colours appear
   iv black appears on either spin.

10 Anya rolls an 8-sided die twice. Find the probability that:

   a exactly one 4 is rolled
   b at least one 4 is rolled.

11 One ball is drawn from each of the bags shown.

   a Draw a tree diagram to illustrate this situation.

   b Find the probability that:

   i 3 blue balls are drawn
   ii green balls are drawn from bags Y and Z
   iii at least one blue ball is drawn.

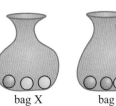

bag X   bag Y   bag Z

12 The diagram shows a simple electrical network.

Each symbol   —⌣—   represents a switch.

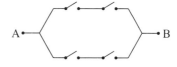

All four switches operate independently, and the probability of each one of them being closed is p.

  a In terms of p, find the probability that the current flows from A to B.

  b Find the least value of p for which the probability of current flow is at least 0.5.

13 Kane plays 3 matches in a darts challenge, alternating between Penny and Quentin as his opponents.
Kane must win 2 matches in a row to win the challenge.
Kane is allowed to choose whether he plays against Penny - Quentin - Penny, or against Quentin - Penny - Quentin.
He knows that Penny is the better darts player.
Which strategy should Kane use to maximise his chances of winning the challenge? Justify your answer.

 G   **DEPENDENT EVENTS**

Suppose a hat contains 5 red and 3 blue tickets. One ticket is randomly chosen, its colour is noted, and it is then put aside and so *not* put back in the hat. A second ticket is then randomly selected. What is the chance that it is red?

If the first ticket was red,   P(second is red) $= \frac{4}{7}$ ⟵——— 4 reds remaining
                                                              ⟵——— 7 to choose from

If the first ticket was blue,   P(second is red) $= \frac{5}{7}$ ⟵——— 5 reds remaining
                                                               ⟵——— 7 to choose from

The probability of the second ticket being red *depends* on what colour the first ticket was. We therefore have **dependent events**.

> Two or more events are **dependent** if the occurrence of one of the events *does affect* the occurrence of the other events.
>
> Events are **dependent** if they are **not independent**.
>
> If A and B are dependent events then
> $$P(A \cap B) = P(A) \times P(B \text{ given that } A \text{ has occurred}).$$

In general, when an experiment involves sampling:

- **without replacement** we have dependent events
- **with replacement** we have independent events.

Not all scenarios we study involve sampling. However, they may still involve dependent events.

For example, the event *Pahal walks to school today* is dependent on the event *it will rain today*.

Example 17   ◀) **Self Tutor**

A box contains 4 red and 2 yellow tickets. Two tickets are randomly selected from the box one by one *without* replacement. Find the probability that:

a both are red   **b** the first is red and the second is yellow.

a   P(both red)

= P(first selected is red ∩ second is red)

= P(first selected is red) × P(second is red given that the first is red)

$= \frac{4}{6} \times \frac{3}{5}$ ⎯⎯⎯⎯⎯ 4 reds out of a total of 6 tickets
⎯⎯⎯⎯⎯ If a red is drawn first, 3 reds remain out of a total of 5.

$= \frac{2}{5}$

b   P(first is red ∩ second is yellow)

= P(first is red) × P(second is yellow given that the first is red)

$= \frac{4}{6} \times \frac{2}{5}$ ⎯⎯⎯⎯⎯ 4 reds out of a total of 6 tickets
⎯⎯⎯⎯⎯ If a red is drawn first, 2 yellows remain out of a total of 5.

$= \frac{4}{15}$

EXERCISE 10G

1 A box contains 7 red and 3 green balls. Two balls are drawn one after another from the box without replacement. Determine the probability that:

  a both are red   **b** the first is green and the second is red.

2 A bag contains 4 blue and 6 white tokens. Two tokens are drawn from the bag one after another, without replacement. Find the probability that:

  a both are blue   **b** the first is blue and the second is white.

Example 18   ◀) **Self Tutor**

A hat contains 20 tickets numbered 1, 2, 3, ..., 20. If three tickets are drawn from the hat without replacement, determine the probability that they are all prime numbers.

> In each fraction, the numerator is the number of outcomes in the event. The denominator is the total number of possible outcomes.

{2, 3, 5, 7, 11, 13, 17, 19} are primes.

∴   8 of the 20 numbers are primes.

∴   P(3 primes)

= P(1st drawn is prime ∩ 2nd is prime ∩ 3rd is prime)

$= \frac{8}{20}$ ⎯⎯⎯⎯⎯ 8 primes out of 20 numbers

$\times \frac{7}{19}$ ⎯⎯⎯⎯⎯ 7 primes out of 19 numbers after a successful first draw

$\times \frac{6}{18}$ ⎯ 6 primes out of 18 numbers after two successful draws

≈ 0.0491

3 A box contains 12 identically shaped chocolates of which 8 are strawberry creams. Three chocolates are selected simultaneously from the box. Determine the probability that:

Drawing three chocolates *simultaneously* implies there is no replacement.

   a they are all strawberry creams

   b none of them are strawberry creams.

4 A lottery has 100 tickets which are placed in a barrel. Three tickets are drawn at random from the barrel, without replacement, to decide 3 prizes. If John has 3 tickets in the lottery, determine his probability of winning:

   a first prize   **b** first and second prize   **c** all 3 prizes   **d** none of the prizes.

5 A hat contains 7 names of players in a tennis squad including the captain and the vice captain. If a team of three is chosen at random by drawing the names from the hat, determine the probability that it does *not* contain:

   a the captain   **b** the captain or the vice captain.

6 Two students are chosen at random from a group of two girls and five boys, all of different ages. Find the probability that the two students chosen will be:

   a two boys   **b** the eldest two students.

Example 19   ◀》 **Self Tutor**

Two boxes each contain 6 petunia plants. Box A contains 2 plants with purple flowers and 4 plants with white flowers. Box B contains 5 plants with purple flowers and 1 plant with white flowers. A box is selected by tossing a coin, and one plant is removed at random from it.

Find the probability that the plant:

   a was taken from box A and has white flowers

   b has purple flowers.

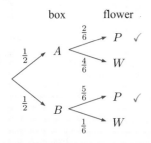

a P(from box A ∩ white flowers)

$= \text{P}(A \cap W)$

$= \frac{1}{2} \times \frac{4}{6}$

$= \frac{1}{3}$

b P(purple flowers)

$= \text{P}(A \cap P) + \text{P}(B \cap P)$

$= \frac{1}{2} \times \frac{2}{6} + \frac{1}{2} \times \frac{5}{6}$ {branches marked ✓}

$= \frac{7}{12}$

7 Of the students in a class playing musical instruments, 60% are female. 20% of the females and 30% of the males play the violin.

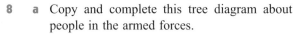

   a Copy and complete the tree diagram.

   b Find the probability that a randomly selected student:

      i is male and does not play the violin

      ii plays the violin.

8 **a** Copy and complete this tree diagram about people in the armed forces.

   b Find the probability that a member of the armed forces:

      i is an officer

      ii is not an officer in the navy

      iii is not an army or air force officer.

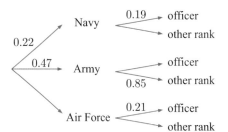

9 The probability of rain tomorrow is $\frac{1}{5}$. If it rains, Mudlark will start favourite in the horse race, with probability $\frac{1}{2}$ of winning. If it is fine, Mudlark only has a 1 in 20 chance of winning.

   a Display the sample space of possible results for the horse race on a tree diagram.

   b Hence determine the probability that Mudlark will win tomorrow.

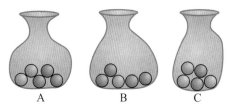

10 Machine A makes 40% of the bottles produced at a factory. Machine B makes the rest. Machine A spoils 5% of its product, while machine B spoils only 2%. Using an appropriate tree diagram, determine the probability that the next bottle inspected at this factory is spoiled.

11 Jar A contains 2 white and 3 red discs. Jar B contains 3 white and 1 red disc. A jar is chosen at random by the flip of a coin, and one disc is randomly selected from it. Determine the probability that the disc is red.

12 The English Premier League consists of 20 teams. Tottenham is currently in 8th place on the table. It has 20% chance of winning and 50% chance of losing against any team placed above it. If a team is placed below it, Tottenham has a 50% chance of winning and a 30% chance of losing. Find the probability that Tottenham will draw its next game.

13 Three bags contain different numbers of blue and red marbles.

A bag is selected using a die which has three A faces, two B faces, and one C face. One marble is then randomly selected from the bag.

Determine the probability that the marble is:

   a blue   **b** red.

Example 20 ◀)) **Self Tutor**

A bag contains 10 balls. 6 balls are black and 4 balls are white. Three balls are drawn from the bag without replacement. Determine the probability that 1 black ball is drawn.

Let B represent drawing a black ball and W represent drawing a white ball.

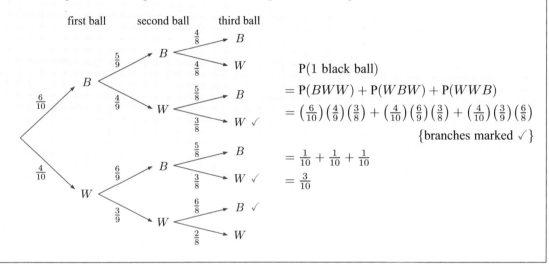

P(1 black ball)

$= P(BWW) + P(WBW) + P(WWB)$

$= \left(\frac{6}{10}\right)\left(\frac{4}{9}\right)\left(\frac{3}{8}\right) + \left(\frac{4}{10}\right)\left(\frac{6}{9}\right)\left(\frac{3}{8}\right) + \left(\frac{4}{10}\right)\left(\frac{3}{9}\right)\left(\frac{6}{8}\right)$

{branches marked ✓}

$= \frac{1}{10} + \frac{1}{10} + \frac{1}{10}$

$= \frac{3}{10}$

14 In a class of 25 students, 11 students participate in extra-curricular activities. Suppose 3 students are randomly selected to be on the student representative council. Find the probability that at least two students selected for the council also participate in extra-curricular activities.

15 A standard deck of playing cards contains 52 cards. Four cards are drawn from a well-shuffled deck without replacement. Find the probability that:

   a two red cards are drawn   **b** at least one black card is drawn.

H   CONDITIONAL PROBABILITY

This Venn diagram shows the numbers of students in a class who study Italian (I) and French (F).

Suppose a student is randomly selected from the class and it is found that the student studies French.

We can determine the probability that this student also studies Italian. We call this a **conditional probability** because it is the probability of I occurring on the *condition* that F has occurred.

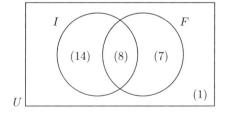

P(I given that F has occurred) $= \frac{8}{15}$ ◀— number of students who study Italian and French
◀— number of students who study French

For events A and B, we use the notation "$A \mid B$" to represent the event "*A given that B has occurred*".

$$P(A \mid B) = \frac{n(A \cap B)}{n(B)}$$

If the outcomes in each of the events are equally likely, notice that:

$$\frac{n(A \cap B)}{n(B)} = \frac{\frac{n(A \cap B)}{n(U)}}{\frac{n(B)}{n(U)}} = \frac{\mathrm{P}(A \cap B)}{\mathrm{P}(B)}$$

This gives us the **conditional probability formula**:

$$\mathbf{P}(A \mid B) = \frac{\mathbf{P}(A \cap B)}{\mathbf{P}(B)}$$

EXERCISE 10H

1 Find $\mathrm{P}(A \mid B)$ if:

  a $\mathrm{P}(A \cap B) = 0.1$ and $\mathrm{P}(B) = 0.4$

  b $\mathrm{P}(A) = 0.3$, $\mathrm{P}(B) = 0.4$, and $\mathrm{P}(A \cup B) = 0.5$

  c A and B are mutually exclusive.

2 The probability that it is cloudy on a particular day is 0.4. The probability that it is cloudy *and* rainy on a particular day is 0.2. Find the probability that it will be rainy on a day when it is cloudy.

3 In a group of 50 students, 40 study Mathematics, 32 study Physics, and each student studies at least one of these subjects.

  a   Use a Venn diagram to find how many students study both subjects.

  b   If a student from this group is randomly selected, find the probability that he or she:

    i   studies Mathematics but not Physics

    ii   studies Physics given that he or she studies Mathematics.

4 Out of 40 boys, 23 have dark hair, 18 have brown eyes, and 26 have dark hair, brown eyes, or both.

  a   Draw a Venn diagram to display this information.

  b   One of the boys is selected at random. Determine the probability that he has:

    i   dark hair and brown eyes

    ii   brown eyes given that he has dark hair.

5 50 hikers participated in an orienteering event during summer. 23 were sunburnt, 22 were bitten by ants, and 5 were both sunburnt and bitten by ants.

  a   Draw a Venn diagram to display this information.

  b   Determine the probability that a randomly selected hiker:

    i   avoided being bitten

    ii   was bitten or sunburnt (or both)

    iii   was bitten given that he or she was sunburnt

    iv   was sunburnt given that he or she was not bitten.

Example 21   ◀)) **Self Tutor**

In a town, 25% of the residents own a cat, 55% own a dog, and 30% do not own either animal.

a   Draw a Venn diagram to describe the situation.

b   Find the probability that a randomly selected resident:

  i   owns a cat given that they own a dog

  ii does not own a dog given that they own a cat.

a   Let C represent residents who own a cat
    and D represent residents who own a dog.

    Let the proportion of residents in $C \cap D$ be x.

    $\therefore$ the proportion in $C \cap D'$ is $0.25 - x$ and the
        proportion in $C' \cap D$ is $0.55 - x$.

    The proportion in $C' \cap D'$ is 0.3.

    $\therefore$ $(0.25 - x) + x + (0.55 - x) = 0.7$

    $\therefore$ $0.8 - x = 0.7$

    $\therefore$ $x = 0.1$

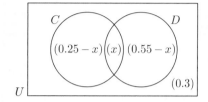

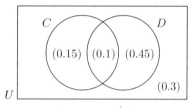

b   i $P(C \mid D) = \dfrac{P(C \cap D)}{P(D)}$

        $= \dfrac{0.1}{0.55}$

        ≈ 0.182

    ii $P(D' \mid C) = \dfrac{P(D' \cap C)}{P(C)}$

        $= \dfrac{0.15}{0.25}$

        $= 0.6$

6   400 families were surveyed. It was found that 90% had a TV set and 80% had a computer. Every family had at least one of these items. One of the families is randomly selected, and it is found that they have a computer. Find the probability that they also have a TV set.

7   In a certain town three newspapers are published. 20% of the population read A, 16% read B, 14% read C, 8% read A and B, 5% read A and C, 4% read B and C, and 2% read all 3 newspapers. A person is selected at random. Use a Venn diagram to help determine the probability that the person reads:

a   none of the papers

b   at least one of the papers

c   exactly one of the papers

d A or B (or both)

e A, given that the person reads at least one paper

f C, given that the person reads either A or B or both.

Example 22 🔊 **Self Tutor**

The top shelf in a cupboard contains 3 cans of pumpkin soup and 2 cans of chicken soup. The bottom shelf contains 4 cans of pumpkin soup and 1 can of chicken soup. Lukas is twice as likely to take a can from the bottom shelf as he is from the top shelf.

Suppose Lukas takes one can of soup without looking at the label. Find the probability that it:

  a   is chicken   **b**   was taken from the top shelf given that it is chicken.

Let T represent the top shelf, B represent the bottom shelf, P represent the pumpkin soup, and C represent the chicken soup.

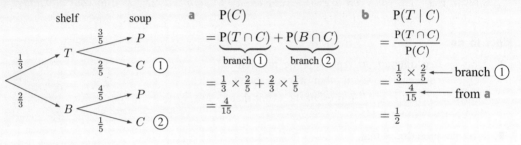

a $P(C)$

$= \underbrace{P(T \cap C)}_{\text{branch } ①} + \underbrace{P(B \cap C)}_{\text{branch } ②}$

$= \frac{1}{3} \times \frac{2}{5} + \frac{2}{3} \times \frac{1}{5}$

$= \frac{4}{15}$

b $P(T \mid C)$

$= \dfrac{P(T \cap C)}{P(C)}$

$= \dfrac{\frac{1}{3} \times \frac{2}{5}}{\frac{4}{15}}$ ⟵ branch ①, from **a**

$= \frac{1}{2}$

---

8 Urn A contains 2 red and 3 blue marbles, and urn B contains 4 red and 1 blue marble. Peter selects an urn by tossing a coin, and takes a marble from that urn.

  a   Determine the probability that the marble is red.

  b   Given that the marble is red, what is the probability that it came from urn B?

9 When Greta's mother goes shopping, the probability that she takes Greta with her is $\frac{2}{5}$. When Greta goes shopping with her mother she gets an ice cream 70% of the time. When Greta does not go shopping with her mother she gets an ice cream 30% of the time.

Determine the probability that:

  a   when Greta's mother goes shopping, she buys Greta an ice cream

  b   Greta went shopping with her mother, given that her mother buys her an ice cream.

10 On a given day, machine X has a 10% chance of malfunctioning and machine Y has a 7% chance of the same.

  a   Last Thursday *exactly one* of the machines malfunctioned. Find the probability that it was machine X.

  b   *At least one* of the machines malfunctioned today. Find the probability that machine Y malfunctioned.

11 A bag contains 2 green tickets and 1 yellow ticket. When a coin is tossed, if the result is heads, one ticket is randomly selected from the bag. Otherwise, *two* tickets are randomly selected from the bag. Given that a green ticket is selected, find the probability that the coin toss was heads.

ACTIVITY   THE MONTY HALL PROBLEM

The Monty Hall problem is a mathematical paradox first posed by **Steve Selvin** to the *American Statistician* in 1975. It became famous after its publication in *Parade* magazine in 1990. The problem is named after the original host of the American television game show *Let's Make a Deal*, on which the problem is loosely based.

The problem as posed in *Parade* reads:

> *Suppose you're on a game show, and you're given the choice of three doors: Behind one door is a car; behind the others, goats. You pick a door, say No. 1, and the host, who knows what's behind the doors, opens another door, say No. 3, which has a goat. He then says to you, "Do you want to switch your choice to door No. 2?" Is it to your advantage to switch your choice?*

What to do:

1 Draw a tree diagram to represent the problem. Let C represent the event that a contestant's choice is correct, and C' represent the event that the choice is incorrect.

2 Find the probability that:

   a the contestant's first choice has the car

   b the contestant's second choice has the car *given* they decide to change their guess.

3 Suppose this game is being played in front of a live studio audience. One of the audience members arrives late, so when they enter the room, they see two closed doors and the third (incorrect) door open. They do not know the contestant's original choice.

   a If this audience member is asked to choose a door, what is the probability they will choose the one with the car?

   b Explain why the contestant has an advantage over this audience member.

I   FORMAL DEFINITION OF INDEPENDENCE

In **Section F** we saw that two events are **independent** if the occurrence of each event does not affect the probability that the other occurs. We can write this definition more formally using conditional probability notation:

A and B are **independent events** if the occurrence of each one
of them does not affect the probability that the other occurs.

This means that $P(A \mid B) = P(A \mid B') = P(A)$
and that $P(B \mid A) = P(B \mid A') = P(B)$.

Using $P(A \cap B) = P(A \mid B)\,P(B)$ we see that

A and B are **independent events** $\Leftrightarrow$ $P(A \cap B) = P(A)\,P(B)$

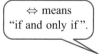

$\Leftrightarrow$ means
"if and only if".

which is the result we saw earlier.

Example 23   🔊 **Self Tutor**

Suppose $P(A) = \frac{2}{5}$, $P(B \mid A) = \frac{1}{3}$, and $P(B \mid A') = \frac{1}{4}$.

   a Find $P(B)$.   **b** Are A and B independent events? Justify your answer.

$$P(B \cap A) = P(B \mid A)\,P(A) = \frac{1}{3} \times \frac{2}{5} = \frac{2}{15}$$

Similarly, $\quad P(B \cap A') = P(B \mid A')\,P(A') = \frac{1}{4} \times \frac{3}{5} = \frac{3}{20}$

∴ the Venn diagram is:

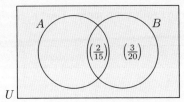

   a $P(B) = \frac{2}{15} + \frac{3}{20} = \frac{17}{60}$

   b $P(B) \neq P(B \mid A)$, so A and B are not independent events.

EXERCISE 10I

1 Suppose $P(R) = 0.4$, $P(S) = 0.5$, and $P(R \cup S) = 0.7$. Are R and S independent events? Justify your answer.

2 Suppose $P(A) = \frac{2}{5}$, $P(B) = \frac{1}{3}$, and $P(A \cup B) = \frac{1}{2}$.

   a Find: **i** $P(A \cap B)$ **ii** $P(B \mid A)$ **iii** $P(A \mid B)$

   b Are A and B independent events? Justify your answer.

3 Suppose $P(X) = 0.5$, $P(Y) = 0.7$, and that X and Y are independent events. Determine the probability of the occurrence of:

   a both X and Y **b** X or Y or both   **c** neither X nor Y

   d X but not Y **e** X given that Y occurs.

4 A and B are independent events. Prove that A' and B' are also independent events.

5 Suppose A and B are independent, mutually exclusive events, and that $P(A) = \frac{5}{7}$. Find $P(B)$.

6 Suppose $P(A \cap B) = 0.1$ and $P(A \cap B') = 0.4$. Given that A and B are independent, find $P(A \cup B')$.

7 Suppose $P(C) = \frac{9}{20}$, $P(D \mid C) = \frac{1}{4}$, and $P(D \mid C') = \frac{1}{5}$.

   a Find $P(D)$.   **b** Are C and D independent events? Justify your answer.

8 What can be deduced if $A \cap B$ and $A \cup B$ are independent events?

J   MAKING PREDICTIONS USING PROBABILITY

DISCUSSION

Suppose you were to flip a coin 100 times.

- How many times do you *expect* the coin to land "heads"?
- Does this mean it *will* land "heads" this many times?
- If it does not land "heads" this many times, does it necessarily mean the coin is unfair?

INVESTIGATION 6   MAKING PREDICTIONS

In these experiments we use theoretical probability to predict the results before actually doing them.

What to do:

1   In this experiment you will roll an ordinary die 60 times.

   a   What *fraction* of the rolls do you expect to be a "1"?

   b   *How many* rolls do you expect to be a "1"?

   c   Use your answers to start filling in the following table. Then perform the experiment and record your results.

Outcome	Theoretical probability	Predicted frequency	Tally	Frequency
1				
2				
3				
4				
5				
6				

   d   Click on the icon to obtain a simulation for rolling a die 60 000 times.   SIMULATION

   i   Predict the frequency for each outcome.

   ii   Run the simulation several times. Do you ever get *exactly* the outcome you predicted? Do you think this means the theoretical argument is flawed?

2   **a**   Display the possible results when two dice are rolled and the results are added together.

   b   In this experiment you will roll two dice 360 times.

   i   Use your illustration from **a** to help find the theoretical probability of each outcome.

   ii   Hence fill in the *predicted frequency* column.

   iii   Perform the experiment, and discuss your results.

Outcome	Theoretical probability	Predicted frequency	Tally	Frequency
2				
3				
4				
5				
6				
7				
8				
9				
10				
11				
12				

3   Suppose you perform an experiment n times, and a particular event has probability p of occurring in each of the trials. How many times do you *expect* the event to occur?

We have previously seen that if we perform an experiment a number of times, then the experimental probability of an event occurring is

$$\text{experimental probability} = \text{relative frequency of event}$$
$$= \frac{\text{number of times event occurs}}{\text{number of trials}}.$$

So, we start with an experiment and use it to generate a probability. In the study of expectation, we go the other way.

Rearranging the equation, we obtain:

$$\text{number of times event occurs} = \text{experimental probability} \times \text{number of trials}.$$

In this case, however, we use a theoretical probability to predict the results.

If there are n trials of an experiment, and an event has probability p of occurring in each of the trials, then the number of times we *expect* the event to occur is np.

DISCUSSION

In most cases, the expected value np will not be an integer. It will therefore be impossible to actually get the "expected" value. Is this a problem?

Example 24
🔊 **Self Tutor**

In his basketball career, Michael Jordan made 83.53% of shots from the free throw line. If he had played one more game and had 18 attempts from the free throw line, how many shots would you expect him to have made?

$n = 18$ throws
$p = \text{P(successfully makes free throw)} = 0.8353$
We would expect him to have made $np = 18 \times 0.8353 \approx 15$ shots.

EXERCISE 10J

1   A goalkeeper has probability $\frac{3}{10}$ of saving a penalty attempt. How many goals would he expect to save from 90 attempts?

2   The coach of a lacrosse team has calculated that Brayden scores on about 23% of his attempts at goal. If Brayden has 68 attempts to score this season, how many times would you expect him to score?

3   A cube with 4 red faces and 2 blue faces is rolled three times.
    a   On any roll, what is the chance of obtaining a red?
    b   For the three rolls, how many times would you expect to roll a red?

4   a   If 2 coins are tossed, what is the chance that they both fall heads?
    b   If the 2 coins are tossed 200 times, on how many occasions would you expect them to both fall heads?

5 During the snow season there is a $\frac{3}{7}$ probability of snow falling on any particular day. If Udo skis for five weeks, on how many days could he expect to see snow falling?

6 If two dice are rolled simultaneously 180 times, on how many occasions would you expect to get a double?

7 In a pre-election poll, residents indicated their voting intentions. The number of voters that favoured each candidate A, B, and C are shown alongside.

A	B	C
165	87	48

  a Estimate the probability that a randomly chosen voter in the electorate will vote for:

  i A   **ii** B   **iii** C.

  b If 7500 people vote in the election, how many do you expect to vote for:

  i A   **ii** B   **iii** C?

8 A test to detect cancer is not always reliable. It gives a positive result 95% of the time if the person does have cancer, and it gives a positive result 3% of the time if the person does not.

The probability that a randomly selected person has cancer is 0.02.

  a Given that a test on a randomly selected person is positive, find the probability that he or she does have cancer.

  b Out of 5000 people on which this test is used, how many people with cancer would you expect to be correctly diagnosed?

THEORY OF KNOWLEDGE

Modern probability theory began in 1653 when gambler Chevalier de Mere contacted mathematician **Blaise Pascal** with a problem on how to divide the stakes when a gambling game is interrupted during play. Pascal involved **Pierre de Fermat**, a lawyer and amateur mathematician, and together they solved the problem. In the process they laid the foundations upon which the laws of probability were formed.

Applications of probability are now found from quantum physics to medicine and industry.

Agner Krarup Erlang

The first research paper on **queueing theory** was published in 1909 by the Danish engineer **Agner Krarup Erlang** who worked for the Copenhagen Telephone Exchange. In the last hundred years this theory has become an integral part of the huge global telecommunications industry, but it is equally applicable to modelling car traffic or queues at your local supermarket.

Statistics and probability are used extensively to predict the behaviour of the global stock market. For example, American mathematician **Edward Oakley Thorp** developed and applied hedge fund techniques for the financial markets in the 1960s.

On the level of an individual investor, money is put into the stock market if there is a good probability that the value of the shares will increase. This investment has risk, however, as witnessed by historic stock market crashes like that of Wall Street in 1929 which triggered the Great Depression, the Black Monday crash of 1987, and the Global Financial Crisis of 2008 - 2009.

1 How does a knowledge of probability theory affect decisions we make?

2 What roles should ethics play in the use of mathematics? You may wish to consider:

- What responsibility does a casino have to operate as a functioning business? What responsibility does it have to the welfare of habitual gamblers? How do these responsibilities affect the way casinos operate?

- By clever mathematical modelling of the global stock markets, you may be able to gain a market advantage. In your gain, does somebody else lose? What rules are in place to protect against financial corruption?

- Do rich countries adopt foreign policies and control trade in order that poor countries remain poor? How much power is associated with financial wealth?

REVIEW SET 10A

1 Kate recorded the number of emails she sent each day for 30 days. Find, to 2 decimal places, the experimental probability that tomorrow she will send:

a 5 emails   b less than 3 emails.

Number of emails	Frequency
0	2
1	5
2	9
3	5
4	4
5	4
6	1

2 A letter of the English alphabet is randomly selected. Let C be the event that the letter is in the word CHEESE.

a List the outcomes in:
   i the sample space U ii the event C.

b Draw a Venn diagram to illustrate U and C.

c Describe in words the meaning of C'.

d Find $P(C)$ and $P(C')$.

3 A coin is tossed and a square spinner labelled A, B, C, D is twirled.

a Draw a 2-dimensional grid to illustrate the sample space.

b Determine the probability of obtaining:
   i a head and consonant   ii a tail and C
   iii a tail or a vowel (or both).

4 Explain what is meant by:

a independent events   b mutually exclusive events.

5 The students A, B, and C have 10%, 20%, and 30% chance of independently solving a certain maths problem. If they all try independently of one another, what is the probability that at least one of them will solve the problem?

6 On any one day, there is a 25% chance of rain and 36% chance that it will be windy.

    a Draw a tree diagram showing the probabilities of wind or rain on a particular day.

    b Hence determine the probability that on a particular day there will be:

        i rain and wind   **ii** rain or wind (or both).

    c What assumption have you made in your answers?

7 A and B are mutually exclusive events where $P(A) = x$ and $P(B') = 0.43$.

    a Write $P(A \cup B)$ in terms of x.   **b** Find x given that $P(A \cup B) = 0.73$.

8 Given $P(Y) = 0.35$ and $P(X \cup Y) = 0.8$, and that X and Y are mutually exclusive events, find:

    a $P(X \cap Y)$ **b** $P(X)$ **c** $P(X$ or Y but not both).

9   **a** Graph the sample space of all possible outcomes when a pair of dice is rolled.

    b Hence determine the probability of getting:

        i a sum of 7 or 11   **ii** a sum of at least 8.

10 In a group of 40 students, 22 study Economics, 25 study Law, and 3 study neither of these subjects.

    a Draw a Venn diagram to display this information.

    b Determine the probability that a randomly chosen student studies:

        i both Economics and Law   **ii** at least one of these subjects

      iii Economics given that they study Law.

11 The probability that a tomato seed will germinate is 0.87. If a market gardener plants 5000 seeds, how many are expected to germinate?

12 A bag contains 3 red, 4 yellow, and 5 blue marbles. Two marbles are randomly selected from the bag with replacement. Find the probability that:

    a both are blue   **b** they are the same colour

    c at least one is red   **d** exactly one is yellow.

13 A survey of 200 people included 90 females. It found that 60 people smoked, 40 of whom were male.

    a Use the given information to complete the two-way table.

    b A person is selected at random. Find the probability that this person is:

	Female	Male	Total
Smoker			
Non-smoker			
Total			

        i a female non-smoker

      ii a male given the person was a non-smoker.

    c If two people from the survey are selected at random, calculate the probability that:

        i both of them are non-smoking females

      ii one is a smoker and the other is a non-smoker.

14 For two events A and B, it is known that $P(A) = \frac{2}{5}$, $P(B) = \frac{3}{10}$, and $P(B \mid A) = \frac{1}{2}$.

    a Calculate $P(A \cap B)$.   **b** Show that A and B are not independent.

    c Calculate $P(A \mid B)$.

REVIEW SET 10B

1 T and M are events such that $n(U) = 30$, $n(T) = 10$, $n(M) = 17$, and $n((T \cup M)') = 5$.

    a Draw a Venn diagram to display this information.

    b Hence find: **i** $P(T \cap M)$ **ii** $P((T \cap M) \mid M)$

2 A school photocopier has a 95% chance of working on any particular day. Find the probability that it will be working on at least one of the next two days.

3 Suppose A and B are independent events, $P(A) = 0.4$, and $P(B) = 0.7$.

    a Calculate $P(A \cap B)$. Hence explain why A and B cannot be mutually exclusive.

    b Calculate $P(A \cup B)$.

4 The probability that a particular salesman will leave his sunglasses behind in any store is $\frac{1}{5}$. Suppose the salesman visits two stores in succession and leaves his sunglasses behind in one of them. What is the probability that the salesman left his sunglasses in the first store?

5 A survey of 50 men and 50 women was conducted to see how many people prefer coffee or tea. It was found that 15 men and 24 women prefer tea.

    a Let C represent the people who prefer coffee and M represent the men. Hence complete the Venn diagram.

    b Calculate $P(M \mid C)$.

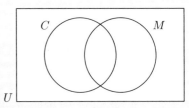

6 Niklas and Rolf play tennis with the winner being the first to win two sets. Niklas has a 40% chance of beating Rolf in any set.

    a Draw a tree diagram showing the possible outcomes.

    b Hence determine the probability that Niklas will win the match.

7 A and B are independent events where $P(A) = 0.8$ and $P(B) = 0.65$. Determine:

    a $P(A \cup B)$ **b** $P(A \mid B)$ **c** $P(A' \mid B')$ **d** $P(B \mid A)$.

8 If I buy 4 tickets in a 500 ticket lottery and the prizes are drawn without replacement, determine the probability that I will win:

    a the first 3 prizes   **b** at least one of the first 3 prizes.

9 The students in a school are all invited to participate in a survey. 48% of the students at the school are males, of whom 16% will participate in the survey. 35% of the females will also participate in the survey. A student is randomly chosen from the school. Find the probability that the student:

    a will participate in the survey

    b is female given that he or she will participate in the survey.

10 For the two events A and B, $P(A) = \frac{3}{7}$ and $P(B') = \frac{2}{3}$.

    a Determine $P(B)$.

    b Calculate $P(A \cup B)$ if A and B are:

        i mutually exclusive   **ii** independent.

11   Jon goes cycling on three random mornings of each week. When he goes cycling he has eggs for breakfast 70% of the time. When he does not go cycling he has eggs for breakfast 25% of the time. Determine the probability that Jon:

    a   has eggs for breakfast

    b   goes cycling given that he has eggs for breakfast.

12   With each pregnancy, a particular woman will give birth to either a single baby or twins. There is a 15% chance of having twins during each pregnancy. Suppose that after 2 pregnancies she has given birth to 3 children. Find the probability that she had twins first.

13   The table alongside shows the number of balloons in a giant party pack.

	Red	Yellow	Blue
Large	12	5	9
Medium	15	8	10
Small	24	11	6

    a   State the:

       i   total number of balloons in the pack

       ii   number of medium balloons in the pack.

    b   One balloon is chosen at random from the pack. Find the probability that:

       i   the balloon is not yellow   **ii**   the balloon is either medium or small.

    c   Two balloons are selected at random from the pack. Find the probability that:

       i   both balloons are red   **ii**   neither of the balloons are large

       iii   exactly one of the balloons is blue   **iv**   at least one of the balloons is blue.

    d   Three balloons are selected at random from the pack. Find the probability that:

       i   all three balloons are small and yellow

       ii   exactly two balloons are medium and red.

14   Answer the questions in the **Opening Problem** on page **240**.

Chapter **11**

Sampling and data

Contents:

OPENING PROBLEM

A supermarket sells 1 kg bags of grapes.

Things to think about:

a Would you expect every bag of grapes to weigh *exactly* 1 kg?

b In what range of weights would you expect most of the bags of grapes to lie?

c Adriana weighed 50 bags of grapes which were delivered to the supermarket on a particular day.

   i Do you think this sample will be *representative* of all the bags of grapes sold by the supermarket? Explain your answer.

   ii What type of graph should Adriana use to display her results?

   iii What would you expect Adriana's graph to look like?

In statistics we collect information about a group of individuals, then analyse this information to draw conclusions about those individuals.

You should already be familiar with these words which are commonly used in statistics:

Data:	information about the characteristics of a group of individuals
Categorical variable:	describes a particular characteristic which can be divided into categories
Quantitative variable:	describes a characteristic which has a numerical value that can be counted or measured
Population:	an entire collection of individuals about which we want to draw conclusions
Census:	the collection of information from the **whole population**
Parameter:	a numerical quantity measuring some aspect of a population
Sample:	a group of individuals selected from a population
Survey:	the collection of information from a **sample**
Statistic:	a quantity calculated from data gathered from a sample, usually used to estimate a population parameter

 # ERRORS IN SAMPLING

A **census** is the most accurate way to investigate a population of interest. However, in most situations it is impractical or impossible to obtain data from the entire population. Instead, we can conduct a **survey** of a well-chosen **sample** of the population.

When we collect data to estimate a characteristic of a population, our estimate will almost certainly be different from the actual characteristic of the population. This difference is referred to as **error**.

There are four main categories of error: **sampling error**, **measurement error**, **coverage error**, and **non-response error**.

Sampling error occurs when a characteristic of a sample differs from that of the whole population. This error is random, and will occur even for samples which are well-chosen to avoid bias.

Measurement error refers to inaccuracies in measurement at the data collection stage. For example, when we record a person's height to the nearest centimetre, the recorded height is slightly different from the person's *exact* height.

Measurement error can also arise from the way survey questions are asked. The question may be worded to lead the respondent to answer in a certain way.   For example, the question "Do you support the dangerous practice of cycling without a helmet?" invites the respondent to answer "no", since the question contains the judgement that riding without a helmet is dangerous. To avoid this type of error, questions should be worded clearly, and in a neutral tone.

Coverage errors occur when a sample does not truly reflect the population we are trying to find information about.

To avoid coverage errors, samples should be **sufficiently large** and **unbiased**.

For example, suppose you are interested in the health of bees on a particular island.

- If you only collect data from 10 bees, you will not get a reliable idea of the health of all bees on the island.

- If you only collect data from one particular bee hive, the sample may not be **representative** of all of the bees on the island. For example, the hive you pick may be stressed and preparing to swarm, whereas its neighbouring hives may be healthy. The sample would therefore be a **biased sample**, and would be unreliable for forming conclusions about the whole population.

Non-response errors occur when a large number of people selected for a survey choose not to respond to it.

For example:

- An online survey is less likely to be completed by elderly people who are unfamiliar with technology. This means that elderly people will be under-represented in the survey.

- In surveys on customer satisfaction, people are more likely to respond if they are unsatisfied.

EXERCISE 11A

1 A new drug called Cobrasyl has been developed for the treatment of high blood pressure in humans. A derivative of cobra venom, it is able to reduce blood pressure to an acceptable level. Before its release, a research team treated 7 high blood pressure patients with the drug, and in 5 cases it reduced their blood pressure to an acceptable level.

   Do you think this sample can be used to draw reliable conclusions about the drug's effectiveness for all patients? Explain your answer.

2 50 people in a Toronto shopping mall were surveyed. It was found that 20 of them had been to an ice hockey game in the past year. From this survey, it was concluded that "40% of people living in Canada have been to an ice hockey game in the past year".

   Give *two* reasons why this conclusion is unreliable.

3 A polling agency is employed to investigate the voting intention of residents in a particular electorate. From the data collected, they want to predict the election result for that electorate in the next election. Explain why each of the following situations may produce a biased sample:

   a A random selection of people in the local large shopping complex is surveyed between 1 pm and 3 pm on a weekday.

   b The members of the local golf club are surveyed.

   c A random sample of people at the local train station between 7 am and 9 am are surveyed.

   d A door to door visit is undertaken, surveying every voter in a particular street.

4 Jennifer wants to estimate the average weight of the 2000 sheep on her farm. She selects a sample of 10 sheep, and weighs them.

Explain why this approach may produce a:

   a coverage error   **b** measurement error.

5 The government has released a new proposal to move funding from education to health. A journalist wants to understand the public's feelings about this proposal. She asks 100 people the question "Do you support the Government's proposed cuts to education?".

   a Explain why this survey may produce a measurement error.

   b How could the question be worded so the public's feelings about the proposal would be more accurately measured?

6 Jack owns 800 apple trees. To determine how many apples the trees are producing, he instructs his four sons to each count the apples from 200 trees.

   a Explain why there will be no sampling error in this process.

   b Two of the sons only count the apples on the tree itself, whilst the other two sons also count the apples on the ground beneath the tree. What type of error is this?

7 A survey company is interested in whether people feel overworked at their jobs. They mail out a survey to 5000 workers, and ask the workers to mail back the survey.

   a Explain why this survey may produce a significant non-response error.

   b What would be the advantages and disadvantages of conducting the survey online instead of by mail?

8 A national sporting organisation has over 300 000 members. Every member is invited to complete an online survey regarding the management structure of the organisation. Only 16% of the members responded.

   a Do you think the non-response error in this situation is likely to produce a biased sample? Explain your answer.

   b Does such a high non-response error necessarily invalidate findings from the survey? Discuss your answer.

DISCUSSION

- Why do you think companies offer incentives for people to complete their surveys?
- Which of the following incentives for completing a survey would be more effective?
  - ▸ A chance to win a prize as shown alongside.
  - ▸ A guaranteed discount or promotional code for the participant to use on their next purchase.
- Is it ethical to offer monetary compensation for completing a survey?

COMPLETE OUR SURVEY
FOR YOUR CHANCE TO
WIN
A $50 GIFT CARD

B | SAMPLING METHODS

In general, the best way to avoid bias when selecting a sample is to make sure the sample is **randomly selected**. This means that each member of the population has the same chance of being selected in the sample.

We will look at five sampling methods:

- **simple random sampling**
- **systematic sampling**
- **convenience sampling**
- **stratified sampling**
- **quota sampling**

SIMPLE RANDOM SAMPLING

Suppose 3 students are to be sampled from a class of 30 students. The names of all students in the class are placed in a barrel, and 3 names are drawn from the barrel.

Notice that:

- Each student has the same chance ($\frac{1}{10}$) of being selected.
- Each set of 3 students is just as likely to be selected as any other. For example, the selection {Bruce, Jane, Sean} is just as likely to occur as {Jane, Peter, Vanessa}.

This type of sampling is called **simple random sampling**.

> For a **simple random sample** of size n from a population:
>
> - Each member of the population has the same chance of being selected in the sample.
> - Each set of n members of the population has the same chance of being selected as any other set of n members.

Instead of drawing names from a barrel, it is usually more practical to number the members of the population, and use a random number generator to select the sample.

You can use your calculator to generate random numbers. In this case, the 8th, 12th, and 25th students would be selected for the sample.

GRAPHICS CALCULATOR INSTRUCTIONS

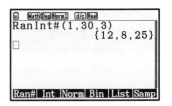

SYSTEMATIC SAMPLING

In **systematic sampling**, the sample is created by selecting members of the population at regular intervals.

For example, an accountancy firm may wish to sample the files of $\frac{1}{10}$th of their clients. They choose a starting file from 1 to 10 (for example, 3), and then select every 10th file after that. So, they would select the 3rd file, then the 13th, 23rd, 33rd, and so on.

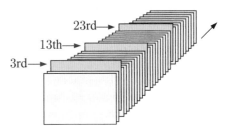

Systematic sampling is useful when not all members of the population are available for sampling at the same time. An example of this is the sampling of cars which pass through a particular intersection during the day.

Example 1

◀)) **Self Tutor**

Management of a large city store wishes to find out whether potential customers like the look of a new product. They decide to sample 5% of the customers using a systematic sample. Show how this sample would be selected.

$5\% = \frac{5}{100} = \frac{1}{20}$

So, every 20th customer will be sampled.

A starting customer is selected from 1 to 20. In this case it is customer 7.

So, the store would select the 7th customer, then the 27th, 47th, 67th, and so on.

```
NORMAL FLOAT AUTO REAL DEGREE MP
randInt(1,20,1)
                              (7)
```

CONVENIENCE SAMPLING

In many situations, people are chosen simply because they are easier to select or more likely to respond.

For example, consider a researcher conducting a survey regarding environmental issues. The researcher decides to stand in a pedestrian mall and ask people walking past. It is easiest for the researcher to ask people who are:

- walking closest to them
- walking slowly
- not already in a conversation or using their phone.

These types of samples are known as **convenience samples** because they are convenient for the experimenter.

DISCUSSION

Do you think convenience samples will often be biased?

Discuss any possible bias if the researcher in the mall was studying:

- mobile internet usage
- personal relationships
- social media
- mental health issues.

STRATIFIED SAMPLING AND QUOTA SAMPLING

Stratified sampling and **quota sampling** are useful when the population can be divided into subgroups, and you want to make sure each subgroup is represented fairly in the sample.

For example, a school may want to know the opinions of its students on which charities it should support in the school fun run. To make sure each year level is represented fairly, the number of students sampled from each year level should be proportional to the fraction of the total number of students that year level represents.

Strata	Samples
Year 8s	
Year 9s	
Year 10s	
Year 11s	
Year 12s	

Example 2 ◀⑴ **Self Tutor**

In our school there are 137 students in Year 8, 152 in Year 9, 174 in Year 10, 168 in Year 11, and 121 in Year 12. A sample of 50 students is needed. How many should be randomly selected from each year?

Total number of students in the school $= 137 + 152 + 174 + 168 + 121 = 752$

For the sample, we want:

number of Year 8 students $= \frac{137}{752} \times 50 \approx 9$

number of Year 9 students $= \frac{152}{752} \times 50 \approx 10$

number of Year 10 students $= \frac{174}{752} \times 50 \approx 12$

number of Year 11 students $= \frac{168}{752} \times 50 \approx 11$

number of Year 12 students $= \frac{121}{752} \times 50 \approx 8$

Year 8 students represent $\frac{137}{752}$ of the school, so they should also represent $\frac{137}{752}$ of the sample.

We should select 9 students from Year 8, 10 from Year 9, 12 from Year 10, 11 from Year 11, and 8 from Year 12.

Ideally, we would want the individuals from each strata to be randomly selected to minimise bias. If this can be done, the sample is a **stratified sample**. Otherwise, if the individuals are specifically selected by the experimenter (such as in a convenience sample) then the sample is a **quota sample**.

EXERCISE 11B

1 Use your calculator to select a random sample of:

   a 6 different numbers between 5 and 25 inclusive

   b 10 different numbers between 1 and 25 inclusive

   c 6 different numbers between 1 and 45 inclusive

   d 5 different numbers between 100 and 499 inclusive.

You may need to generate additional random numbers if a number appears more than once.

2 Click on the icon to obtain a printable calendar for 2019 showing the weeks of the year. Each day is numbered.

CALENDAR

Using a random number generator, choose a sample from the calendar of:

   a five different dates   b a complete week starting with a Monday   c a month

   d three different months   e three consecutive months   f four different Wednesdays.

Explain your method of selection in each case.

January	February	March	April	May
1 Tu (1) Wk 1	1 Fr (32)	1 Fr (60)	1 Mo (91)	1 We (121)
2 We (2)	2 Sa (33)	2 Sa (61)	2 Tu (92) Wk 14	2 Th (122)
3 Th (3)	3 Su (34)	3 Su (62)	3 We (93)	3 Fr (123)
4 Fr (4)	4 Mo (35)	4 Mo (63)	4 Th (94)	4 Sa (124)
5 Sa (5)	5 Tu (36) Wk 6	5 Tu (64) Wk 10	5 Fr (95)	5 Su (125)
6 Su (6)	6 We (37)	6 We (65)	6 Sa (96)	6 Mo (126)
7 Mo (7)	7 Th (38)	7 Th (66)	7 Su (97)	7 Tu (127) Wk 19
8 Tu (8) Wk 2	8 Fr (39)	8 Fr (67)	8 Mo (98)	8 We (128)
9 We (9)	9 Sa (40)	9 Sa (68)	9 Tu (99) Wk 15	9 Th (129)
...	...	...	...	...

3   A chocolate factory produces 80 000 blocks of chocolate per day. Today, the factory operator wants to sample 2% of the blocks for quality testing. He uses a systematic sample, starting from the 17th block.

   a   List the first five blocks to be sampled.

   b   Find the total size of the sample.

4   An annual dog show averages 3540 visitors. The catering manager is conducting a survey to investigate the proportion of visitors who will spend more than €20 on food and drinks at the show. He decides to survey the first 40 people through the gate.

   a   Identify the sampling method used.

   b   Discuss any problems with the sampling method.

   c   Suggest a better sampling method that includes a suitable sample size and which better represents the population.

5   A library manager is interested in the number of people using the library each day. She decides to perform a count every 28th day for one year, starting next Monday.

   a   What type of sampling method is this?

   b   How many days will be in her sample?

   c   Explain why the sample may be biased.

6   A sporting club wants to ask its members some questions about the clubhouse. The club has 80 tennis members, 60 lawn bowls members, and 20 croquet members.

   a   How many members does the club have in total?

   b   The club decides to use a sample of 40. How many members of each sport should be sampled?

7   A large retail store has 10 departmental managers, 24 supervisors, 65 senior sales staff, 98 junior sales staff, and 28 shelf packers. The company director wishes to interview a sample of 30 staff to obtain their view of operating procedures. How many of each group should be selected for the sample?

8   Mona wants to gauge the opinions of her peers on the design of the school's yearbook. She uses her own home room class as her sample.

   a   Explain why Mona's sample is a convenience sample.

   b   In what ways will Mona's sample be biased?

   c   Suggest a more appropriate sampling method that Mona should use.

9   Lucian is a school counsellor. He wants to raise awareness of student cyber-bullying with the students' parents. Lucian therefore wants to find out whether students at the school have discussed the issue with their parents.

   a   Explain why it might not be practical for Lucian to use a simple random sample or systematic sample.

   b   Lucian wants to make sure that each gender is appropriately represented in his sample. Should he use a stratified sample or quota sample?

10 The 200 students in Years 11 and 12 at a high school were asked whether or not they had ever smoked a cigarette. The replies received were:

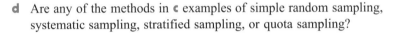

```
nnnny   nnnyn   ynnnn   yynyy   ynyny   ynnyn   nyynn   yynyn   ynynn   nyynn
ynnyn   yynyy   nnyyy   yyyyy   nnnyy   nnnnn   nnyny   yynny   nnnyy   ynyyn
nynnn   ynyyn   nnyny   ynyyy   ynnnn   yyyyn   yynnn   nynyn   yyyny   ynnyy
nynnn   yynny   nyynn   yynyn   ynynn   nyyyn   ynnyy   nyyny   nnyny   ynnnn
```

    a Why is this considered to be a census?

    b Find the actual proportion of all students who said they had smoked.

    c Discuss the validity and usefulness of the following sampling methods which could have been used to estimate the proportion in **b**:

      i sampling the first five replies

      ii sampling the first ten replies

      iii sampling every second reply

      iv sampling the fourth member of every group of five

      v randomly selecting 30 numbers from 1 to 200 and choosing the response corresponding to that number

      vi sampling 20% of Year 11 students and 20% of Year 12 students.

    d Are any of the methods in **c** examples of simple random sampling, systematic sampling, stratified sampling, or quota sampling?

DISCUSSION

The so-called "Brexit" referendum of 2016 to determine whether the United Kingdom would remain part of the European Union is one of the most controversial democratic referendums in recent history.

  1 Was the referendum a census or a sample?

  2 What sampling errors may have been present? In what ways might the sample have been biased?

  3 33 551 983 votes were counted in the referendum, and it was decided by a simple majority of 51.9% to 48.1% that the United Kingdom would leave. This is shown in the first pie chart.

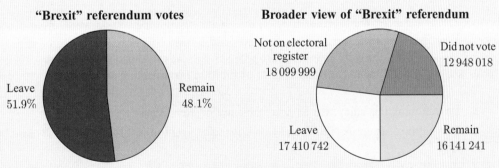

"Brexit" referendum votes

Leave 51.9%   Remain 48.1%

Broader view of "Brexit" referendum

Not on electoral register 18 099 999

Did not vote 12 948 018

Leave 17 410 742

Remain 16 141 241

In the second pie chart we take a broader view to include those who did not vote and those not on the electoral register.

    a Do you think that the United Kingdom leaving the European Union can be considered "the will of the people"?

    b Do you think it is a good idea to have a non-compulsory referendum which can be carried with only a simple majority?

THEORY OF KNOWLEDGE

Clinical trials are commonly used in medical research to test the effectiveness of new treatments for conditions or diseases. They require randomly sampling patients who have the condition or disease in question.

A clinical trial usually involves dividing the sampled individuals into 2 groups:

- A **control group** that serves as the baseline for comparison. This group is usually given either a placebo or the best currently available treatment.
- A **treatment group** that receives the new treatment to be tested.

Ideally, the two groups should be as similar as possible so that differences between the results for the two groups more accurately reflect the differences between treatments, rather than the differences between individuals.

1 Are clinical trials necessarily practical for studying treatments of extremely rare diseases?

2 How should groups be sampled?

As clinical trials are experiments involving people, the consideration of **ethics** is particularly important. In 1975, the **Declaration of Helsinki** was written by the World Medical Association to provide guidelines on human experimentation.

Key points of the Declaration include:

- Patients must be made fully aware of all possible risks before they give their consent to participate.
- Patients must never be given a treatment that is known to be inferior.
- Patients are allowed to withdraw from the study at any time.

The full Declaration can be found at www.wma.net/policy/current-policies/.

3 Are these ethical guidelines applicable to *any* experiment or survey that involves people?

4 Are there the same ethical concerns about experiments involving:

    a animals   **b** non-living things?

In June 2014, Facebook published a study on the effects of omitting certain words from posts in a user's "News feed" on their moods and emotions[1]. This study was heavily criticised for its lack of ethical consideration. The only consent to use people's data was obtained within Facebook's general Terms and Conditions document, which must be agreed to upon making an account.

5 Do you think this study was an acceptable use of users' data?

6 Do you think using the Terms and Conditions document to justify "informed consent" is *fair*?

7 Are ethics more important than research?

[1] Adam D. I. Kramer, Jamie E. Guillory, and Jeffrey T. Hancock. "Experimental evidence of massive-scale emotional contagion through social networks". In: *Proceedings of the National Academy of Sciences* 111.24 (2014), pp. 8788 - 8790. ISSN: 0027-8424. DOI: 10.1073/pnas.1320040111. eprint: http://www.pnas.org/content/111/24/8788.full.pdf. URL: http://www.pnas.org/content/111/24/8788.

TYPES OF DATA

When we collect data, we measure or observe a particular feature or **variable** associated with the population. The variables we observe are described as either **categorical** or **numerical**.

CATEGORICAL VARIABLES

A **categorical variable** describes a particular quality or characteristic.

The data is divided into **categories**, and the information collected is called **categorical data**.

Some examples of categorical data are:

- *computer operating system*:   The categories could be Windows, macOS, or Linux.
- *gender*:   The categories are male and female.

QUANTITATIVE OR NUMERICAL VARIABLES

A **quantitative variable** has a numerical value. The information collected is called **numerical data**.

Quantitative variables can either be **discrete** or **continuous**.

A **discrete quantitative variable** or just **discrete variable** takes exact number values. It is usually a result of **counting**.

Some examples of discrete variables are:

- *the number of apricots on a tree*:
     The variable could take the values 0, 1, 2, 3, ... up to 1000 or more.
- *the number of players in a game of tennis*:
     The variable could take the values 2 or 4.

A **continuous quantitative variable** or just **continuous variable** can take any numerical value within a certain range. It is usually a result of **measuring**.

Some examples of continuous variables are:

- *the times taken to run a 100 m race*:
     The variable would likely be between 9.5 and 25 seconds.
- *the distance of each hit in baseball*:
     The variable could take values from 0 m to 100 m.

Example 3 **Self Tutor**

Classify each variable as categorical, discrete, or continuous:

a the number of heads when 3 coins are tossed

b the brand of toothpaste used by the students in a class

c the heights of a group of 15 year old children.

a We count the number of heads. The result could be 0, 1, 2, or 3. It is a discrete variable.

b The variable describes the brands of toothpaste. It is a categorical variable.

c We measure the height of each child. The data can take any value between certain limits, though when measured we round off the data to an accuracy determined by the measuring device. It is a continuous variable.

EXERCISE 11C

1 Classify each variable as categorical, discrete, or continuous.
If the variable is categorical, list some possible categories.
If the variable is quantitative, suggest possible values or a range of values the variable may take.

a The number of brothers a person has.
b The colours of lollies in a packet.
c The time children spend brushing their teeth each day.
d The heights of the trees in a garden.
e The brand of car a person drives.
f The number of petrol pumps at a service station.
g The most popular holiday destinations.
h The scores out of 10 in a diving competition.
i The amount of water a person drinks each day.
j The number of hours spent per week at work.
k The average temperatures of various cities.
l The items students ate for breakfast before coming to school.
m The number of televisions in each house.

2 Consider the following statistics for a tennis player:

Name: Vance McFarland
Age: 28
Height: 191 cm
Country: Ireland
Tournament wins: 14
Average serving speed: 185 $km\,h^{-1}$
Ranking: 6
Career prize money: £3 720 000

Classify each variable as categorical, discrete, or continuous.

D | ## SIMPLE DISCRETE DATA

ORGANISING DISCRETE DATA

One of the simplest ways to organise data is using a **tally and frequency table** or just **frequency table**.

For example, consider the data set:

$$
\begin{array}{ccccc}
1\ 3\ 1\ 2\ 4 & \quad 2\ 4\ 1\ 5\ 3 & \quad 1\ 3\ 2\ 2\ 4 \\
1\ 3\ 4\ 1\ 2 & \quad 3\ 2\ 4\ 1\ 3 & \quad 2\ 1\ 2\ 5\ 2
\end{array}
$$

A **tally** is used to count the number of 1s, 2s, 3s, and so on. As we read the data from left to right, we place a vertical stroke in the tally column. We use ∦ to represent 5 occurrences.

The **frequency** column summarises the number of occurrences of each particular data value.

The **relative frequency** of a data value is the frequency divided by the total number of recorded values. It indicates the proportion of results which take that value.

Value	Tally	Frequency (f)	Relative frequency
1	∦ |||	8	≈ 0.267
2	∦ ||||	9	0.3
3	∦		6	0.2
4	∦	5	≈ 0.167
5	||	2	≈ 0.0667
	Total	30	

A tally column is not essential for a frequency table, but is useful in the counting process.

DISPLAYING DISCRETE DATA

Discrete data is displayed using a **column graph**. For this type of graph:

- The possible data values are placed on the horizontal axis.
- The frequency of data values is read from the vertical axis.
- The column widths are equal and the column height represents the frequency of the data value.
- There are gaps between columns to indicate the data is discrete.

A column graph for the data set above is shown alongside.

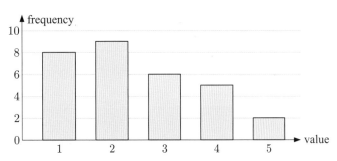

The **mode** of a data set is the most frequently occurring value. On a column graph, the mode will have the highest column. In this case the mode is 2.

DESCRIBING THE DISTRIBUTION OF A DATA SET

A column graph allows us to quickly observe the **distribution** or **shape** of the data set. We can describe the distribution as:

- **Symmetric**
- **Negatively skewed**
- **Positively skewed**

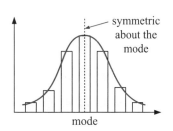

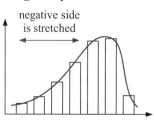

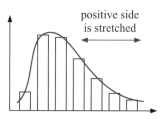

Outliers are data values that are either much larger or much smaller than the general body of data.

Outliers appear separated from the body of data on a column graph.

If an outlier is a genuine piece of data, it should be retained for analysis. However, if it is found to be the result of an error in the data collection process, it should be removed from the data.

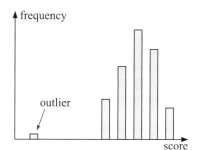

Example 4   ◀⫶) Self Tutor

30 children attended a library holiday programme. Their year levels at school were:

8	7	6	7	7	7	9	7	7	11	8	10	8	8	9
10	7	7	8	8	8	8	7	6	6	6	6	9	6	9

a Record this information in a frequency table. Include a column for relative frequency.

b Construct a column graph to display the data.

c What is the modal year level of the children?

d Describe the shape of the distribution. Are there any outliers?

e What percentage of the children were in Year 8 or below?

f What percentage of the children were above Year 9?

a

Year level	Tally	Frequency	Relative frequency
6	卌 ǀ	6	0.2
7	卌 ǀǀǀǀ	9	0.3
8	卌 ǀǀǀ	8	≈ 0.267
9	ǀǀǀǀ	4	≈ 0.133
10	ǁ	2	≈ 0.067
11	ǀ	1	≈ 0.033
	Total	30	

b

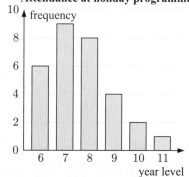

c The modal year level is Year 7.

d The distribution of children's year levels is positively skewed.
There are no outliers.

e $\dfrac{6+9+8}{30} \times 100\% \approx 76.7\%$ of the children were in Year 8 or below.

or the sum of the relative frequencies is $0.2 + 0.3 + 0.267 = 0.767$

∴ 76.7% were in Year 8 or below.

f $\dfrac{2+1}{30} \times 100\% = 10\%$ of the children were above Year 9.

or $0.067 + 0.033 = 0.1$ ∴ 10% were above Year 9.

Due to rounding, the relative frequencies will not always appear to add to *exactly* 1.

EXERCISE 11D

1 In the last football season, the Flames scored the following numbers of goals in each game:

$$2 \quad 0 \quad 1 \quad 4 \quad 0 \quad 1 \quad 2 \quad 1 \quad 1 \quad 0 \quad 3 \quad 1$$
$$3 \quad 0 \quad 1 \quad 1 \quad 6 \quad 2 \quad 1 \quad 3 \quad 1 \quad 2 \quad 0 \quad 2$$

a What is the variable being considered here?

b Explain why the data is discrete.

c Construct a frequency table to organise the data. Include a column for relative frequency.

d Draw a column graph to display the data.

e What is the modal score for the team?

f Describe the distribution of the data. Are there any outliers?

g In what percentage of games did the Flames fail to score?

2 Prince Edward High School prides itself on the behaviour of its students. However, from time to time they misbehave and as a result are placed on detention. The studious school master records the number of students on detention each week throughout the year:

$$0 \quad 2 \quad 1 \quad 5 \quad 0 \quad 1 \quad 4 \quad 2 \quad 3 \quad 1 \quad 4 \quad 3 \quad 0 \quad 2 \quad 9 \quad 2 \quad 1 \quad 5 \quad 0 \quad 3$$
$$6 \quad 4 \quad 2 \quad 1 \quad 5 \quad 1 \quad 0 \quad 2 \quad 1 \quad 4 \quad 3 \quad 1 \quad 2 \quad 0 \quad 4 \quad 3 \quad 2 \quad 1 \quad 2 \quad 3$$

a Construct a column graph to display the data.

b What is the modal number of students on detention in a week?

c Describe the distribution of the data, including the presence of outliers.

d In what percentage of weeks were more than 4 students on detention?

3 Each time Joan visits the cinema, she records the number of previews for other films which are shown before the feature. She has obtained these results:

$$2 \quad 4 \quad 3 \quad 1 \quad 3 \quad 2 \quad 3 \quad 4 \quad 2 \quad 5 \quad 2 \quad 3$$
$$4 \quad 3 \quad 6 \quad 5 \quad 4 \quad 3 \quad 3 \quad 6 \quad 3 \quad 4 \quad 6 \quad 4$$
$$3 \quad 1 \quad 4 \quad 2 \quad 5 \quad 4 \quad 3 \quad 5 \quad 4 \quad 5$$

a Construct a frequency table to organise the data.

b Draw a column graph to display the data.

c Find the mode of the data.

d Describe the distribution of the data. Are there any outliers?

e On what percentage of occasions were at least 3 previews shown?

4 A random sample of people were asked "How many times did you eat out last week?" A column graph was used to display the results.

a How many people were surveyed?

b Find the mode of the data.

c How many people surveyed did not eat out at all last week?

d What percentage of people surveyed ate out more than three times last week?

e Describe the distribution of the data.

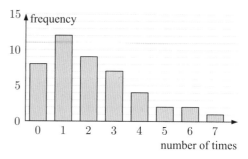

E   GROUPED DISCRETE DATA

A local kindergarten is concerned about the number of vehicles passing by between 8:45 am and 9:00 am. Over 30 consecutive weekdays they recorded data:

27, 30, 17, 13, 46, 23, 40, 28, 38, 24, 23, 22, 18, 29, 16,
35, 24, 18, 24, 44, 32, 52, 31, 39, 32, 9, 41, 38, 24, 32

In situations like this there are many different data values with very low frequencies. This makes it difficult to study the distribution of the data. It is more meaningful to **group** the data into **class intervals** and then compare the frequencies of the classes.

For the data given we use class intervals of width 10. The frequency table for the grouped data is shown alongside.

The **modal class**, or class with the highest frequency, is from 20 to 29 cars.

Number of cars	Tally	Frequency
0 to 9	|	1
10 to 19	⊮⊬⊮	5
20 to 29	⊮⊬⊮ ⊮⊬⊮	10
30 to 39	⊮⊬⊮ ||||	9
40 to 49	||||	4
50 to 59	|	1
	Total	30

We construct **column graphs** for grouped discrete data in the same way as for simple data.

Vehicles passing kindergarten between 8:45 am and 9:00 am

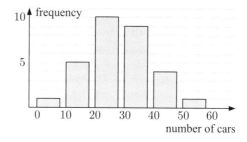

DISCUSSION

- If we are given a set of raw data, how can we efficiently find the lowest and highest data values?
- If the data values are grouped in classes on a frequency table or column graph, do we still know what the lowest and highest values are?

EXERCISE 11E

1 Arthur catches the train to school from a suburban train station. Over the course of 30 days he counts the number of people waiting at the station when the train arrives.

$$\begin{array}{cccccccccc}
17 & 25 & 32 & 19 & 45 & 30 & 22 & 15 & 38 & 8 \\
21 & 29 & 37 & 25 & 42 & 35 & 19 & 31 & 26 & 7 \\
22 & 11 & 27 & 44 & 24 & 22 & 32 & 18 & 40 & 29
\end{array}$$

    a Construct a tally and frequency table for this data using class intervals 0 - 9, 10 - 19, ..., 40 - 49.

    b On how many days were there less than 10 people at the station?

    c On what percentage of days were there at least 30 people at the station?

    d Draw a column graph to display the data.

    e Find the modal class of the data.

2 A selection of businesses were asked how many employees they had. The results are displayed on this column graph.

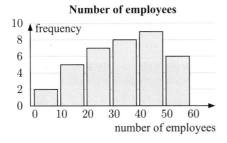

Number of employees

    a How many businesses were surveyed?

    b Find the modal class.

    c Describe the distribution of the data.

    d What percentage of businesses surveyed had less than 30 employees?

    e Can you determine the highest number of employees a business had?

3 A city council is interested in the number of houses in each street of a suburb, because it intends to place collection bins for unwanted clothing. The data they find is:

$$\begin{array}{cccccccccccccc}
42 & 15 & 20 & 6 & 34 & 19 & 8 & 5 & 11 & 38 & 56 & 23 & 24 & 24 \\
35 & 47 & 22 & 36 & 39 & 18 & 14 & 44 & 25 & 6 & 34 & 35 & 28 & 12 \\
27 & 32 & 36 & 34 & 30 & 40 & 32 & 12 & 17 & 6 & 37 & 32
\end{array}$$

    a Construct a frequency table for this data using class intervals 0 - 9, 10 - 19, ..., 50 - 59.

    b Hence draw a column graph to display the data.

    c Write down the modal class.

    d What percentage of the streets contain at least 20 houses?

F   CONTINUOUS DATA

When we measure data that is **continuous**, we cannot write down an exact value. Instead we write down an approximation which is only as accurate as the measuring device.

Since no two data values will be *exactly* the same, it does not make sense to talk about the frequency of a particular value. Instead we group the data into **class intervals** of **equal width**. We can then talk about the frequency of each class interval.

A special type of graph called a **frequency histogram** or just **histogram** is used to display continuous data. This is similar to a column graph, but the "columns" are joined together and the values at the edges of each column indicate the boundaries of that class interval.

The **modal class**, or class of values that appears most often, is easy to identify from a frequency histogram.

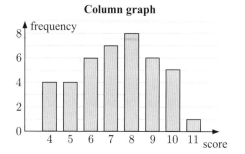

Column graph

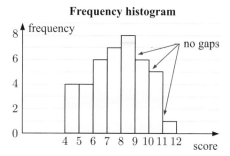

Frequency histogram

no gaps

INVESTIGATION   CHOOSING CLASS INTERVALS

When dividing data values into intervals, the choice of how many intervals to use is important. It affects not only the width of each class interval, but how much detail of the distribution is seen on the histogram.

What to do:

1   Click on the icon to access a demonstration which draws histograms of data sets   DEMO
    with different sizes and distributions.

    a   Select the symmetrical data set with $n = 1000$ data values.
        Use the slider to vary the number of intervals used in the histogram.

        i   Comment on what happens to the *shape* of the histogram.
        ii   Are there features of the data that can only be seen when there are many class intervals?
        iii   When there are many class intervals, is the frequency axis necessarily useful?

    b   Repeat your investigation in **a** for other values of n. Try $n = 100$, $10\,000$, and $100\,000$.
        Record your observations.

    c   For each value $n = 100$, 1000, $10\,000$, and $100\,000$, try using $\approx \sqrt{n}$ class intervals.
        Discuss whether you think this is an appropriate number.

2   Experiment with the other distribution types. If the distribution is not symmetric, do you need more or fewer class intervals?

Example 5   ◀ᴺ Self Tutor

A sample of 20 juvenile lobsters was randomly selected from a tank containing several hundred. The length of each lobster was measured in cm, and the results were:

4.9	5.6	7.2	6.7	3.1	4.6	6.0	5.0	3.7	7.3
6.0	5.4	4.2	6.6	4.7	5.8	4.4	3.6	4.2	5.4

a   Organise the data using a frequency table, and hence graph the data.

b   State the modal class and explain what this means.

c   Describe the distribution of the data.

a The variable *length of a lobster* is continuous, even though lengths have been rounded to the nearest mm.

The shortest length is 3.1 cm and the longest is 7.3 cm, so we will use class intervals of width 1 cm.

Length (l cm)	Frequency
$3 \leqslant l < 4$	3
$4 \leqslant l < 5$	6
$5 \leqslant l < 6$	5
$6 \leqslant l < 7$	4
$7 \leqslant l < 8$	2

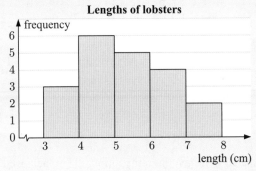

Lengths of lobsters

b The modal class $4 \leqslant l < 5$ occurs most frequently. More lobsters have lengths in this interval than in any other interval.

c The distribution is positively skewed with no outliers.

EXERCISE 11F

1 A frequency table for the heights of a volleyball squad is given alongside.

a Explain why *height* is a continuous variable.

b Construct a frequency histogram for the data. Carefully mark and label the axes, and include a heading for the graph.

c What is the modal class? Explain what this means.

d Describe the distribution of the data.

Height (H cm)	Frequency
$170 \leqslant H < 175$	1
$175 \leqslant H < 180$	8
$180 \leqslant H < 185$	9
$185 \leqslant H < 190$	11
$190 \leqslant H < 195$	9
$195 \leqslant H < 200$	3
$200 \leqslant H < 205$	3

2 For the following data, state whether a frequency histogram or a column graph should be used, and draw the appropriate graph.

a The number of matches in 30 match boxes:

Number of matches per box	47	49	50	51	52	53	55
Frequency	1	1	9	12	4	2	1

b The heights of 25 gymnasts (to the nearest cm):

Height (h cm)	Frequency
$120 \leqslant h < 130$	1
$130 \leqslant h < 140$	2
$140 \leqslant h < 150$	7
$150 \leqslant h < 160$	14
$160 \leqslant h < 170$	1

3 A school has conducted a survey of 60 students to investigate the time it takes for them to travel to school. The following data gives their travel times to the nearest minute.

12	15	16	8	10	17	25	34	42	18	24	18	45	33	38
45	40	3	20	12	10	10	27	16	37	45	15	16	26	32
35	8	14	18	15	27	19	32	6	12	14	20	10	16	14
28	31	21	25	8	32	46	14	15	20	18	8	10	25	22

  a Is travel time a discrete or continuous variable?

  b Construct a frequency table for the data using class intervals $0 \leqslant t < 10$, $10 \leqslant t < 20$, ..., $40 \leqslant t < 50$.

  c Hence draw a histogram to display the data.

  d Describe the distribution of the data.

  e What is the modal travelling time?

4 A group of 25 junior athletes participated in a javelin competition. They achieved the following distances in metres:

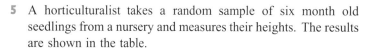

17.6	25.7	21.3	30.9	13.0	31.6	22.3	28.3	7.4
38.4	19.1	24.0	40.0	16.2	42.9	31.9	28.1	41.8
13.6	27.4	33.7	9.2	23.3	39.8	25.1		

  a Choose suitable class intervals to group the data.

  b Organise the data in a frequency table.

  c Draw a frequency histogram to display the data.

  d Find the modal class.

  e What percentage of athletes threw the javelin 30 m or further?

5 A horticulturalist takes a random sample of six month old seedlings from a nursery and measures their heights. The results are shown in the table.

Height (h mm)	Frequency
$300 \leqslant h < 325$	12
$325 \leqslant h < 350$	18
$350 \leqslant h < 375$	42
$375 \leqslant h < 400$	28
$400 \leqslant h < 425$	14
$425 \leqslant h < 450$	6

  a Display the data on a frequency histogram.

  b How many of the seedlings are 400 mm or higher?

  c What percentage of the seedlings are between 350 mm and 400 mm high?

  d In total there are 1462 seedlings in the nursery. Estimate the number of seedlings which measure:

  i less than 400 mm   **ii** between 375 and 425 mm.

6 The weights, in grams, of 50 laboratory rats are given below.

261	133	173	295	265	142	140	271	185	251
166	100	292	107	201	234	239	159	153	263
195	151	156	117	144	189	234	171	233	182
165	122	281	149	152	289	168	260	256	156
239	203	101	268	241	217	254	240	214	221

  a Choose suitable class intervals to group the data.

  b Organise the data in a frequency table.

  c Draw a frequency histogram to display the data.

  d What percentage of the rats weigh less than 200 grams?

REVIEW SET 11A

1 Andrew is interested in the cultural background of the students at his school. He puts together a survey which he hands out to students in his Italian class.

   a Explain why Andrew's sample may be biased.

   b Suggest an alternative sampling method that Andrew can use so that his results will be more representative of his population of interest.

2 A golf club has 1800 members with ages shown alongside. A member survey is to be undertaken to determine the proportion of members who are in favour of changes to dress regulations.

   a Explain why the golf club would not question all members on the proposed changes to dress regulations.

   b If a sample size of 350 is used, how many of each age group will be surveyed?

Age range	Members
under 18	257
18 - 39	421
40 - 54	632
55 - 70	356
over 70	134

3 Classify each variable as discrete or continuous:

   a the number of pages in a book

   b the distance travelled by hikers in one day

   c the attendance figures for a music festival.

4 On a Saturday night, a team of police officers set up a drug and alcohol testing station to test drivers leaving the centre of town on a major road.

   a What type of sampling method is this?

   b Do you think the sample will be biased? If so, do you think it is *sensible* for it to be biased? Explain your answer.

5 This column graph shows the number of rounds a player wins in a judo tournament.

   a Is the *number of rounds won* a discrete or continuous variable?

   b State the modal number of rounds won.

   c Describe the distribution of the data.

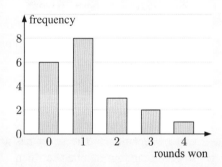

6 Ryan measured the heights of 87 randomly selected boys at his school. His results are summarised alongside.

   a Calculate the relative frequency of each class interval.

   b What percentage of boys measured between 160 cm and 180 cm?

   c Construct a histogram to display the data.

   d Identify the modal class.

   e Describe the distribution of the data.

Height (h cm)	Frequency
$140 \leqslant h < 150$	1
$150 \leqslant h < 160$	13
$160 \leqslant h < 170$	40
$170 \leqslant h < 180$	30
$180 \leqslant h < 190$	3
Total	87

7 A parking inspector recorded the number of parking tickets she issued each day for four weeks. Her results are shown below:

| 2 | 4 | 2 | 3 | 5 | 0 | 3 | 3 | 2 | 4 | 6 | 3 | 3 | 3 |
| 4 | 1 | 3 | 3 | 4 | 5 | 2 | 3 | 1 | 3 | 1 | 2 | 5 | 4 |

   a Construct a tally and frequency table to organise the data.

   b Draw a column graph to display the data.

   c Describe the distribution of the data. Are there any outliers?

8 The data supplied below is the diameter (in cm) of a number of bacteria colonies as measured by a microbiologist 12 hours after seeding.

| 0.4 | 2.1 | 3.4 | 3.9 | 4.7 | 3.7 | 0.8 | 3.6 | 4.1 | 4.9 | 2.5 | 3.1 | 1.5 | 2.6 | 4.0 |
| 1.3 | 3.5 | 0.9 | 1.5 | 4.2 | 3.5 | 2.1 | 3.0 | 1.7 | 3.6 | 2.8 | 3.7 | 2.8 | 3.2 | 3.3 |

   a Is the *diameter of bacteria colonies* a discrete or continuous variable?

   b Organise the data into 5 class intervals of equal width.

   c Draw a histogram to display the data.   **d** State the modal class.

   e Describe the distribution.

REVIEW SET 11B

1 Classify each variable as categorical, discrete, or continuous:

   a the number of pages in a daily newspaper

   b the maximum daily temperature in a city

   c a person's favourite flavour of ice cream

   d the position taken by a player on a lacrosse field

   e the time it takes to run one kilometre

   f the length of a person's feet

   g a person's shoe size

   h the cost of a bicycle.

2 A sales promoter decides to visit 10 houses in a street and offer special discounts on a new window treatment. The street has 100 houses numbered from 1 to 100. The sales promoter selects a random number between 1 and 10 inclusive and calls on the house with that street number. After this the promoter calls on every tenth house.

   a What sampling technique is used by the sales promoter?

   b Explain why every house in the street has an equal chance of being visited.

   c Explain why this is not a simple random sample.

3 Petra emailed a questionnaire to her teacher colleagues about general student behaviour in their classes.

   a Explain why Petra's questionnaire may produce a high non-response error.

   b Of the 20 teachers who were emailed the questionnaire, 10 responded. Petra decides to use these 10 responses as her sample. Explain why Petra is likely to encounter a coverage error.

4 The column graph shows the marks out of 20 that were scored for a test.

a Describe the distribution of the data.

b What percentage of the students scored 13 or more marks?

c What percentage of the students scored less than 5 marks?

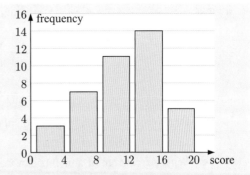

5 The winning margins in 100 rugby games were recorded as follows:

Margin (points)	1 - 10	11 - 20	21 - 30	31 - 40	41 - 50
Frequency	13	35	27	18	7

a Draw a column graph to present this information.

b In what percentage of games was the winning margin:

   i 20 points or less   **ii** more than 30 points?

c Can you tell from the table what the lowest winning margin was? Explain your answer.

6 The Dzungarian or Przewalski's horse is an endangered species native to the Mongolian steppes. The adult horses in an established breeding program are weighed in kg. The results are:

    274 298 302 316 296 279 325
    303 286 318 286 325 306 303
    261 315 326 293 281

a Explain why the *mass of a horse*, m kg, is a continuous quantitative variable.

b Organise the data in a frequency table using the intervals $260 \leqslant m < 270$, $270 \leqslant m < 280$, ..., $320 \leqslant m < 330$.

c Identify the modal class.

d Draw a histogram to display the data.

e Hence describe the distribution of the data.

7 The data below are the lengths, in metres, of yachts competing in a sailing race.

    14.7 14.1 21.6 16.2 15.7 12.8 10.1 13.9 14.4 13.0
    11.7 14.6 17.2 13.4 12.1 11.3 13.1 21.6 23.5 16.4
    14.4 15.8 12.6 19.7 18.0 16.2 27.4 21.9 14.4 12.4

a Is the data discrete or continuous?

b Organise the data using a frequency table.

c Draw an appropriate graph to display the data.

d Describe the distribution of the data.

8 The students in a class were asked how many films they watched in the last month. The results are given below:

$$2 \quad 0 \quad 1 \quad 5 \quad 0 \quad 3 \quad 8 \quad 4 \quad 2 \quad 4$$
$$1 \quad 4 \quad 0 \quad 0 \quad 1 \quad 0 \quad 6 \quad 1 \quad 5 \quad 4$$
$$3 \quad 1 \quad 4 \quad 2 \quad 0 \quad 0 \quad 1 \quad 3$$

a Organise the data using a frequency table.

b Draw an appropriate graph to display the data.

c Identify the mode of the data.

d What percentage of students saw:

  i At least one film in the last month

  ii less than 3 films in the last month?

Chapter 12

Statistics

Contents:

OPENING PROBLEM

Nick believes he has devised a series of stretches which can help relieve back pain. He invites people with back pain to perform the stretches for several weeks.

The participants rate their level of back pain on a scale of 1 to 10 (10 being the greatest) before and after the experiment:

Before:	7	9	5	6	9	7	10	6	8	9
	8	7	9	8	10	4	8	6	7	8

After:	4	7	6	3	8	5	9	4	5	8
	7	6	5	4	7	2	5	3	4	6

Things to think about:

a What statistics can we calculate to measure the *centre* of each data set?

b How can we use a graph to make a visual comparison between the data sets?

c Do you believe that Nick's stretching exercises reduce back pain? Explain your answer.

In the previous Chapter, we looked at how data can be collected, organised, and displayed. By looking at appropriate graphs, we can get an idea of a data set's **distribution**.

We can get a better understanding of a data set if we can locate its **middle** or **centre**, and measure its **spread** or dispersion. Knowing one of these without the other is often of little use.

However, whatever statistics we calculate, it is essential to view and interpret them in the context of what we are studying.

A   MEASURING THE CENTRE OF DATA

There are three statistics that are used to measure the **centre** of a data set. These are the **mode**, the **mean**, and the **median**.

THE MODE

In the previous Chapter we saw that:

- For discrete data, the **mode** is the most frequently occurring value in the data set.
- For continuous data, we cannot talk about a mode in this way because no two data values will be *exactly* equal. Instead we talk about a **modal class**, which is the class or group that has the highest frequency.

If a data set has two values which both occur most frequently, we say it is **bimodal**.

If a data set has three or more values which all occur most frequently, the mode is not an appropriate measure of centre to use.

THE MEAN

The **mean** of a data set is the statistical name for its arithmetic average.

For the data set $\{x_1, x_2, x_3, ..., x_n\}$,

$$\text{mean} = \frac{\textbf{sum of all data values}}{\textbf{the number of data values}}$$

$$= \frac{x_1 + x_2 + x_3 + ... + x_n}{n}$$

$$= \frac{\sum\limits_{i=1}^{n} x_i}{n}$$

We use $\overline{x}$ to represent the mean of a **sample**, and μ to represent the mean of a **population**.

In many cases we do not have data from all of the members of a population, so the exact value of μ is unknown. Instead we collect data from a sample of the population, and use the mean of the sample $\overline{x}$ as an approximation for μ.

μ is the Greek letter "mu" which we pronounce as "mew".

THE MEDIAN

The **median** is the *middle value* of an ordered data set.

An ordered data set is obtained by listing the data from the smallest to the largest value.

The median splits the data in halves. Half of the data values are less than or equal to the median, and half are greater than or equal to it.

For example, if the median mark for a test is 73% then you know that half the class scored less than or equal to 73% and half scored greater than or equal to 73%.

For an **odd number** of data values, the median is one of the original data values.

For an **even number** of data values, the median is the average of the two middle values, and hence may not be in the original data set.

If there are n data values listed in order from smallest to largest,

the median is the $\left(\dfrac{n+1}{2}\right)$th data value.

For example:

If $n = 13$, $\dfrac{n+1}{2} = 7$, so the median is the 7th ordered data value.

If $n = 14$, $\dfrac{n+1}{2} = 7.5$, so the median is the average of the 7th and 8th ordered data values.

DEMO

Example 1 ◀) **Self Tutor**

The numbers of faulty products returned to an electrical goods store each day over a 21 day period are:

    3 4 4 9 8 8 6 4 7 9 1 3 5 3 5 9 8 6 3 7 1

a For this data set, find:
    i the mean   ii the median   iii the mode.

b On the 22nd day there were 9 faulty products returned. How does this affect the measures of the centre?

a   i   mean $= \dfrac{3 + 4 + 4 + ... + 3 + 7 + 1}{21}$ ◀— sum of all the data values

                                      21 ◀————— 21 data values

                $= \dfrac{113}{21}$

                ≈ 5.38 faulty products

   ii   As $n = 21$, $\dfrac{n+1}{2} = 11$

       The ordered data set is: ~~1 1 3 3 3 3 4 4 4 5~~ 5 ~~6 6 7 7 8 8 8 9 9 9~~

                                              ↑
                                    11th value

       $\therefore$ median $= 5$ faulty products

   iii   3 is the data value which occurs most often, so the mode is 3 faulty products.

b We expect the mean to increase since the new data value is greater than the old mean.

    In fact, the new mean $= \dfrac{113 + 9}{22} = \dfrac{122}{22} \approx 5.55$ faulty products.

    Since $n = 22$, $\dfrac{n+1}{2} = 11.5$

    The new ordered data set is:

                    ~~1 1 3 3 3 3 4 4 4 5~~ 5 6 ~~6 7 7 8 8 8 9 9 9 9~~

                             two middle data values

    $\therefore$ the new median $= \dfrac{5+6}{2} = 5.5$ faulty products.

    The new data set has two modes which are 3 and 9 faulty products.

You can use your **graphics calculator** or the **statistics package** to find measures of centre.

 GRAPHICS CALCULATOR INSTRUCTIONS

STATISTICS PACKAGE

EXERCISE 12A

1 Phil kept a record of the number of cups of coffee he drank each day for 15 days:

                 2, 3, 1, 1, 0, 0, 4, 3, 0, 1, 2, 3, 2, 1, 4

Without using technology, find the   a mode   b median   c mean   of the data.

2 For each data set, find the: i mean   ii median   iii mode.

   a   2, 3, 3, 3, 4, 4, 4, 5, 5, 5, 5, 6, 6, 6, 6, 6, 7, 7, 8, 8, 8, 9, 9

   b   10, 12, 12, 15, 15, 16, 16, 17, 18, 18, 18, 18, 19, 20, 21

   c   22.4, 24.6, 21.8, 26.4, 24.9, 25.0, 23.5, 26.1, 25.3, 29.5, 23.5

Check your answers using technology.

3 The sum of 7 scores is 63. What is their mean?

4 The scores obtained by two ten-pin bowlers over a 10 game series are:

Gordon: 160, 175, 142, 137, 151, 144, 169, 182, 175, 155
Ruth: 157, 181, 164, 142, 195, 188, 150, 147, 168, 148

Who had the higher mean score?

5 Consider the two data sets:

Data set A: 3, 4, 4, 5, 6, 6, 7, 7, 7, 8, 8, 9, 10
Data set B: 3, 4, 4, 5, 6, 6, 7, 7, 7, 8, 8, 9, 15

a Find the mean of both data set A and data set B.

b Find the median of both data set A and data set B.

c Comment on your answers to **a** and **b**.

6 An Indian dessert shop keeps a record of how many motichoor ladoo and malai jamun they sell each day for a month:

Motichoor ladoo								**Malai jamun**							
62	76	55	65	49	78	71	82	37	52	71	59	63	47	56	68
79	47	60	72	58	82	76	67	43	67	38	73	54	55	61	49
50	61	70	85	77	69	48	74	50	48	53	39	45	60	46	51
63	56	81	75	63	74	54		38	57	41	72	50	44	76	

a Find the:

  i mean number of motichoor ladoo and malai jamun sold

  ii median number of motichoor ladoo and malai jamun sold.

b Which item was more popular? Explain your answer.

7 A bus and tram travel the same route many times during the day. The drivers counted the number of passengers on each trip one day, as listed below.

	Bus							**Tram**				
30	43	40	53	70	50	63	58	68	43	45	70	79
41	38	21	28	23	43	48	38	23	30	22	63	73
20	26	35	48	41	33		25	35	60	53		

a Use technology to calculate the mean and median number of passengers for both the *Bus* and *Tram* data.

b Which method of transport do you think is more popular? Explain your answer.

8 A basketball team scored 43, 55, 41, and 37 points in their first four matches.

a Find the mean number of points scored for these four matches.

b What score does the team need to shoot in their next match to maintain the same mean score?

c The team scores only 25 points in the fifth match.

  i Will this increase or decrease their overall mean score? Explain your answer.

  ii Find the mean number of points scored for the five matches.

Example 2   🔊 **Self Tutor**

If 6 people have a mean mass of 53.7 kg, find their total mass.

$$\frac{\text{sum of masses}}{6} = 53.7 \text{ kg}$$

$$\therefore \quad \text{sum of masses} = 53.7 \times 6$$

$$\therefore \quad \text{the total mass} = 322.2 \text{ kg}$$

---

9   This year, the mean monthly sales for a clothing store have been €15 467. Calculate the total sales for the store for the year.

10 While on a 12 day outback safari, Bill drove an average of 262 km per day. How far did Bill drive in total while on the safari?

11 Given $\bar{x} = 11.6$ and $n = 10$, calculate $\displaystyle\sum_{i=1}^{10} x_i$.

12 Towards the end of a season, a netballer had played 14 matches and scored an average of 16.5 goals per game. In the final two matches of the season she scored 21 goals and 24 goals. Find the netballer's average for the whole season.

13 Find x if 5, 9, 11, 12, 13, 14, 17, and x have a mean of 12.

14 Find a if 3, 0, a, a, 4, a, 6, a, and 3 have a mean of 4.

15 Over the entire assessment period, Aruna averaged 35 out of a possible 40 marks for her Mathematics tests. However, when checking her files, she could only find 7 of the 8 tests. For these she scored 29, 36, 32, 38, 35, 34, and 39. How many marks out of 40 did she score for the eighth test?

16 A sample of 10 measurements has a mean of 15.7, and a sample of 20 measurements has a mean of 14.3. Find the mean of all 30 measurements.

17 The mean and median of a set of 9 measurements are both 12. Seven of the measurements are 7, 9, 11, 13, 14, 17, and 19. Find the other two measurements.

INVESTIGATION 1   EFFECTS OF OUTLIERS

We have seen that an **outlier** or **extreme value** is a value which is much greater than, or much less than, the other values.

Your task is to examine the effect of an outlier on the three measures of centre.

What to do:

1 Consider the set of data: 4, 5, 6, 6, 6, 7, 7, 8, 9, 10.   Calculate:

  a the mean   **b** the mode   **c** the median.

2 Suppose we introduce the extreme value 100 to the data, so the data set is now: 4, 5, 6, 6, 6, 7, 7, 8, 9, 10, 100.   Calculate:

  a the mean   **b** the mode   **c** the median.

3 Comment on the effect that the extreme value has on:

  a the mean   **b** the mode   **c** the median.

4 Which of the three measures of centre is most affected by the inclusion of an outlier?

5 Discuss situations with your class when it would *not* be appropriate to use a particular measure of centre of a data set.

B ▌ CHOOSING THE APPROPRIATE MEASURE

The mean, mode, and median can all be used to indicate the centre of a set of numbers. The most appropriate measure will depend upon the type of data under consideration. When selecting which one to use for a given set of data, you should keep the following properties in mind.

Statistic	Properties
Mode	• gives the most usual value • only takes common values into account • not affected by extreme values
Mean	• commonly used and easy to understand • takes all values into account • affected by extreme values
Median	• gives the halfway point of the data • only takes middle values into account • not affected by extreme values

For example:

- A shoe store is investigating the sizes of shoes sold over one month. The mean shoe size is not useful to know, since it probably will not be an actual shoe size. However, the mode shows at a glance which size the store most commonly has to restock.

- On a particular day a computer shop makes sales of $900, $1250, $1000, $1700, $1140, $1100, $1495, $1250, $1090, and $1075. In this case the mode is meaningless, the median is $1120, and the mean is $1200. The mean is the best measure of centre as the salesman can use it to predict average profit.

- When looking at real estate prices, the mean is distorted by the few sales of very expensive houses. For a typical house buyer, the median will best indicate the price they should expect to pay in a particular area.

EXERCISE 12B

1 The selling prices of the last 10 houses sold in a certain district were as follows:

$$\$346\,400, \quad \$327\,600, \quad \$411\,000, \quad \$392\,500, \quad \$456\,400,$$
$$\$332\,400, \quad \$348\,000, \quad \$329\,500, \quad \$331\,400, \quad \$362\,500$$

a Calculate the mean and median selling prices. Comment on your results.

b Which measure would you use if you were:

  i a vendor wanting to sell your house

  ii looking to buy a house in the district?

2 The annual salaries of ten office workers are:

$$\$33\,000, \quad \$56\,000, \quad \$33\,000, \quad \$48\,000, \quad \$34\,000,$$
$$\$33\,000, \quad \$33\,000, \quad \$48\,000, \quad \$33\,000, \quad \$42\,000$$

    a Find the mode, mean, and median salaries of this group.

    b Explain why the mode is an unsatisfactory measure of the centre in this case.

    c Is the median a satisfactory measure of the centre of this data set?

3 The following raw data is the daily rainfall, to the nearest millimetre, for a month:

$$3, 1, 0, 0, 0, 0, 0, 2, 0, 0, 3, 0, 0, 0, 7, 1, 1, 0, 3, 8, 0, 0, 0, 42, 21, 3, 0, 3, 1, 0, 0$$

    a Use technology to find the mean, median, and mode of the data.

    b Explain why the median is not the most suitable measure of centre for this set of data.

    c Explain why the mode is not the most suitable measure of centre for this set of data.

    d Identify the outliers in this data set.

    e The outliers are genuine pieces of data and not the result of recording errors. Should they be removed before calculating statistics?

4 Esmé runs a day-tour business in Amsterdam. She wants to offer a "family package" that includes the charges for two adults and their children. To investigate the number of children she should include in the package, she asks 30 randomly selected customers with children how many children they have. Their responses are:

$$2 \quad 2 \quad 2 \quad 3 \quad 4 \quad 1 \quad 1 \quad 2 \quad 1 \quad 1 \quad 1 \quad 2 \quad 2 \quad 3 \quad 4$$
$$1 \quad 4 \quad 4 \quad 2 \quad 3 \quad 1 \quad 1 \quad 1 \quad 2 \quad 1 \quad 1 \quad 2 \quad 2 \quad 3 \quad 2$$

    a Calculate the mean, median, and modal number of children per family.

    b Is the mode a useful statistic in this case?

    c Suggest how many children Esmé should include in the package, giving reasons for your answer.

THEORY OF KNOWLEDGE

We have seen that the mean, the median, and mode are all statistics that give an *indication* of a data set's centre. The actual things that they measure are quite different!

- The mode is the value with the highest frequency. It is a measure of centre in terms of *frequency*.
- The median divides the data into halves. It is a measure of centre in terms of *proportion*.
- The mean is the arithmetic average. It can be thought of as the "balancing point" of the data set's distribution.

Other less commonly used measures for a data set $\{x_1, x_2, ..., x_n\}$ include:

- the **geometric mean** $= \sqrt[n]{x_1 \times x_2 \times .... \times x_n}$

- the **mid-range value** $= \dfrac{\text{maximum} + \text{minimum}}{2}$.

We have seen that the most appropriate measure of centre will depend on what we are investigating. In a way, we change how the "centre" of a data set is defined to suit the purpose of our investigation.

1 When we have data that is heavily skewed, the mode will be on the far left or far right on its column graph.

a Does the mode give an accurate indication of a data set's centre in these cases?

b Is the relationship between mode and the centre of a data set purely coincidental?

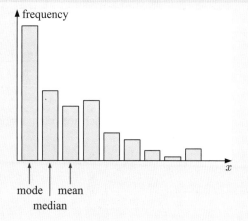

2 For what kinds of data sets would the geometric mean and the mid-range value be useful?

3 How would *you* define the "centre" of a data set?

4 What makes a measure of centre objectively "better" than another measure?

5 Is there a *canonical* measure of centre, which means a measure of centre that is "better" than any other in all cases?

C   USING FREQUENCY TABLES

We have already seen how to organise data into a **frequency table** like the one alongside.

The mode of the data is found directly from the *Frequency* column.

Value	Frequency
3	1
4	1
5	3
6	7
mode → 7	15
8	8
9	5

THE MEAN

Adding a "Product" column to the table helps to add the data values.

For example, the value 7 occurs 15 times, and these add to $15 \times 7 = 105$.

Value (x)	Frequency (f)	Product (xf)
3	1	$3 \times 1 = 3$
4	1	$4 \times 1 = 4$
5	3	$5 \times 3 = 15$
6	7	$6 \times 7 = 42$
7	15	$7 \times 15 = 105$
8	8	$8 \times 8 = 64$
9	5	$9 \times 5 = 45$
Total	$\sum f = 40$	$\sum xf = 278$

Since the mean $= \dfrac{\text{sum of all data values}}{\text{the number of data values}}$, we find

$$\overline{x} = \frac{x_1 f_1 + x_2 f_2 + x_3 f_3 + \dots + x_k f_k}{f_1 + f_2 + f_3 + \dots + f_k} \qquad \text{where } k \text{ is the number of } different \text{ values in the data.}$$

$$\therefore \quad \overline{x} = \frac{\sum\limits_{j=1}^{k} x_j f_j}{\sum\limits_{j=1}^{k} f_j} \quad \text{which we often abbreviate as} \quad \frac{\sum x f}{\sum f}.$$

In this case the mean $= \dfrac{278}{40} = 6.95$.

THE MEDIAN

Since $\dfrac{n+1}{2} = \dfrac{41}{2} = 20.5$, the median is the average of the 20th and 21st ordered data values.

In the table, the blue numbers show the accumulated frequency values, or **cumulative frequency**.

We can see that the 20th and 21st ordered data values are both 7s.

$\therefore$ the median $= \dfrac{7+7}{2} = 7$

Value	Frequency	Cumulative frequency
3	1	1 ← one number is 3
4	1	2 ← two numbers are 4 or less
5	3	5 ← five numbers are 5 or less
6	7	12 ← 12 numbers are 6 or less
7	15	27 ← 27 numbers are 7 or less
8	8	35 ← 35 numbers are 8 or less
9	5	40 ← all numbers are 9 or less
Total	40	

Example 3 ◆) **Self Tutor**

The table below shows the number of aces served by a sample of tennis players in their first sets of a tournament.

Number of aces	1	2	3	4	5	6
Frequency	4	11	18	13	7	2

Determine the: **a** mean   **b** median   **c** mode   for this data.

Number of aces (x)	Frequency (f)	Product (xf)	Cumulative frequency
1	4	4	4
2	11	22	15
3	18	54	33
4	13	52	46
5	7	35	53
6	2	12	55
Total	$\sum f = 55$	$\sum x f = 179$	

a $\bar{x} = \dfrac{\sum xf}{\sum f}$

$= \dfrac{179}{55}$

≈ 3.25 aces

In this case $\dfrac{\sum xf}{\sum f}$ is short for $\dfrac{\displaystyle\sum_{j=1}^{6} x_j f_j}{\displaystyle\sum_{j=1}^{6} f_j}$.

b There are 55 data values, so $n = 55$. $\dfrac{n+1}{2} = 28$, so the median is the 28th ordered data

value. From the cumulative frequency column, the 16th to 33rd ordered data values are 3 aces.

∴ the 28th ordered data value is 3 aces.

∴ the median is 3 aces.

c Looking down the frequency column, the highest frequency is 18. This corresponds to 3 aces, so the mode is 3 aces.

EXERCISE 12C

1 The table alongside shows the number of people in cars on a road.

Calculate the:

   a mode   **b** median   **c** mean.

Check your answers using your graphics calculator.

GRAPHICS
CALCULATOR
INSTRUCTIONS

Number of people	Frequency
1	13
2	8
3	4
4	5
Total	30

2 The frequency table alongside shows the number of phone calls made in a day by 50 fifteen-year-olds.

  a For this data set, find the:

    i mean   **ii** median   **iii** mode.

  b Construct a column graph for the data and show the position of the mean, median, and mode on the horizontal axis.

  c Describe the distribution of the data.

  d Why is the mean larger than the median?

  e Which measure of centre would be the most suitable for this data set?

Number of phone calls	Frequency
0	5
1	8
2	13
3	8
4	6
5	3
6	3
7	2
8	1
11	1

3

Number of matches	Frequency
47	5
48	4
49	11
50	6
51	3
52	1
Total	30

A company claims that their match boxes contain 50 matches on average. The Consumer Protection Society conducts a survey to assess the company's claim. The results of the survey are shown alongside.

  a Calculate the:

    i mode   **ii** median   **iii** mean.

  b Do the results support the company's claim?

  c In a court for "false advertising", the company won their case against the Consumer Protection Society. Suggest how they did this.

4   Families at a school in Manchester were surveyed, and the number of children in each family was recorded. The results of the survey are shown alongside.

Number of children	Frequency
1	5
2	28
3	15
4	8
5	2
6	1
Total	59

   a Calculate the:
      i mean   ii mode   iii median.
   b The average British family has 2.075 children. How does this school compare to the national average?
   c Describe the skewness of the data.
   d How has the skewness of the data affected the measures of the centre of the data set?

5   The column graph shows the weekly pocket money for a class of children.

   a Construct a frequency table from the graph.
   b Determine the total number of children in the class.
   c Find the:
      i mean   ii median   iii mode   of the data.
   d Which of the measures of centre can be found easily using the graph only?

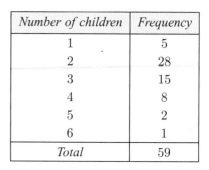

Column graph of pocket money

6   Out of 31 measurements, 15 are below 10 cm and 12 are above 11 cm. Find the median if the other 4 measurements are 10.1 cm, 10.4 cm, 10.7 cm, and 10.9 cm.

7   In an office of 20 people there are only 4 salary levels paid:

   $100 000 (1 person), $84 000 (3 people),
   $70 000 (6 people), $56 000 (10 people)

   a Calculate:
      i the median salary   ii the modal salary
      iii the mean salary.
   b Which measure of central tendency might be used by the boss who is against a pay rise for the other employees?

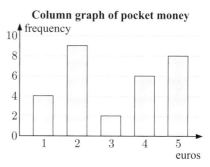

8   The table shows the test scores for a class of students. A pass is a score of 5 or more.

Score	2	3	4	5	6	7	8
Frequency	0	2	3	5	x	4	1

   a Given that the mean score was 5.45, find x.
   b Find the percentage of students who passed.

D   GROUPED DATA

When information has been gathered in groups or classes, we use the **midpoint** or **mid-interval value** to represent all data values within each interval.

We are assuming that the data values within each class are evenly distributed throughout that interval. The mean calculated is an **approximation** of the actual value, and we cannot do better than this without knowing each individual data value.

INVESTIGATION 2   MID-INTERVAL VALUES

When mid-interval values are used to represent all data values within each interval, what effect will this have on estimating the mean of the grouped data?

The table alongside summarises the marks out of 50 received by students who sat a Physics examination. The exact results for each student have been lost.

Marks	Frequency
0 - 9	2
10 - 19	31
20 - 29	73
30 - 39	85
40 - 49	28

What to do:

1 Suppose that all of the students scored the lowest possible result in their class interval, so 2 students scored 0, 31 students scored 10, and so on.

Calculate the mean of these results, and hence complete:

"The mean Physics examination mark must be *at least* ......"

2 Now suppose that all of the students scored the highest possible result in their class interval. Calculate the mean of these results, and hence complete:

"The mean Physics examination mark must be *at most* ......"

3 We now have two extreme values between which the actual mean must lie.

Now suppose that all of the students scored the mid-interval value in their class interval. We assume that 2 students scored 4.5, 31 students scored 14.5, and so on.

    a Calculate the mean of these results.

    b How does this result compare with lower and upper limits found in **1** and **2**?

    c Copy and complete:

      "The mean Physics examination mark was approximately ......"

4 Discuss with your class how accurate you think an estimate of the mean using mid-interval values will be. How is this accuracy affected by the number and width of the class intervals?

Example 4   ◀) Self Tutor

The table below shows the ages of bus drivers. Estimate the mean age, to the nearest year.

Age (years)	21 - 25	26 - 30	31 - 35	36 - 40	41 - 45	46 - 50	51 - 55
Frequency	11	14	32	27	29	17	7

Age (years)	Frequency (f)	Midpoint (x)	xf
21 - 25	11	23	253
26 - 30	14	28	392
31 - 35	32	33	1056
36 - 40	27	38	1026
41 - 45	29	43	1247
46 - 50	17	48	816
51 - 55	7	53	371
Total	$\sum f = 137$		$\sum xf = 5161$

$$\overline{x} = \frac{\sum xf}{\sum f}$$

$$= \frac{5161}{137}$$

$$\approx 37.7$$

∴ the mean age of the drivers is about 38 years.

EXERCISE 12D

1 Simone recorded the lengths of her phone calls for one week. The results are shown in the table alongside.

Time (t min)	Frequency
$0 \leqslant t < 10$	17
$10 \leqslant t < 20$	10
$20 \leqslant t < 30$	9
$30 \leqslant t < 40$	4

The midpoint of an interval is the average of its endpoints.

    a How many phone calls did she make during the week?

    b Estimate the mean length of the calls.

2 50 students sat a Mathematics test. Estimate the mean score given these results:

Score	0 - 9	10 - 19	20 - 29	30 - 39	40 - 49
Frequency	2	5	7	27	9

GRAPHICS CALCULATOR INSTRUCTIONS

Check your answers using your calculator.

3 A teacher recorded the number of children who used the school's playground each day for 50 days.

Number of children	Frequency
21 - 30	8
31 - 40	16
41 - 50	14
51 - 60	12
Total	50

    a On how many days was the playground used by more than 40 children?

    b Find the modal class.

    c Estimate the mean of the data.

4 The table shows the petrol sales in one day by a number of city service stations.

Amount of petrol (P L)	Frequency
$2000 < P \leqslant 3000$	4
$3000 < P \leqslant 4000$	4
$4000 < P \leqslant 5000$	9
$5000 < P \leqslant 6000$	14
$6000 < P \leqslant 7000$	23
$7000 < P \leqslant 8000$	16

    a How many service stations were involved in the survey?

    b Estimate the total amount of petrol sold for the day by the service stations.

    c Estimate the mean amount of petrol sold for the day.

    d Find the modal class for this distribution. Explain your answer.

5 The data below shows the runs scored by Jeff over an entire cricket season.

$$
\begin{array}{cccccccc}
17 & 5 & 22 & 13 & 6 & 0 & 15 & 20 \\
14 & 7 & 28 & 36 & 13 & 28 & 9 & 18 \\
2 & 23 & 12 & 27 & 5 & 22 & 3 & 0 \\
32 & 8 & 13 & 25 & 9 & & &
\end{array}
$$

    a Organise the data into the groups   0 - 9,   10 - 19, 20 - 29,   30 - 39.

    b Use your grouped data to estimate the mean number of runs scored.

    c Use the raw data to find the exact mean number of runs scored. How accurate was your estimate in **b**?

6 The manager of a bank decides to investigate the time customers wait to be served. The results for 300 customers are shown in the table alongside.

Waiting time (t min)	Frequency
$0 \leqslant t < 1$	p
$1 \leqslant t < 2$	42
$2 \leqslant t < 3$	50
$3 \leqslant t < 4$	78
$4 \leqslant t < 5$	60
$5 \leqslant t < 6$	30
$6 \leqslant t < 7$	16

    a Determine the value of p.

    b Estimate the mean waiting time.

    c What percentage of customers waited for at least 5 minutes?

7 This frequency histogram illustrates the results of an aptitude test given to a group of people seeking positions in a company.

    a How many people took the test?

    b Estimate the mean score for the test.

    c What fraction of the people scored less than 100 for the test?

    d What percentage of the people scored more than 130 for the test?

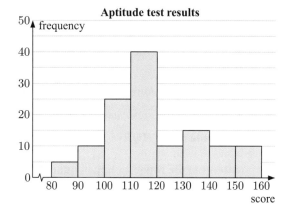

Aptitude test results

E   MEASURING THE SPREAD OF DATA

Consider the following statements:

- The mean height of 20 boys in a Year 12 class was found to be 175 cm.
- A carpenter used a machine to cut 20 planks of length 175 cm.

Even though the means of the two data sets are the same, there will clearly be a greater *variation* in the heights of boys than in the lengths of the planks.

Commonly used statistics that measure the spread of a data set are:

- the **range**
- the **variance**
- the **interquartile range**
- the **standard deviation**.

We will look at variance and standard deviation later in the Chapter.

THE RANGE

The **range** is the difference between the **maximum** data value and the **minimum** data value.

$$\textbf{range} = \textbf{maximum} - \textbf{minimum}$$

As a statistic for discussing the spread of a data set, the range is not considered to be particularly reliable. This is because it only uses two data values. It may be influenced by extreme values or outliers.

However, the range is useful for purposes such as choosing class intervals.

Example 5	◀)) Self Tutor

The weight, in kilograms, of the pumpkins in Herb's crop are:

2.3, 3.1, 2.7, 4.1, 2.9, 4.0, 3.3, 3.7, 3.4, 5.1, 4.3, 2.9, 4.2

Find the range of the data.

Range = maximum − minimum
$$= 5.1 - 2.3$$
$$= 2.8 \text{ kg}$$

THE INTERQUARTILE RANGE

The median divides the ordered data set into two halves, and these halves are divided in half again by the **quartiles**.

The middle value of the *lower* half is called the **lower quartile** (Q_1).

The middle value of the *upper* half is called the **upper quartile** (Q_3).

The **interquartile range** (**IQR**) is the range of the middle half of the data.

> The median is sometimes referred to as Q_2 because it is the 2nd quartile.

interquartile range = upper quartile − lower quartile
$$\mathbf{IQR = Q_3 - Q_1}$$

Example 6	◀)) Self Tutor

For the data set   5 5 7 3 8 2 3 4 6 5 7 6 4,   find:

a the median   **b** Q_1 and Q_3 **c** the interquartile range.

The ordered data set is: 2 3 3 4 4 5 5 5 6 6 7 7 8   (13 data values)

a Since $n = 13$, $\dfrac{n+1}{2} = 7$ ∴ the median is the 7th data value.

~~2 3 3 4 4 5~~ 5 ~~5 6 6 7 7 8~~

∴ median = 5

b Since the median is a data value we now ignore it and split the remaining data into two:

> The lower and upper halves of the data must have the same number of data values.

```
    lower half      upper half
  2 3 3 4 4 5    5 6 6 7 7 8
```

Q_1 = median of lower half $= \dfrac{3+4}{2} = 3.5$

Q_3 = median of upper half $= \dfrac{6+7}{2} = 6.5$

c IQR $= Q_3 - Q_1$
$$= 6.5 - 3.5$$
$$= 3$$

Notice how the data set in **Example 6** can be summarised:

$$\text{range} = 8 - 2 = 6$$

2 3 3 4 4 5 5 5 6 6 7 7 8

lower quartile   median   upper quartile
Q_1 Q_2 Q_3

$$\text{IQR} = 6.5 - 3.5$$
$$= 3$$

Example 7   ◀) **Self Tutor**

For the data set   12 24 17 10 16 29 22 18 32 20, find:

a the median   **b** Q_1 and Q_3 **c** the interquartile range.

The ordered data set is: 10 12 16 17 18 20 22 24 29 32   (10 data values)

a Since $n = 10$, $\dfrac{n+1}{2} = 5.5$ $\therefore$ the median is the average of the 5th and 6th data values.

~~10 12 16 17~~ 18 20 ~~22 24 29 32~~

$\therefore$ median $= \dfrac{\text{5th value} + \text{6th value}}{2} = \dfrac{18 + 20}{2} = 19$

b We have an even number of data values, so we include all data values when we split the data set into two:

lower half   upper half $Q_1 = $ median of lower half $= 16$

$\overbrace{10\ 12\ 16\ 17\ 18}$ $\overbrace{20\ 22\ 24\ 29\ 32}$ $Q_3 = $ median of upper half $= 24$

c $\text{IQR} = Q_3 - Q_1 = 24 - 16 = 8$

Technology can be used to help calculate the interquartile range. Your graphics calculator gives the values of Q_1 and Q_3, from which the interquartile range is found using $\text{IQR} = Q_3 - Q_1$.

```
          Rad Normal  ab/c Real
1-Variable
minX  =10                       ↑
Q1    =16
Med   =19
Q3    =24
maxX  =32
Mod   =10                       ↓
```

GRAPHICS
CALCULATOR
INSTRUCTIONS

STATISTICS
PACKAGE

EXERCISE 12E

1 For each of the following data sets, make sure the data is ordered and then find:

i the median   **ii** the lower and upper quartiles
iii the range   **iv** the interquartile range.

a 5, 6, 9, 10, 11, 13, 15, 16, 18, 20, 21

b 7, 7, 10, 13, 14, 15, 18, 19, 21, 21, 23, 24, 24, 26

c 21, 24, 19, 32, 15, 43, 38, 29

d 32, 45, 26, 28, 52, 57, 41, 69, 33, 20

Check your answers using your graphics calculator.

2 Natalie and Karen scored the following numbers of goals in their last 12 netball games:

> *Natalie*:   29   48   34   39   26   49   28   36   41   46   29   46
> *Karen*:   28   50   38   24   12   47   25   20   44   21   48   22

 a Find the range and interquartile range for:
   i Natalie   ii Karen.
 b Who was the more consistent netball player?

3 Jane and Ashley's monthly telephone bills are shown below:

> *Jane*: $35, $47, $29, $38, $29, $34, $42, $29, $36, $40, $36, $31
> *Ashley*: $19, $24, $26, $19, $23, $40, $35, $59, $32, $42, $26, $24

 a Find the mean and median for each data set.
 b Find the range and interquartile range for each data set.
 c Which person generally pays more for their telephone bills?
 d Which person has the greater variability in their telephone bills?

4   a Find the range and interquartile range for the data set:

> 9   12   7   15   14   22   18   11   20   15
> 20   10   13   67   25   18   11   7   14   19

 b Identify the outlier in the data set.
 c Recalculate the range and interquartile range with the outlier removed.
 d Which measure of spread is more affected by the outlier?

5 Derrick and Gareth recorded the number of minutes they slept each night for 15 nights:

> *Derrick*:   420, 435, 440, 415, 380, 400, 430, 450, 210, 445, 425, 445, 450, 420, 425
> *Gareth*:   360, 420, 460, 430, 480, 340, 450, 490, 500, 460, 330, 470, 340, 480, 370

 a Calculate the range and interquartile range for each data set.
 b Which person's data has the lower:
   i range   ii interquartile range?
 c Which measure of spread is more appropriate for determining who is generally the more consistent sleeper? Explain your answer.

6 a, b, c, d, e, f, g, h, i, j, k, l, and m are 13 data values which have been arranged in *ascending* order.
 a Which variable represents the median?
 b Write down an expression for:
   i the range   ii the interquartile range.

7 A data set has the following known measures of centre and spread:

Measure	median	mode	range	interquartile range
Value	9	7	13	6

Find the new value of each of these measures if every member of the data set is:
 a increased by 2   b doubled.

DISCUSSION

Consider the data set:

$$5, \quad 7, \quad 7, \quad 8, \quad 9, \quad 11, \quad 11, \quad 12, \quad 14, \quad 14, \quad 15$$

1 Calculate Q_1, Q_3, and the IQR:

- by hand
- using your graphics calculator
- using a spreadsheet.

Do you get the same answers in all 3 cases?

2 If there is an odd number of data values, some statistical packages calculate quartiles by *including* the median in each half of the data.

a Check to see whether your spreadsheet calculates quartiles this way.

b Does this method necessarily change the *interpretation* of the calculated values?

c Are statistical packages that do this necessarily "wrong"?

F BOX AND WHISKER DIAGRAMS

A **box and whisker diagram** or simply **box plot** is a visual display of some of the descriptive statistics of a data set. It shows:

- the minimum value
- the lower quartile (Q_1)
- the median (Q_2)   These five numbers form the
- the upper quartile (Q_3)   **five-number summary** of the data set.
- the maximum value

For the data set in **Example 7** on page **321**, the five-number summary and box plot are:

minimum $= 10$
$Q_1 = 16$
median $= 19$
$Q_3 = 24$
maximum $= 32$

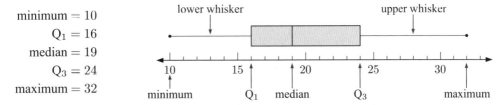

You should notice that:

- The rectangular box represents the "middle" half of the data set.
- The lower whisker represents the 25% of the data with smallest values.
- The upper whisker represents the 25% of the data with greatest values.

INTERPRETING A BOX PLOT

A set of data with a **symmetric distribution** will have a symmetric box plot.

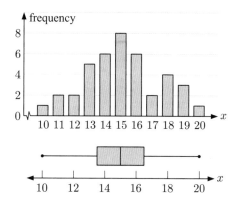

The whiskers of the box plot are the same length and the median line is in the centre of the box.

A set of data which is **positively skewed** will have a positively skewed box plot.

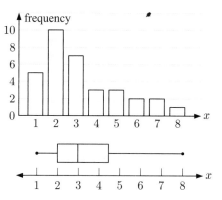

The upper whisker is longer than the lower whisker and the median line is closer to the left hand side of the box.

A set of data which is **negatively skewed** will have a negatively skewed box plot.

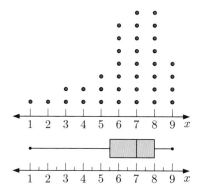

The lower whisker is longer than the upper whisker and the median line is closer to the right hand side of the box.

Example 8   ◀) **Self Tutor**

Consider the data set: 8 2 3 9 6 5 3 2 2 6 2 5 4 5 5 6

a   Find the five-number summary for this data.

b   Draw a box plot for the data.

c   Find the:

  i   range   ii   interquartile range.

d   Find the percentage of data values which are less than 3.

STATISTICS
PACKAGE

a The ordered data set is:

2 2 2 2 3 3 4 5 ⦙ 5 5 5 6 6 6 8 9   {16 data values}

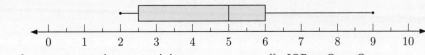

$Q_1 = 2.5$ median $= 5$ $Q_3 = 6$

The five-number summary is: $\begin{cases} \text{minimum} = 2 & Q_1 = 2.5 \\ \text{median} = 5 & Q_3 = 6 \\ \text{maximum} = 9 \end{cases}$

b

| | 0 | 1 | 2 | 3 | 4 | 5 | 6 | 7 | 8 | 9 | 10 |

c **i** range = maximum − minimum   **ii** IQR $= Q_3 - Q_1$

         $= 9 - 2$ $= 6 - 2.5$

         $= 7$ $= 3.5$

d Using the ordered data set in **a**, 4 out of 16 data values are less than 3.

$\therefore$ 25% of the data values are less than 3.

> Part **d** can be seen from the original data set. We cannot read it straight from the box plot because the box plot does not tell us that all of the data values are integers.

EXERCISE 12F

1 The box plot below summarises the points scored by a basketball team.

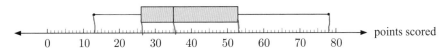

| | 0 | 10 | 20 | 30 | 40 | 50 | 60 | 70 | 80 | points scored |

a Locate:

   i the median   **ii** the maximum value   **iii** the minimum value

   iv the upper quartile   **v** the lower quartile.

b Calculate: **i** the range   **ii** the interquartile range.

2 The box plot below summarises the class results for a test out of 100 marks.

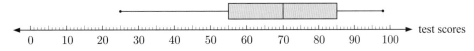

| | 0 | 10 | 20 | 30 | 40 | 50 | 60 | 70 | 80 | 90 | 100 | test scores |

a Copy and complete the following statements about the test results:

   i The highest mark scored for the test was ...... and the lowest mark was ......

   ii Half of the class scored a mark greater than or equal to ......

   iii The top 25% of the class scored at least ...... marks.

   iv The middle half of the class had scores between ...... and ......

b Find the range of the data set.

c Find the interquartile range of the data set.

3 For the following data sets:

    i Construct a five-number summary.
    ii Draw a box plot.
    iii Find the range.
    iv Find the interquartile range.

STATISTICS PACKAGE

GRAPHICS CALCULATOR INSTRUCTIONS

    a 3, 4, 5, 5, 5, 6, 6, 6, 7, 7, 8, 8, 9, 10
    b 3, 7, 0, 1, 4, 6, 8, 8, 8, 9, 7, 5, 6, 8, 7, 8, 8, 2, 9
    c 23, 44, 31, 33, 26, 17, 30, 35, 47, 31, 51, 47, 20, 31, 28, 49, 26, 49

4 Enid counts the number of beans in 33 pods. Her results are:

    5, 8, 10, 4, 2, 12, 6, 5, 7, 7, 5, 5, 5, 13, 9, 3, 4, 4, 7, 8, 9, 5, 5, 4, 3, 6, 6, 6, 6, 9, 8, 7, 6

    a Find the median, lower quartile, and upper quartile of the data set.
    b Find the interquartile range of the data set.
    c Draw a box plot of the data set.

5 Ranji counts the number of bolts in several boxes and tabulates the data as follows:

Number of bolts	33	34	35	36	37	38	39	40
Frequency	1	5	7	13	12	8	0	1

    a Find the five-number summary for this data set.
    b Find the: **i** range   **ii** IQR.
    c Draw a box plot of the data set.

GAME

Click on the icon to play a card game about box plots.

CARD GAME

G   OUTLIERS

We have seen that **outliers** are extraordinary data that are separated from the main body of the data.

However, we have so far identified outliers rather informally by looking at the data directly, or at a column graph of the data.

A commonly used test to identify outliers involves the calculation of upper and lower boundaries:

- **upper boundary = upper quartile + 1.5 × IQR**
  Any data larger than the upper boundary is an outlier.
- **lower boundary = lower quartile − 1.5 × IQR**
  Any data smaller than the lower boundary is an outlier.

Outliers are marked with an asterisk on a box plot. It is possible to have more than one outlier at either end.

Each whisker extends to the last value that is not an outlier.

Example 9

◄)) **Self Tutor**

Test the following data for outliers. Hence construct a box plot for the data.

$$3, \ 7, \ 8, \ 8, \ 5, \ 9, \ 10, \ 12, \ 14, \ 7, \ 1, \ 3, \ 8, \ 16, \ 8, \ 6, \ 9, \ 10, \ 13, \ 7$$

The ordered data set is:

$$1 \ 3 \ 3 \ 5 \ 6 \ 7 \ 7 \ 7 \ 8 \ 8 \vdots 8 \ 8 \ 9 \ 9 \ 10 \ 10 \ 12 \ 13 \ 14 \ 16 \quad \{n = 20\}$$

min $= 1$ 　　$Q_1 = 6.5$ 　　median $= 8$ 　　$Q_3 = 10$ 　　max $= 16$

IQR $= Q_3 - Q_1 = 3.5$

Test for outliers: 　　upper boundary 　　and 　　lower boundary

$\qquad\qquad\qquad\qquad$ = upper quartile $+ 1.5 \times$ IQR $\qquad$ = lower quartile $- 1.5 \times$ IQR

$\qquad\qquad\qquad\qquad$ = $10 + 1.5 \times 3.5$ $\qquad\qquad\qquad$ = $6.5 - 1.5 \times 3.5$

$\qquad\qquad\qquad\qquad$ = 15.25 $\qquad\qquad\qquad\qquad\qquad$ = 1.25

16 is above the upper boundary, so it is an outlier.
1 is below the lower boundary, so it is an outlier.

Each whisker is drawn to the last value that is not an outlier.

EXERCISE 12G

1 A data set has lower quartile $= 31.5$, median $= 37$, and upper quartile $= 43.5$.

  a Calculate the interquartile range for this data set.

  b Calculate the boundaries that identify outliers.

  c The smallest values of the data set are 13 and 20. The largest values are 52 and 55. Which of these are outliers?

  d Draw a box plot of the data set.

2 James goes bird watching for 25 days. The number of birds he sees each day are:

$$12, \ 5, \ 13, \ 16, \ 8, \ 10, \ 12, \ 18, \ 9, \ 11, \ 14, \ 14,$$
$$22, \ 9, \ 10, \ 7, \ 9, \ 11, \ 13, \ 7, \ 10, \ 6, \ 13, \ 3, \ 8$$

  a Find the median, lower quartile, and upper quartile of the data set.

  b Find the interquartile range of the data set.

  c Find the lower and upper boundaries, and hence identify any outliers.

  d Draw a box plot of the data set.

3 Match each graph with its box plot:

a

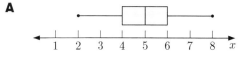

b

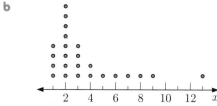

c

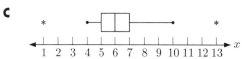

d

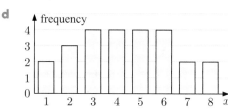

A

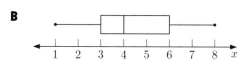

B

C

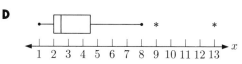

D

4 The data below shows the number of properties sold by a real estate agent each week in 2018:

$$\begin{array}{cccccccccccccc}
2 & 2 & 1 & 3 & 2 & 2 & 2 & 2 & 1 & 4 & 1 & 5 & 1 \\
1 & 1 & 2 & 2 & 2 & 3 & 1 & 7 & 2 & 2 & 2 & 0 & 2 \\
2 & 4 & 4 & 3 & 3 & 1 & 0 & 2 & 4 & 1 & 2 & 1 & 3 \\
0 & 2 & 3 & 1 & 2 & 1 & 3 & 4 & 2 & 2 & 2 & 1 & 3
\end{array}$$

a Draw a column graph to display the data.

b From the column graph, does the data appear to have any outliers?

c Calculate the upper and lower boundaries to test for outliers and hence check your answer to **b**.

d Construct a box plot for the data.

DISCUSSION

Consider the data in the column graph alongside.
The data has $Q_1 = 2$ and $Q_3 = 4$.

1 Calculate the IQR and the upper and lower boundaries for outliers.

2 According to the upper and lower boundaries, the data value "8" is an outlier. Do you agree that "8" should be considered an outlier of this data set?

3 Do you think the given rule for detecting outliers will be effective for data that is heavily skewed?

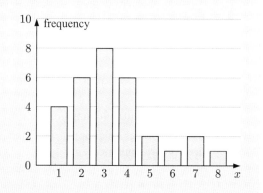

PARALLEL BOX AND WHISKER DIAGRAMS

A **parallel box and whisker diagram** or **parallel box plot** enables us to make a *visual comparison* of the distributions of two data sets. We can easily compare descriptive statistics such as their median, range, and interquartile range.

Example 10 ◀)) Self Tutor

A hospital trialling a new anaesthetic has collected data on how long the new and old drugs take before the patient becomes unconscious. They wish to know which drug acts faster and which is more predictable.

Old drug times (s): 8, 12, 9, 8, 16, 10, 14, 7, 5, 21,
13, 10, 8, 10, 11, 8, 11, 9, 11, 14

New drug times (s): 8, 12, 7, 8, 12, 11, 9, 8, 10, 8,
10, 9, 12, 8, 8, 7, 10, 7, 9, 9

Draw a parallel box plot for the data sets and use it to compare the two drugs.

The five-number summaries are:

For the old drug: $\min = 5$ For the new drug: $\min = 7$
              $Q_1 = 8$ $Q_1 = 8$
           median $= 10$ median $= 9$
              $Q_3 = 12.5$ $Q_3 = 10$
              $\max = 21$ $\max = 12$

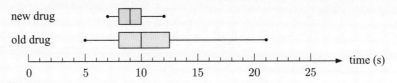

Using the median, 50% of the time the new drug takes 9 seconds or less, compared with 10 seconds for the old drug. So, the new drug is generally a little quicker.

Comparing the spreads:

range for old drug $= 21 - 5$ range for new drug $= 12 - 7$
              $= 16$ $= 5$

IQR for old drug $= Q_3 - Q_1$ IQR for new drug $= Q_3 - Q_1$
              $= 12.5 - 8$ $= 10 - 8$
              $= 4.5$ $= 2$

The new drug times are less "spread out" than the old drug times, so the new drug is more predictable.

EXERCISE 12H

1 The following parallel box plots compare the times students in Years 9 and 12 spend on homework.

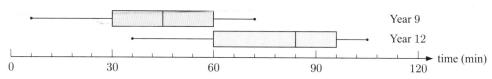

a Copy and complete:

Statistic	Year 9	Year 12
minimum		
Q_1		
median		
Q_3		
maximum		

b For each group, determine the:

    i range   **ii** interquartile range.

c Determine whether the following statements are true or false, or if there is not enough information to tell:

    i On average, Year 12 students spend about twice as much time on homework as Year 9 students.

    ii Over 25% of Year 9 students spend less time on homework than all Year 12 students.

2 The amounts of money withdrawn from an ATM were recorded on a Friday and on a Saturday. The results are displayed on the parallel box plot shown.

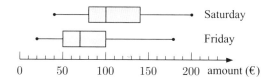

a Find the five-number summary for each data set.

b For each data set, determine the

    i range   **ii** interquartile range.

3 After the final examination, the results of two classes studying the same subject were compiled in this parallel box plot.

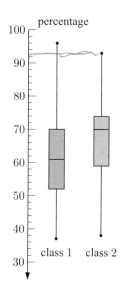

a In which class was:

    i the highest mark   **ii** the lowest mark

    iii there a larger spread of marks?

b Find the interquartile range of class 1.

c Find the range of class 2.

d Students who scored at least 70% received an achievement award. Find the percentage of students who received an award in:

    i class 1   **ii** class 2.

e Describe the distribution of marks in:

    i class 1   **ii** class 2.

f Copy and complete:

The students in class ...... generally scored higher marks.

The marks in class ...... were more varied.

4 The data below are the durations, in minutes, of Kirsten and Erika's last 25 phone calls.

    Kirsten: 1.7 2.0 3.9 3.4 0.9 1.4 2.5 1.1 5.1 4.2 1.5 2.6 0.8
                  4.0 1.5 1.0 2.9 3.2 2.5 0.8 1.8 3.1 6.9 2.3 1.2

    Erika: 2.0 4.8 1.2 7.5 3.2 5.7 3.9 0.2 2.7 6.8 3.4 5.2 3.2
              7.2 1.7 11.5 4.0 2.4 3.7 4.2 10.7 3.0 2.0 0.9 5.7

    a Find the five-number summary for each data set.

    b Display the data in a parallel box plot.

    c Compare and comment on the distributions of the data.

5 Emil and Aaron play in the same handball team and are fierce but friendly rivals when it comes to scoring. During a season, the numbers of goals they scored in each match were:

    Emil: 1 6 2 0 3 4 1 4 2 3 0 3 2 4 3 4 3 3
              3 4 2 4 3 2 3 3 0 5 3 5 3 2 4 3 4 3

    Aaron: 7 2 4 8 1 3 4 2 3 0 5 3 5 2 3 1 2 0
              4 3 4 0 3 3 0 2 5 1 1 2 2 5 1 4 0 1

    a Is the variable discrete or continuous?

    b Enter the data into a graphics calculator or statistics package.

    c Produce a column graph for each data set.

    d Describe the shape of each distribution.

    e Compare the measures of the centre of each distribution.

    f Compare the spreads of each distribution.

    g Draw a parallel box plot for the data.

    h What conclusions can be drawn from the data?

6 A manufacturer of light globes claims that their new design has a 20% longer life than those they are presently selling. Forty of each globe are randomly selected and tested. Here are the results to the nearest hour:

Old type: 103   96 113 111 126 100 122 110   84 117 103 113 104 104
              111   87   90 121   99 114 105 121   93 109   87 118   75 111
               87 127 117 131 115 116   82 130 113   95 108 112

New type: 146 131 132 160 128 119 133 117 139 123 109 129 109 131
              191 117 132 107 141 136 146 142 123 144 145 125 164 125
              133 124 153 129 118 130 134 151 145 131 133 135

    a Is the variable discrete or continuous?

    b Enter the data into a graphics calculator or statistics package. Compare the measures of centre and spread.

    c Draw a parallel box plot.

    d Describe the shape of each distribution.

    e What conclusions, if any, can be drawn from the data?

CUMULATIVE FREQUENCY GRAPHS

If we want to know the number or proportion of scores that lie above or below a particular value, we add a **cumulative frequency** column to a **frequency table**, and use a graph called a **cumulative frequency graph** to represent the data.

The cumulative frequencies are plotted and the points joined by a smooth curve. This differs from an ogive or cumulative frequency polygon where neighbouring points are joined by straight lines.

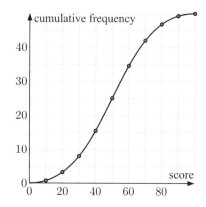

PERCENTILES

A **percentile** is the score below which a certain percentage of the data lies.

For example:

- the 85th percentile is the score below which 85% of the data lies.
- If your score in a test is the 95th percentile, then 95% of the class have scored less than you.

Notice that:
- the **lower quartile** (Q_1) is the 25th percentile
- the **median** (Q_2) is the 50th percentile
- the **upper quartile** (Q_3) is the 75th percentile.

A cumulative frequency graph provides a convenient way to find percentiles.

Example 11   ◀⏵ Self Tutor

The data shows the results of the women's marathon at the 2008 Olympics, for all competitors who finished the race.

a Add a cumulative frequency column to the table.

b Represent the data on a cumulative frequency graph.

c Use your graph to estimate the:

  i median finishing time

  ii number of competitors who finished in less than 155 minutes

  iii percentage of competitors who took more than 159 minutes to finish

  iv time taken by a competitor who finished in the top 20% of runners completing the marathon.

Time (t min)	Frequency
$146 \leqslant t < 148$	8
$148 \leqslant t < 150$	3
$150 \leqslant t < 152$	9
$152 \leqslant t < 154$	11
$154 \leqslant t < 156$	12
$156 \leqslant t < 158$	7
$158 \leqslant t < 160$	5
$160 \leqslant t < 168$	8
$168 \leqslant t < 176$	6

a

Time (t min)	Frequency	Cumulative frequency
$146 \leqslant t < 148$	8	8
$148 \leqslant t < 150$	3	11
$150 \leqslant t < 152$	9	20
$152 \leqslant t < 154$	11	31
$154 \leqslant t < 156$	12	43
$156 \leqslant t < 158$	7	50
$158 \leqslant t < 160$	5	55
$160 \leqslant t < 168$	8	63
$168 \leqslant t < 176$	6	69

$8 + 3 = 11$ competitors completed the marathon in less than 150 minutes.

50 competitors completed the marathon in less than 158 minutes.

b

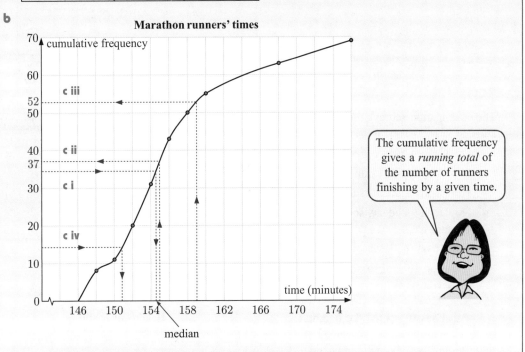

Marathon runners' times

The cumulative frequency gives a *running total* of the number of runners finishing by a given time.

c

i The median is the 50th percentile. As 50% of 69 is 34.5, we start with the cumulative frequency 34.5 and find the corresponding time.

The median ≈ 154.5 min.

ii Approximately 37 competitors took less than 155 min to complete the race.

iii $69 - 52 = 17$ competitors took more than 159 min.

$\therefore \quad \frac{17}{69} \approx 24.6\%$ took more than 159 min.

iv As 20% of 69 is 13.8, we start with the cumulative frequency 14 and find the corresponding time.

The top 20% of competitors took less than 151 min.

Another way to calculate percentiles is to add a separate scale to the cumulative frequency graph.

For example, on the graph alongside, the cumulative frequency is read from the axis on the left side, and each value corresponds to a percentile on the right side.

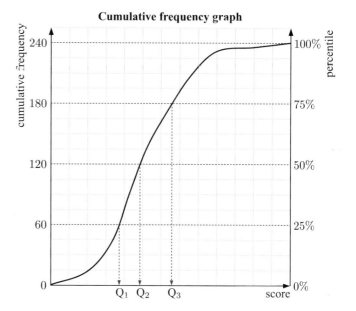

Cumulative frequency graph

EXERCISE 12I

1   The examination scores of a group of students are shown in the table.

a   Draw a cumulative frequency graph for the data.

b   Find the median examination mark.

c   How many students scored 65 marks or less?

d   How many students scored at least 50 but less than 70 marks?

e   If the pass mark was 45, how many students failed?

f   If the top 16% of students were awarded credits, what was the credit mark?

Score (x)	Frequency
$10 \leqslant x < 20$	2
$20 \leqslant x < 30$	5
$30 \leqslant x < 40$	7
$40 \leqslant x < 50$	21
$50 \leqslant x < 60$	36
$60 \leqslant x < 70$	40
$70 \leqslant x < 80$	27
$80 \leqslant x < 90$	9
$90 \leqslant x < 100$	3

2   A botanist has measured the heights of 60 seedlings and has presented her findings on this cumulative frequency graph.

a   How many seedlings have heights of 5 cm or less?

b   What percentage of seedlings are taller than 8 cm?

c   Find the median height.

d   Find the interquartile range for the heights.

e   Find the 90th percentile for the data and explain what this value represents.

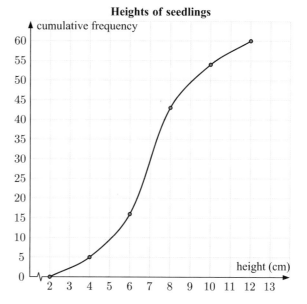

Heights of seedlings

3 The following table summarises the age groups of car drivers involved in accidents in a city for a given year.

   a Draw a cumulative frequency graph for the data.

   b Estimate the median age of the drivers involved in accidents.

   c Estimate the percentage of drivers involved in accidents who had an age of 23 or less.

   d Estimate the probability that a driver involved in an accident is aged:

     i 27 years or less   **ii** 27 years.

Age (x years)	Number of accidents
$16 \leqslant x < 20$	59
$20 \leqslant x < 25$	82
$25 \leqslant x < 30$	43
$30 \leqslant x < 35$	21
$35 \leqslant x < 40$	19
$40 \leqslant x < 50$	11
$50 \leqslant x < 60$	24
$60 \leqslant x < 80$	41

4 The following data are the lengths of 30 trout caught in a lake during a fishing competition. The measurements were rounded *down* to the next centimetre.

$$31 \quad 38 \quad 34 \quad 40 \quad 24 \quad 33 \quad 30 \quad 36 \quad 38 \quad 32 \quad 35 \quad 32 \quad 36 \quad 27 \quad 35$$
$$40 \quad 34 \quad 37 \quad 44 \quad 38 \quad 36 \quad 34 \quad 33 \quad 31 \quad 38 \quad 35 \quad 36 \quad 33 \quad 33 \quad 28$$

   a Construct a cumulative frequency table for trout lengths, x cm, using the intervals $24 \leqslant x < 27$, $27 \leqslant x < 30$, and so on.

   b Draw a cumulative frequency graph for the data.

   c Hence estimate the median length.

   d Use the original data to find its median and compare your answer with **c**.

5 The following cumulative frequency graph displays the performances of 80 competitors in a cross-country race.

Cross-country race times

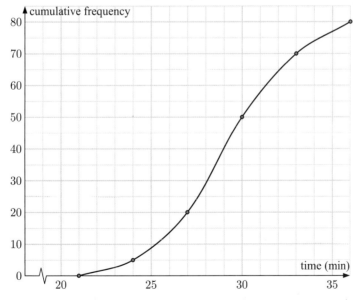

   a Find the lower quartile.

   b Find the median.

   c Find the upper quartile.

   d Find the IQR.

   e Estimate the 40th percentile.

   f Use the cumulative frequency curve to complete the following table:

Time (t min)	$21 \leqslant t < 24$	$24 \leqslant t < 27$	$27 \leqslant t < 30$	$30 \leqslant t < 33$	$33 \leqslant t < 36$
Number of competitors					

6 The table shows the lifetimes of a sample of electric light globes.

a Draw a cumulative frequency graph for the data.

b Estimate the median life of a globe.

c Estimate the percentage of globes which had a life of 2700 hours or less.

d Estimate the number of globes which had a life between 1500 and 2500 hours.

Life (l hours)	Number of globes
$0 \leqslant l < 500$	5
$500 \leqslant l < 1000$	17
$1000 \leqslant l < 2000$	46
$2000 \leqslant l < 3000$	79
$3000 \leqslant l < 4000$	27
$4000 \leqslant l < 5000$	4

7 The following frequency distribution was obtained by asking 50 randomly selected people to measure the length of their feet. Their answers are given to the nearest centimetre.

Foot length (cm)	20	21	22	23	24	25	26	27	28	29	30
Frequency	1	1	0	3	5	13	17	7	2	0	1

a Between what limits are lengths rounded to 20 cm?

b Rewrite the frequency table to show the data in the class intervals you have just described.

c Hence draw a cumulative frequency graph for the data.

d Estimate:

  i the median foot length

  ii the number of people with foot length 26 cm or more.

J   VARIANCE AND STANDARD DEVIATION

The problem with using the range and the IQR as measures of spread or dispersion is that both of them only use two values in their calculation. As a result, some data sets can have their spread characteristics hidden when only the range or IQR are quoted.

So we need to consider alternative measures of spread which take into account all data values of a data set. We therefore turn to the **variance** and **standard deviation**.

POPULATION VARIANCE AND STANDARD DEVIATION

The **population variance** of a data set $\{x_1, x_2, x_3, ..., x_n\}$ is

$$\sigma^2 = \frac{\sum\limits_{i=1}^{n} (x_i - \mu)^2}{n}$$

where μ is the population mean
and n is the number of data values.

The variance is the average of the squares of the distances from the mean.

We observe that if the data values x_i are situated close together around the mean μ, then the values $(x_i - \mu)^2$ will be small, and so the variance will be small.

The **standard deviation** is the square root of the variance.

> The **population standard deviation** of a data set $\{x_1,\ x_2,\ x_3,\ ....,\ x_n\}$ is
>
> $$\sigma = \sqrt{\dfrac{\displaystyle\sum_{i=1}^{n}(x_i - \mu)^2}{n}}.$$

The standard deviation measures the degree to which the data *deviates* from the mean.

The square root in the standard deviation is used to correct the units. For example, if x_i is the weight of a student in kg, the variance σ^2 would be in kg^2, and σ would be in kg.

The standard deviation is a **non-resistant** measure of spread. This is due to its dependence on the mean and because extreme data values will give large values for $(x_i - \mu)^2$. It is only a useful measure if the distribution is approximately symmetrical.

The IQR and percentiles are more appropriate tools for measuring spread if the distribution is considerably skewed.

In this course you are only expected to use technology to calculate variance and standard deviation. However, we present both methods in the following Example to help you understand standard deviations better.

GRAPHICS
CALCULATOR
INSTRUCTIONS

Example 12   ◀) Self Tutor

Find the population variance and standard deviation for the data set:

$$3 \quad 12 \quad 8 \quad 15 \quad 7$$

The mean $\mu = \dfrac{3 + 12 + 8 + 15 + 7}{5} = 9$

The population variance $\sigma^2 = \dfrac{\sum(x - \mu)^2}{n}$

$= \dfrac{86}{5}$

$= 17.2$

The population standard deviation $\sigma = \sqrt{17.2}$

≈ 4.15

x	$x - \mu$	$(x - \mu)^2$
3	-6	36
12	3	9
8	-1	1
15	6	36
7	-2	4
Total		86

Casio fx-CG50	TI-84 Plus CE	HP Prime
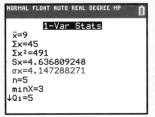		

SAMPLE VARIANCE AND STANDARD DEVIATION

In the screenshots on the previous page, you can see that near the population standard deviation σ, there is a statistic s with a similar value.

Technically, if we have data which is a *sample* from a large population, the **sample standard deviation** s provides a better estimate for the actual population standard deviation than if we use the formula for σ on the sample. However, this is beyond the scope of this course.

In this course you are expected to calculate all standard deviations as though they were populations. The important thing is that you recognise that the two statistics exist, and that you are using the correct one.

EXERCISE 12J

1   Consider the following data sets:

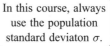

> In this course, always use the population standard deviaton σ.

    Data set A: 10   7   5   8   10

    Data set B: 4   12   11   14   1   6

  a   Show that each data set has mean 8.

  b   Which data set appears to have the greater spread? Explain your answer.

  c   Find the population variance and standard deviation of each data set. Use technology to check your answers.

2   Skye recorded the number of pets owned by each student in her class.

$$0 \quad 2 \quad 3 \quad 1 \quad 2 \quad 4 \quad 0 \quad 0 \quad 1 \quad 5 \quad 2 \quad 3 \quad 6$$
$$2 \quad 3 \quad 1 \quad 1 \quad 0 \quad 4 \quad 1 \quad 1 \quad 0 \quad 2 \quad 1 \quad 2 \quad 0$$

  a   Use technology to find the population standard deviation of the data.

  b   Find the population variance of the data.

3   The ages of members of an Olympic water polo team are: 22, 25, 23, 28, 29, 21, 20, 26.

  a   Calculate the mean and population standard deviation for this group.

  b   The same team members are chosen to play in the next Olympic Games 4 years later. Calculate the mean and population standard deviation of their ages at the next Olympic Games.

  c   Comment on your results in general terms.

4   A hospital selected a sample of 20 patients and asked them how many glasses of water they had consumed that day. The results were:

$$5 \quad 2 \quad 1 \quad 0 \quad 4 \quad 1 \quad 0 \quad 2 \quad 7 \quad 4$$
$$8 \quad 2 \quad 7 \quad 6 \quad 1 \quad 2 \quad 3 \quad 8 \quad 0 \quad 2$$

Find the population standard deviation of the data.

5   Kylie is interested in the ages of spectators at a rugby match. She selects a sample of 30 spectators and records their ages.

$$17 \quad 24 \quad 30 \quad 10 \quad 42 \quad 48 \quad 37 \quad 19 \quad 28 \quad 53 \quad 29 \quad 40 \quad 11 \quad 21 \quad 9$$
$$43 \quad 22 \quad 59 \quad 46 \quad 52 \quad 31 \quad 13 \quad 7 \quad 26 \quad 32 \quad 47 \quad 22 \quad 15 \quad 26 \quad 42$$

Calculate the mean and population standard deviation of the data.

6   Danny and Jennifer recorded how many hours they spent on homework each day for 14 days.

    Danny: $3\frac{1}{2}$, $3\frac{1}{2}$, 4, $2\frac{1}{2}$, 3, $3\frac{1}{2}$, 3, $1\frac{1}{2}$, 3, 4, $2\frac{1}{2}$, 4, 4, 3

    Jennifer: $2\frac{1}{2}$, 1, $2\frac{1}{2}$, 2, 2, $2\frac{1}{2}$, $1\frac{1}{2}$, 2, 2, $2\frac{1}{2}$, 2, 2, 2, $1\frac{1}{2}$

a Calculate the mean number of hours each person spent on homework.

b Which person generally studies for longer?

c Calculate the population standard deviation σ for each data set.

d Which person studies more consistently?

7 Tyson wants to compare the swimming speeds of boys and girls at his school. He randomly selects 10 boys and 10 girls, and records the time, in seconds, each person takes to swim two laps of the 25 m school pool.

> *Boys*:   32.2, 26.4, 35.6, 30.8, 28.5, 40.2, 27.3, 38.9, 29.0, 31.3
>
> *Girls*:   36.2, 33.5, 28.1, 39.8, 31.6, 35.7, 37.3, 36.0, 39.7, 29.8

a Copy and complete the table:

	Boys	Girls
Mean $\overline{x}$		
Median		
Standard deviation σ		
Range		

b Which group:

i generally swims faster   **ii** has the greater spread of swimming speeds?

c How could Tyson improve the reliability of his findings?

8 Two baseball coaches compare the number of runs scored by their teams in their last ten games:

Rockets	0	10	1	9	11	0	8	5	6	7
Bullets	4	3	4	1	4	11	7	6	12	5

a Show that the two teams have the same mean and range of runs scored.

b Which team's performance do you suspect is more variable over the period? Check your answer by finding the population standard deviation for each data set.

c Does the range or the standard deviation give a better indication of variability?

9 The number of visitors to a museum and an art gallery each day during December are shown.

> *Museum*:   1108 1019 850   1243 1100 923   964   847   918   820   781
> 963   814   881   742   911   1101 952   864   943   1087 1132
> 906   1050 0   826   986   1040 1127 1084 981

> *Art gallery*: 1258 1107 1179 1302 1236 1386 1287 1313 1269 1332 1094
> 1153 1275 1168 1086 1276 1342 1153 1227 1305 1187 1249
> 1300 1156 1074 1168 1299 1257 1134 1259 1366

a For each data set, calculate the:

i mean   **ii** population standard deviation.

b Which place had the greater spread of visitor numbers?

c **i** Identify the outlier in the *Museum* data.

ii Give a reason why this outlier may have occurred.

iii Do you think it is reasonable to remove the outlier when comparing the numbers of visitors to these places? Explain your answer.

iv Recalculate the mean and population standard deviation with the outlier removed.

v Discuss the effect of the outlier on the population standard deviation.

10 Find the population standard deviation of this data set.

Value	Frequency
3	1
4	3
5	11
6	5

GRAPHICS CALCULATOR INSTRUCTIONS

11 The table shows the ages of squash players at the Junior National Squash Championship.

Age	11	12	13	14	15	16	17	18
Frequency	2	1	4	5	6	4	2	1

Find the mean and population standard deviation of the ages.

12 The column graphs show two distributions:

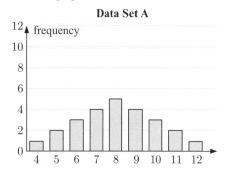

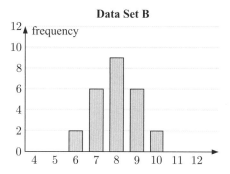

a By looking at the graphs, which distribution appears to have wider spread?

b Find the mean of each data set.

c Find the population standard deviation for each data set. Comment on your answers.

d The other measures of spread for the two data sets are given in the table. In what way does the standard deviation give a better description of how the data is distributed?

Data set	Range	IQR
A	8	3
B	4	2

13 The table alongside shows the results obtained by female and male students in a test out of 20 marks.

a Looking at the table:

  i Which group appears to have scored better in the test?

  ii Which group appears to have a greater spread of scores?

Justify your answers.

b Calculate the mean and population standard deviation for each group.

Score	Females	Males
12	0	1
13	0	0
14	0	2
15	0	3
16	2	4
17	6	2
18	5	0
19	1	1
20	1	0

14 Brianna and Jess are conducting a survey of their class.

Brianna asked every student (including Jess and herself) how many children there are in their family. Jess asked every student (including Brianna and herself) how many siblings or step-siblings they have.

How will their results compare in terms of mean and standard deviation? Explain your answer.

Example 13   ◄)) **Self Tutor**

Estimate the standard deviation for this distribution of examination scores:

Mark	Frequency	Mark	Frequency
0 - 9	1	50 - 59	16
10 - 19	1	60 - 69	24
20 - 29	2	70 - 79	13
30 - 39	4	80 - 89	6
40 - 49	11	90 - 99	2

Class interval	Mid-interval value	Frequency
0 - 9	4.5	1
10 - 19	14.5	1
20 - 29	24.5	2
30 - 39	34.5	4
40 - 49	44.5	11
50 - 59	54.5	16
60 - 69	64.5	24
70 - 79	74.5	13
80 - 89	84.5	6
90 - 99	94.5	2

For continuous data or data grouped in classes, use the mid-interval value to represent all data in that interval.

Casio fx-CG50	TI-84 Plus CE	TI-*n*spire

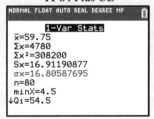
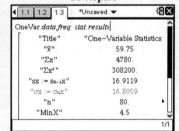

The standard deviation ≈ 16.8.

15 The lengths of 30 randomly selected 12-day old babies were measured and the following data obtained.

For the given data, estimate the:

   a mean   **b** standard deviation.

Length (L cm)	Frequency
$40 \leqslant L < 42$	1
$42 \leqslant L < 44$	1
$44 \leqslant L < 46$	3
$46 \leqslant L < 48$	7
$48 \leqslant L < 50$	11
$50 \leqslant L < 52$	5
$52 \leqslant L < 54$	2

16 A traffic survey revealed that the following numbers of vehicles passed through a suburban intersection in 5 minute intervals during the day.

Vehicles	1 - 5	6 - 10	11 - 15	16 - 20	21 - 25	26 - 30	31 - 35	36 - 40
Frequency	4	16	22	28	14	9	5	2

For the given data, estimate the:

  a mean   **b** standard deviation.

17 The weekly wages of 200 randomly selected steel workers are given alongside:

For the given data, estimate the:

  a mean   **b** standard deviation.

Wage (W)	Number of workers
$720 \leqslant W < 740$	17
$740 \leqslant W < 760$	38
$760 \leqslant W < 780$	47
$780 \leqslant W < 800$	57
$800 \leqslant W < 820$	18
$820 \leqslant W < 840$	10
$840 \leqslant W < 860$	10
$860 \leqslant W < 880$	3

18 The hours worked last week by 40 employees of a local clothing factory were as follows:

$$38 \quad 40 \quad 46 \quad 32 \quad 41 \quad 39 \quad 44 \quad 38 \quad 40 \quad 42 \quad 38 \quad 40 \quad 43 \quad 41$$
$$47 \quad 36 \quad 38 \quad 39 \quad 34 \quad 40 \quad 48 \quad 30 \quad 49 \quad 40 \quad 40 \quad 43 \quad 45 \quad 36$$
$$35 \quad 39 \quad 42 \quad 44 \quad 48 \quad 36 \quad 38 \quad 42 \quad 46 \quad 38 \quad 39 \quad 40$$

  a Calculate the mean and standard deviation for this data.

  b Now group the data into classes 30 - 33, 34 - 37, and so on. Calculate the mean and standard deviation using these groups. Examine any differences between the two sets of answers.

INVESTIGATION 3   **TRANSFORMING DATA**

In this Investigation we will explore the effects of transforming a data set on its mean and standard deviation.

We will use this data set as a basis: 4 2 3 3 5 2 9 7 3 5

                                        2 1 5 3 6 6 3 3 6 7

What to do:

1 Calculate the mean and population standard deviation for the data set.

2   **a** Suppose we add 5 to each data value. Calculate the mean and population standard deviation for the new data set.

  b What do you expect to happen to the mean and standard deviation if k is added to each value in a data set?

  c Check your answer by:

    i adding 11 to each data value   **ii** subtracting 3 from each data value.

3   **a** Suppose we multiply each value in the original data set by 4. Calculate the mean and population standard deviation for the new data set.

  b What do you expect to happen to the mean and standard deviation if each value in a data set is multiplied by a?

c Check your answer by:

    i multiplying each value by 9   **ii** dividing each value by 4.

4 Suppose a data set $\{x_i\}$ has mean μ and standard deviation σ. Write down the mean and standard deviation for the data set:

    a $\{ax_i\}$ **b** $\{x_i + k\}$ **c** $\{ax_i + k\}$

INVESTIGATION 4 — ESTIMATING THE VARIANCE AND STANDARD DEVIATION OF A POPULATION

In this Investigation we consider the accuracy of using a sample to make inferences about a whole population. This will help you to see why statisticians have a subtly different formula for the standard deviation of a sample.

The Year 12 students at a school were asked to record how many minutes they spent travelling to school. The results were collected in a survey the following morning.

There are a total of 150 Year 12 students at the school, and these are split into 6 classes.

What to do:

1 Click on the icon to obtain a spreadsheet containing all of the responses to the survey.

SPREADSHEET

    a Use the frequency table in the spreadsheet to draw a histogram for the data. Describe this distribution.

    b The summary statistics in the spreadsheet are calculated using all of the survey responses, and hence are the *true* population values. Find the true population variance.

2 10 students were randomly selected from each class to form 6 samples. Their responses to the survey are shown below:

Sample 1:	10	14	16	9	16	15	15	21	9	21
Sample 2:	11	9	11	16	16	13	10	12	21	16
Sample 3:	12	10	14	7	13	11	21	20	15	9
Sample 4:	20	19	19	19	13	19	22	15	10	19
Sample 5:	19	13	23	11	17	4	14	21	13	11
Sample 6:	19	11	16	6	8	13	10	22	20	11

    a Calculate the *sample* statistics s and s^2 for each sample.

    b Calculate the *population* statistics σ and σ^2 for each sample.

    c Which set of estimates from **a** and **b** are generally closer to the true population variance and standard deviation?

    d Does your answer to **c** explain why we have different variance and standard deviation formulae for a sample as opposed to a population?

3 To see which set of estimators (population or sample) are better at estimating the true population variance and standard deviation, we will consider a simulation based on the survey responses from the school.

Click on the icon to obtain a spreadsheet with 1000 simulations of the survey results. The values s, s^2, σ, and σ^2 are calculated for each simulated sample. The average values for each estimator are shown in the table on the sheet labelled "Summary".

SPREADSHEET

	A	B	C	D	E	F
1	**Actual values**				**Estimator**	**Average estimate**
2	μ	15		*Variance*	σ^2	23.794
3	σ	5			s^2	25.046
4	σ^2	25		*Standard*	σ	4.814
5	n	20		*deviation*	s	4.939

Based on the calculations in the spreadsheet, which set of estimates (population or sample) are generally closer to the true values? Does your conclusion agree with your answer to **2 c**?

4 Change the values for μ and σ in the spreadsheet. This will now effectively simulate the results for a different distribution, perhaps the travel times for the students at a different school. Does your choice of μ or σ affect your conclusion regarding the choice of estimators?

5 Why is it important to have accurate estimates of the variance and standard deviation of a population?

REVIEW SET 12A

1 For each of the following data sets, find the: **i** mean   **ii** median.

   a 0, 2, 3, 3, 4, 5, 5, 6, 6, 7, 7, 8   **b** 2.9, 3.1, 3.7, 3.8, 3.9, 3.9, 4.0, 4.5, 4.7, 5.4

2 Katie loves cats. She visits every house in her street to find out how many cats live there. The responses are given below:

Number of cats	0	1	2	3	4	5
Frequency	36	9	11	5	1	1

   a Draw a graph to display this data.

   b Describe the distribution.

   c Find the:

      i mode   **ii** mean   **iii** median.

   d Which of the measures of centre is most appropriate for this data? Explain your answer.

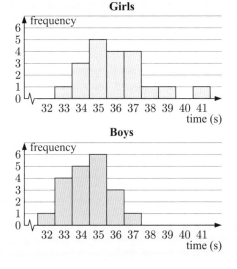

3 The histograms alongside show the times for the 50 metre freestyle recorded by members of a swimming squad.

   a Copy and complete:

Distribution	Girls	Boys
median		
mean		
modal class		

   b Discuss the distributions of times for the boys and girls. What conclusion can you make?

4 The data set 4, 6, 9, a, 3, b has a mean and mode of 6. Find the values of a and b given that $a > b$.

5 Consider the data set: $k - 2$, k, $k + 3$, $k + 3$.

    a Show that the mean of the data set is equal to $k + 1$.

    b Suppose each number in the data set is increased by 2. Find the new mean of the data set in terms of k.

6 The winning margins in 100 basketball games were recorded. The results are summarised alongside.

    a Explain why you cannot calculate the mean winning margin from the table exactly.

    b Estimate the mean winning margin.

Margin (points)	Frequency
1 - 10	13
11 - 20	35
21 - 30	27
31 - 40	18
41 - 50	7

7 The table alongside compares the mass of guinea pigs at birth with their mass when they are two weeks old.

    a Find the mean birth mass.

    b Find the mean mass after two weeks.

    c Find the mean increase over the two weeks.

Guinea Pig	Mass (g) at birth	Mass (g) at 2 weeks
A	75	210
B	70	200
C	80	200
D	70	220
E	74	215
F	60	200
G	55	206
H	83	230

8 Consider this data set:

    19, 7, 22, 15, 14, 10, 8, 28, 14, 18, 31, 13, 18, 19, 11, 3, 15, 16, 19, 14

    a Find the five-number summary for the data.   **b** Find the range and IQR.

    c Draw a box plot of the data set.

9 Katja's golf scores for her last 20 rounds were:

        90   106   84   103   112   100   105   81   104   98

       107   95   104   108   99   101   106   102   98   101

For this data set, find the:

    a median   **b** interquartile range   **c** mean   **d** standard deviation.

10 The parallel box plot alongside shows the 100 metre sprint times for the members of two athletics squads.

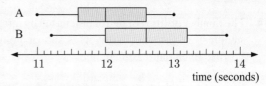

    a Determine the five-number summaries for both A and B.

    b For each group, calculate the range and interquartile range.

    c Copy and complete:

       i The members of squad ...... generally ran faster because ......

      ii The times in squad ...... are more varied because ......

11 80 senior students ran 400 metres in a Physical Education program. Their times were recorded and the results were used to produce the cumulative frequency graph shown.

Estimate:

   a the median

   b the interquartile range

   c the time corresponding to the top 10% of runners.

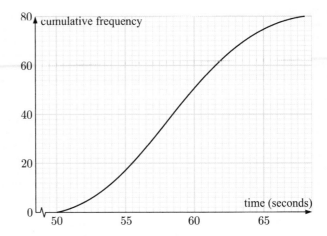

12 This cumulative frequency curve shows the times taken for 200 students to travel to school by bus.

   a Estimate how many of the students spent between 10 and 20 minutes travelling to school.

   b 30% of the students spent more than m minutes travelling to school. Estimate the value of m.

   c Use the cumulative frequency curve to complete the following table:

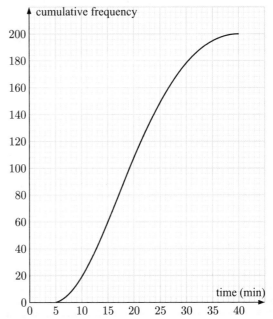

Time (t min)	Frequency
$5 \leqslant t < 10$	
$10 \leqslant t < 15$	
$\vdots$	
$35 \leqslant t < 40$	

13 Find the population variance and standard deviation for each data set:

   a 117, 129, 105, 124, 123, 128, 131, 124, 123, 125, 108

   b 6.1, 5.6, 7.2, 8.3, 6.6, 8.4, 7.7, 6.2

14 The number of litres of petrol purchased by a random sample of motor vehicle drivers is shown alongside. For the given data, estimate the:

   a mean   **b** standard deviation.

Litres (L)	Number of vehicles
$15 \leqslant L < 20$	5
$20 \leqslant L < 25$	13
$25 \leqslant L < 30$	17
$30 \leqslant L < 35$	29
$35 \leqslant L < 40$	27
$40 \leqslant L < 45$	18
$45 \leqslant L < 50$	7

15 Pratik is a quality control officer for a biscuit company. He needs to check that 250 g of biscuits go into each packet, but realises that the weight in each packet will vary slightly.

   a Would you expect the standard deviation for the whole population to be the same for one day as it is for one week? Explain your answer.

   b If a sample of 100 packets is measured each day, what measure would be used to check:

     i that an average of 250 g of biscuits goes into each packet

     ii the variability of the mass going into each packet?

   c Explain the significance of a low standard deviation in this case.

REVIEW SET 12B

1 Heike is preparing for an athletics carnival. She records her times in seconds for the 100 m sprint each day for 4 weeks.

$$
\begin{array}{llllllll}
\textit{Week 1}: & 16.4 & 15.2 & 16.3 & 16.3 & 17.1 & 15.5 & 14.9 \\
\textit{Week 2}: & 14.9 & 15.7 & 15.1 & 15.1 & 14.7 & 14.7 & 15.3 \\
\textit{Week 3}: & 14.3 & 14.2 & 14.6 & 14.6 & 14.3 & 14.3 & 14.4 \\
\textit{Week 4}: & 14.0 & 14.0 & 13.9 & 14.0 & 14.1 & 13.8 & 14.2 \\
\end{array}
$$

   a Calculate Heike's mean and median time for each week.

   b Do you think Heike's times have improved over the 4 week period? Explain your answer.

2 A die was rolled 50 times.
The results are shown in the table alongside.
Find the:

   a mode   **b** mean   **c** median.

Number	Frequency
1	10
2	7
3	8
4	5
5	12
6	8

3 The data in the table alongside has mean 5.7.

   a Find the value of x.

   b Find the median of the distribution.

Value	2	5	x	$x+6$
Frequency	3	2	4	1

4 A set of 14 data is: 6, 8, 7, 7, 5, 7, 6, 8, 6, 9, 6, 7, p, q.
The mean and mode of the set are both 7. Find p and q.

5 The table alongside shows the number of patrons visiting an art gallery on various days.
Estimate the mean number of patrons per day.

Number of patrons	Frequency
250 - 299	14
300 - 349	34
350 - 399	68
400 - 449	72
450 - 499	54
500 - 549	23
550 - 599	7

6 Draw a box and whisker diagram for the following data:

      11, 12, 12, 13, 14, 14, 15, 15, 15, 16, 17, 17, 18.

7 Consider the data set: 120, 118, 132, 127, 135, 116, 122, 93, 128.

    a Find the standard deviation for the data.

    b Find the upper and lower quartiles of the data set.

    c Are there any outliers in the data set?

    d Draw a box plot to display the data.

8 The number of peanuts in a jar varies slightly from jar to jar. Samples of 30 jars were taken for each of two brands X and Y, and the number of peanuts in each jar was recorded.

		Brand X							*Brand Y*			
871	885	878	882	889	885		909	906	913	891	898	901
916	913	886	905	907	898		894	894	928	893	924	892
874	904	901	894	897	899		927	907	901	900	907	913
908	901	898	894	895	895		921	904	903	896	901	895
910	904	896	893	903	888		917	903	910	903	909	904

    a Copy and complete this table:

	Brand X	Brand Y
min		
Q_1		
median		
Q_3		
max		
IQR		

    b Display the data on a parallel box plot.

    c Comment on which brand:

        i has more peanuts per jar   **ii** has a more consistent number of peanuts per jar.

9 120 people caught whooping cough in an outbreak. The times for them to recover were recorded, and the results were used to produce the cumulative frequency graph shown.

Estimate:

    a the median

    b the interquartile range.

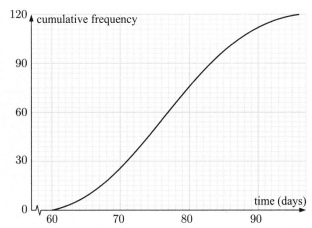

10 Consider the data in the table below:

Scores (x)	$0 \leqslant x < 10$	$10 \leqslant x < 20$	$20 \leqslant x < 30$	$30 \leqslant x < 40$	$40 \leqslant x < 50$
Frequency	1	13	27	17	2

    a Construct a cumulative frequency graph for the data.

    b Estimate the:

        i median   **ii** interquartile range   **iii** mean   **iv** standard deviation.

11 Consider the frequency table alongside:

a Find the values of p and m.

b Hence find the mode, median, and range of the data.

c Given that $\sum\limits_{i=1}^{5} x_i f_i = 254$, write the mean $\overline{x}$ as a fraction.

Score	Frequency	Cumulative frequency
6	2	2
7	4	m
8	7	13
9	p	25
10	5	30

12 To test the difficulty level of a new computer game, a company measures the time taken for a group of players to complete the game. Their results are displayed in the table alongside.

a How many players were surveyed?

b Write down the modal class.

c Draw a cumulative frequency graph for the data.

d The game is considered too easy if either the mean or median completion time is below 90 minutes.

  i Estimate the median completion time using your cumulative frequency graph.

  ii Estimate the mean completion time.

  iii Hence comment on whether the game is too easy.

e Complete this sentence:

The middle 50% of players completed the game in times between ...... and ...... minutes.

Completion time (t min)	Number of players
$0 \leqslant t < 30$	1
$30 \leqslant t < 60$	4
$60 \leqslant t < 90$	12
$90 \leqslant t < 120$	18
$120 \leqslant t < 150$	7
$150 \leqslant t < 180$	2

13 The table below shows the number of matches in a sample of boxes.

Number	47	48	49	50	51	52
Frequency	21	29	35	42	18	31

a Find the mean and standard deviation for this data.

b Does this result justify a claim that the average number of matches per box is 50?

14 A random sample of weekly supermarket bills was recorded in the table alongside.

For the given data, estimate the:

a mean   **b** standard deviation.

Bill (€b)	Number of families
$140 \leqslant b < 160$	27
$160 \leqslant b < 180$	32
$180 \leqslant b < 200$	48
$200 \leqslant b < 220$	25
$220 \leqslant b < 240$	37
$240 \leqslant b < 260$	21
$260 \leqslant b < 280$	18
$280 \leqslant b < 300$	7

15 Friends Kevin and Felicity each selected a sample of 20 crossword puzzles. The times they took, in minutes, to complete each puzzle were:

Kevin					Felicity				
37	53	47	33	39	33	36	41	26	52
49	37	48	32	36	38	49	57	39	44
39	42	34	29	52	48	25	34	27	53
48	33	56	39	41	38	34	35	50	31

a Find the mean of each data set.

b Find the population standard deviation for each data set.

c Who generally solves crossword puzzles faster?

d Who is more consistent in their time taken to solve the puzzles?

ANSWERS

EXERCISE 1A

1   **a** $m = 3$, $c = 7$ **b** $m = -2$, $c = -5$
  c $m = \frac{2}{3}$, $c = -\frac{1}{3}$ **d** $m = -4$, $c = 11$
  e $m = -1$, $c = -6$ **f** $m = -\frac{6}{5}$, $c = \frac{9}{5}$
  g $m = -\frac{7}{9}$, $c = \frac{2}{9}$ **h** $m = \frac{1}{3}$, $c = -\frac{1}{2}$
  i $m = -\frac{5}{8}$, $c = \frac{3}{8}$

2   **a** $y = 3x - 11$ **b** $y = -2x - 1$ **c** $y = \frac{1}{4}x - 4$
  d $y = -\frac{2}{3}x - \frac{25}{3}$ **e** $y = 2x - 9$ **f** $y = -\frac{3}{4}x + 4$

3   **a**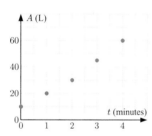
  b Yes, the variables are linearly related as the points all lie on a straight line.
  c gradient is 3, y-intercept is 5
  d $y = 3x + 5$
  e $y = 35$

4 $\approx 7.88\%$

5   **a** *Pond P*: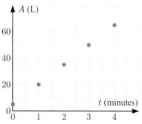

  Pond Q:

  b Pond Q; the points on the graph of pond Q all lie on a straight line.
  c   **i** The gradient is 15 which means that the amount of water increases by 15 L each minute.
    The A-intercept is 5 which means that the amount of water in the pond initially was 5 L.
    ii $A = 15t + 5$ **iii** 125 L

6   **a** The gradient is -10 which means that the balance in the account decreases by \$10 each year.
    The y-intercept is 90 which means that the initial balance was \$90.
  b $y = -10x + 90$ **c** 9 years

7   **a** $-\frac{23}{910}$ **b** $y = -\frac{23}{910}x + 46$

8   **a** 150 metres
  b The height of the helicopter above sea level increases by 120 metres each minute after taking off.
  c 390 metres   **d** 4 minutes 10 seconds

9   **a** $4x + y = 6$ **b** $5x - y = 3$ **c** $3x + 4y = 5$
  d $2x + 9y = 8$ **e** $3x - 5y = 1$ **f** $5x - 6y = -18$

10   **a** $y = -5x + 2$ **b** $y = -\frac{3}{7}x + \frac{2}{7}$ **c** $y = -\frac{4}{3}x - \frac{1}{3}$
  d $y = 2x - 6$ **e** $y = \frac{3}{13}x + \frac{4}{13}$ **f** $y = \frac{10}{3}x - \frac{7}{3}$

11 $ax + by = d$ can be written as $y = -\frac{a}{b}x + \frac{d}{b}$ which has the form $y = mx + c$. $\therefore$ $m = -\frac{a}{b}$

12   **A** and **D**, **B** and **C**

13   **C** and **D** are both perpendicular to **A**.

14   **a** $4x + y = 6$ **b** $x - 2y = 13$ **c** $5x + 3y = 8$
  d $7x - 6y = 17$

15   **a** $y = 2x + 5$ **b** $y = -x + 9$ **c** $y = -5x - 12$
  d $y = \frac{2}{3}x - 8$ **e** $y = \frac{7}{5}x - \frac{11}{5}$ **f** $y = -\frac{5}{6}x + \frac{19}{6}$

16   **a** $2x - y = -2$ **b** $3x + 10y = 8$ **c** $8x + 5y = -13$

17   **a** $y = \frac{3}{4}x - \frac{5}{4}$ **b** $-\frac{5}{4}$

18   **a** $y = 3x + 1$ **b** $2x - y = 7$ **c** $y = \frac{1}{2}x + \frac{11}{2}$
  d $2x - y = -3$

19   **a** yes   **b** no   **c** yes   **d** yes

20   **a** $c = 7$ **b** $m = 11$ **c** $t = 8$

21   **a** $k = -3$ **b** $k = -51$ **c** $k = -12$

22   **a** $x - y + 2 = 0$ **b** -2

EXERCISE 1B

1   **a** 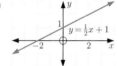   **b**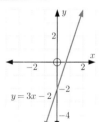

  c 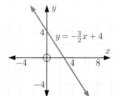   **d**

  e   **f**

  g 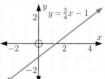   **h**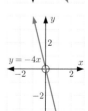

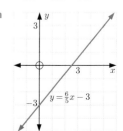

i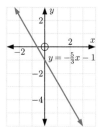

2 a 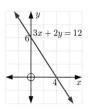 **b**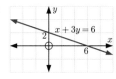

c 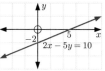 **d**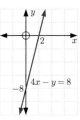

e 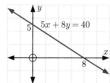 **f**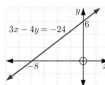

g 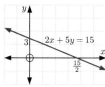 **h**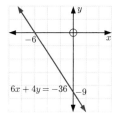

i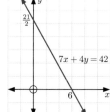

3 a $m = -\frac{3}{4}$, $c = 2$ **b** **i** yes   **ii** no   **iii** yes

c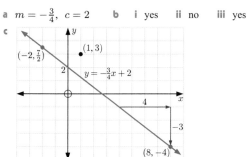

4 a x-intercept 9, y-intercept -6
b **i** yes   **ii** no   **c** $c = -8$
d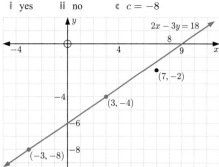

5 a \$30   **b**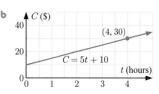

6 a x serves of nigiri at \$4.50 each and y serves of sashimi at \$9 each adds up to a total of \$45.
∴ $4.5x + 9y = 45$
b 3 serves of sashimi   **d**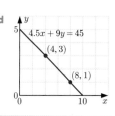
c 8 serves of nigiri

EXERCISE 1C

1 a $(4, 4)$ **b** 3   **c** $-\frac{1}{3}$ **d** $x + 3y = 16$

2 a $2x - y = 3$ **b** $3x - y = 2$ **c** $x - y = 5$
d $2x - y = 2$ **e** $x = \frac{9}{2}$ **f** $8x + 6y = 35$

3 a $2x - 3y = 2$ **b** $2(1) - 3(0) = 2$ ✓
c PR $=$ QR $= \sqrt{26}$ units

4 a AB $=$ BC $=$ CD $=$ AD $= \sqrt{29}$ units
∴ ABCD is a rhombus.
b $y = -x$ **c** B: $2 = -(-2)$ ✓ D: $-1 = -(1)$ ✓

5 a **i** $\frac{3}{2}$ **ii** $-\frac{2}{3}$ **b** $2x + 3y - 21 = 0$

6 a **Hint:** Start by finding the gradient and midpoint of [AB].
b We can find the perpendicular bisector of any two points A(x_1, y_1) and B(x_2, y_2) by substituting in the values of x_1, x_2, y_1, and y_2.

7 a **i** $x + y = 6$ **ii** $x - 3y = 0$ **iii** $x + 3y = 9$
b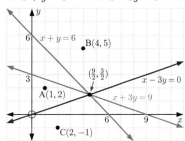

The perpendicular bisectors all intersect at $\left(\frac{9}{2}, \frac{3}{2}\right)$.
A, B, and C are all equidistant from this point.

c The perpendicular bisectors of each pair of points will meet at a single point. As the three points are equidistant from the point of intersection, a circle centred at the point of intersection that passes through one of them will pass through all of them.

8 a i $9x + 11y = -37$ ll $3x + y = -10$
   iii $3x - 7y = -3$

b
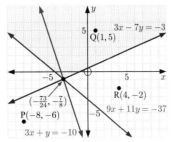

EXERCISE 1D.1

1 a $x = -2$, $y = -4$ b $x = 1$, $y = -3$
  c $x = 6$, $y = 7$
2 a $x = 3$, $y = 2$ b $x = 6$, $y = 1$
  c $x = 2$, $y = -12$
3 a The lines are parallel, so there are no solutions.
  b The lines are coincident. There are infinitely many solutions.
  c The lines are parallel, so there are no solutions.

EXERCISE 1D.2

1 a $x = 3$, $y = 5$ b $x = 1$, $y = -1$
  c $x = -1$, $y = 8$ d $x = \frac{1}{2}$, $y = 2\frac{1}{2}$
  e $x = \frac{2}{3}$, $y = -4$ f $x = 3\frac{3}{25}$, $y = 1\frac{16}{25}$
2 a $x = 5$, $y = 8$ b $x = -7$, $y = -2$
  c $x = -5$, $y = -2$ d $x = \frac{1}{3}$, $y = -1\frac{1}{3}$
  e $x = -4$, $y = -\frac{1}{4}$ f $x = -1\frac{11}{31}$, $y = -\frac{4}{31}$
3 a $x = -3$, $y = 3\frac{1}{2}$ b $x = -2\frac{1}{4}$, $y = 3$
  c $x = 8$, $y = -2\frac{1}{3}$ d $x = \frac{2}{3}$, $y = 2\frac{2}{3}$
  e $x = \frac{1}{4}$, $y = \frac{3}{4}$ f $x = \frac{1}{3}$, $y = 2\frac{1}{4}$

EXERCISE 1D.3

1 a $x = 2$, $y = 1$ b $x = 3$, $y = -1$
  c $x = -4$, $y = 5$ d $x = 4$, $y = -3$
  e $x = 6$, $y = -2$ f $x = 1\frac{1}{2}$, $y = -2\frac{1}{2}$
2 a $x = 3$, $y = 7$ b $x = -5$, $y = 2$
  c $x = -1$, $y = -6$ d $x = \frac{1}{3}$, $y = 4$
  e $x = -3$, $y = 1\frac{1}{2}$ f $x = \frac{1}{4}$, $y = 1\frac{1}{4}$
3 a $x = 5$, $y = -2$ b $x = -3$, $y = -4$
  c $x = 7$, $y = -3$ d $x = 1\frac{1}{4}$, $y = -\frac{3}{4}$
  e $x = -4\frac{1}{2}$, $y = -2\frac{1}{2}$ f $x = -28\frac{2}{3}$, $y = -17\frac{2}{3}$

EXERCISE 1E

1 plate: £7, bowl: £9
2 waltz: 3 minutes, sonatina: 7 minutes
3 short cable: 2.5 m, long cable: 4.2 m
4 a 10 points   b 6 points
   ˙9 cans of paint   6 $125

7 a $\approx$ 496 m
  b after $\approx$ 25 min 26 s, or after $\approx$ 9615 m
8 a $12\frac{1}{4}$ units^2 b $1\frac{4}{25}$ units^2

REVIEW SET 1A

1 a
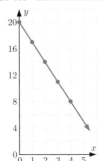

  b Yes, the variables are linearly related as the points all lie on a straight line.
  c gradient is -3, y-intercept is 20
  d $y = -3x + 20$
  e $y = -1$

2 a The gradient is $\frac{3}{40} = 0.075$, which means that the weekly income of a salesperson increases by £0.075 for each pound increase in sales that week.
  The I-intercept is 50, which means that the weekly income of a salesperson is £50 before any sales are made.
  b $I = 0.075S + 50$ c £305

3 a $y = -\frac{1}{3}x + 4$ b $x + 3y - 12 = 0$
4 a $3x - 2y = 12$ b 4   5 a yes   b yes
6 a
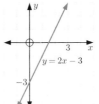
  b
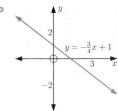
  c
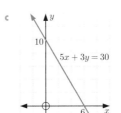
  d
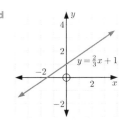
  e
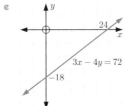
  f
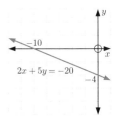

7 a $y = -1$ b $3x - 2y = 9$
8 a $x = 3$, $y = 4$ b $x = -3$, $y = 3$
9 a $x = 1$, $y = 7$ b $x = -1$, $y = 2$
10 a $x = 3$, $y = -1$ b $x = -4$, $y = 3$
11 a $m = -\frac{1}{2}$, $c = 4$ b yes   c $k = -2$

d

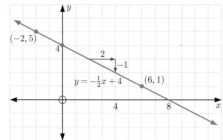

12 **a** €60   **b** €35   13 3 batteries

14 **a** **i** $7x + 5y = -6$ **ii** $5x - 7y = 1$

b ABCD is a square.

REVIEW SET 1B

1 **a** The gradient is 10 which means that the speed increases by 10 m s^{-1} each second.
The y-intercept is 5 which means that the initial speed was 5 m s^{-1}.

b $y = 10x + 5$ **c** 85 m s^{-1}

2 **a** $5x - y = 11$ **b** $x + 4y = -19$

3 **a** $y = 3x + 1$ **b** $5x - 2y = -3$

4 **a** $k = 7$ **b** $k = -11$

5 **a** 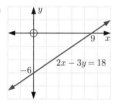   **b**

c 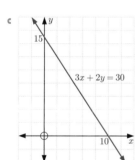   **d**

e 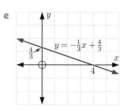   **f**

6 $y = x - 3$

7 **a** **i** $\frac{1}{5}$ **ii** -5 **b** $5x + y = 22$

8 **a** $x = -2$, $y = -5$ **b** $x = 4$, $y = -2$

9 **a** $x = \frac{1}{3}$, $y = 4$ **b** $x = -2$, $y = 4$

10 **a** $x = 3$, $y = -\frac{1}{2}$ **b** $x = 1\frac{1}{2}$, $y = -3\frac{1}{2}$

11 **a** $m = \frac{2}{3}$ **b** **i** yes   **ii** no

c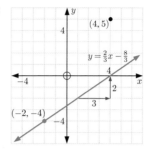

12 15 books   13 6 two hour lessons

14 **a** **i** $2x + y = 7$ **ii** $x + 3y = 11$ **iii** $x - 2y = -4$

b

All three perpendicular bisectors intersect at $(2, 3)$.
A, B, and C are all equidistant from this point.

EXERCISE 2A

1 **a** $5 \in D$ **b** $6 \notin G$ **c** $d \notin \{$all English vowels$\}$
   d $\{2, 5\} \subseteq \{1, 2, 3, 4, 5, 6\}$
   e $\{3, 8, 6\} \nsubseteq \{1, 2, 3, 4, 5, 6\}$

2 **a** finite   **b** infinite   **c** infinite

3 **a** $A = \{1, 2, 4, 8\}$, $n(A) = 4$
   b $A = \{4, 6, 8, 9, 10, 12, 14, 15, 16, 18\}$, $n(A) = 10$
   c $A = \{A, R, D, V, K\}$, $n(A) = 5$
   d $A = \{$January, February, March, April, May, June, July, August, September, October, November, December$\}$
   $n(A) = 12$
   e $A = \{41, 43, 47\}$, $n(A) = 3$

4 **a** **i** 6   **ii** 3
   b **i** true   **ii** false   **iii** true   **iv** true   **v** true

5 **a** subsets of S: $\varnothing$, $\{1\}$, $\{2\}$, $\{1, 2\}$
   subsets of T: $\varnothing$, $\{1\}$, $\{2\}$, $\{3\}$, $\{1, 2\}$, $\{1, 3\}$, $\{2, 3\}$, $\{1, 2, 3\}$
   b yes   **c** $\frac{1}{2}$

6 Each of the four elements can be *included* or *not included* in a subset.
   $\therefore$ the set has $2 \times 2 \times 2 \times 2 = 16$ subsets.

7 **a** $A = \{31, 37\}$, $B = \{32, 34, 36, 38\}$,
   $C = \{32, 33, 34, 35, 36, 38, 39\}$, $D = \varnothing$
   b **i** 2   **ii** 0   **c** **i** A, D **ii** B, D
   d **i** true   **ii** false   **iii** false

8 $x = 3$

EXERCISE 2B

1 **a** **i** $A \cap B = \{9\}$
   ii $A \cup B = \{5, 6, 7, 8, 9, 10, 11, 12, 13\}$
   b **i** $A \cap B = \varnothing$ **ii** $A \cup B = \{1, 2, 3, 4, 5, 6, 7, 8\}$
   c **i** $A \cap B = \{1, 3, 5, 7\}$
   ii $A \cup B = \{1, 2, 3, 4, 5, 6, 7, 8, 9\}$

d **i** $A \cap B = \{5, 8\}$

   ii $A \cup B = \{0, 1, 3, 4, 5, 8, 11, 13, 14\}$

2 **a** disjoint   **b** not disjoint

3 **a** A and B, there is no number between 20 and 30 that is both even and odd.

   b $A \cap C = \{22, 24, 26, 28\}$, $A \subset C$ **c** 9

4 **a** True, $R \cap S = \varnothing$ tells us that R and S have no elements in common, and hence are disjoint.

   b True, every element of $A \cap B$ is an element of A, and every element of $A \cap B$ is an element of B.

   c True, if $A \cap B = A \cup B$ then there are no elements that are in only A or only B. $\therefore$ $A = B$.

EXERCISE 2C

1 **a** $A' = \{1, 4, 5, 9\}$

   b No, since 1 is neither prime nor composite.

2 **a** $M' = \{$February, March, April, May, August, September, October, November, December$\}$

   b $A' = \{$June, July, September, October, November, December$\}$

3 **a** $A = \{10, 12, 15, 20\}$ **b** $B = \{12, 15, 18\}$

   c $A' = \{11, 13, 14, 16, 17, 18, 19\}$

   d $B' = \{10, 11, 13, 14, 16, 17, 19, 20\}$

   e $A \cap B = \{12, 15\}$ **f** $A \cup B = \{10, 12, 15, 18, 20\}$

   g $A' \cap B = \{18\}$

   h $A' \cup B = \{11, 12, 13, 14, 15, 16, 17, 18, 19\}$

   i $A \cap B' = \{10, 20\}$

   j $A \cup B' = \{10, 11, 12, 13, 14, 15, 16, 17, 19, 20\}$

   k $A' \cap B' = \{11, 13, 14, 16, 17, 19\}$

   l $A' \cup B' = \{10, 11, 13, 14, 16, 17, 18, 19, 20\}$

4 **a** **i** 7   **ii** 3   **iii** 4   **iv** 4   **v** 3

   b For any set S within a universal set U,
   $n(S) + n(S') = n(U)$.

5 **a** 9   **b** 11

EXERCISE 2D

1

Number	$\mathbb{N}$	$\mathbb{Z}$	$\mathbb{Q}$	$\mathbb{R}$
6	✓	✓	✓	✓
$-\frac{3}{8}$	✗	✗	✓	✓
1.8	✗	✗	✓	✓
$1.\overline{8}$	✗	✗	✓	✓
-17	✗	✓	✓	✓
$\sqrt{64}$	✓	✓	✓	✓
$\frac{\pi}{2}$	✗	✗	✗	✓
$\sqrt{-3}$	✗	✗	✗	✗
$-\sqrt{3}$	✗	✗	✗	✓

2 **a** false   **b** true   **c** true   **d** false

   e true   **f** false   **g** true   **h** true

3 **a** true   **b** true   **c** false   **d** true

   e false   **f** true   **g** true   **h** false

4 **a** finite   **b** infinite   **c** infinite

5 $\mathbb{Z}^- \cup \{0\}$

EXERCISE 2E

1 **a** **i** The set of all x such that x is an integer between -1 and 7, including -1 and 7.

   ii $A = \{-1, 0, 1, 2, 3, 4, 5, 6, 7\}$ **iii** 9

b **i** The set of all x such that x is a natural number between -2 and 8.

   ii $A = \{0, 1, 2, 3, 4, 5, 6, 7\}$ **iii** 8

c **i** The set of all real x such that x is greater than or equal to 0, and less than or equal to 1.

   ii not possible

   iii A is an infinite set, $n(A)$ is undefined.

d **i** The set of all x such that x is a rational number greater than or equal to 5, and less than or equal to 6.

   ii not possible

   iii A is an infinite set, $n(A)$ is undefined.

2 **a**

c

e (3) **f** (6)

g (2, 6) **h** (3.6, 10.2)

i (3, 6) **j** (2, 4)

k (3, 7, 12) **l** (0, 5, 10)

3 **a** $\{x \in \mathbb{Z} \mid -100 < x < 100\}$ **b** $\{x \in \mathbb{R} \mid x > 1000\}$

   c $\{x \in \mathbb{Q} \mid 2 \leqslant x \leqslant 3\}$

4 **a** $\{x \mid x \geqslant 8\}$ **b** $\{x \mid -1 \leqslant x < 4\}$

   c $\{x \in \mathbb{Z} \mid -3 < x < 4\}$

   d $\{x \mid x < -5\} \cup \{x \mid x > 1\}$ **e** $\{x \mid x < \frac{3}{2}\}$

   f $\{x \in \mathbb{N} \mid x \leqslant 4\} \cup \{x \in \mathbb{N} \mid x = 6\}$

   g $\{x \mid x \leqslant -2\} \cup \{x \mid x \geqslant 3\}$

   h $\{x \mid x < -2\} \cup \{x \mid 0 < x < 2\}$

   i $\{x \mid 1 \leqslant x \leqslant 4\} \cup \{x \mid x \geqslant 6\}$

5 **a** $A \subseteq B$ **b** $A \nsubseteq B$ **c** $A \subseteq B$ **d** $A \subseteq B$

   e $A \nsubseteq B$ **f** $A \nsubseteq B$

6 **a** $C' = \{x \in \mathbb{Z} \mid x \geqslant -4\}$ **b** $C' = \{x \in \mathbb{Q} \mid 2 < x < 8\}$

7 **a** $A = \{2, 3, 4, 5, 6, 7\}$ **b** $A' = \{0, 1, 8\}$

   c $B = \{5, 6, 7, 8\}$ **d** $B' = \{0, 1, 2, 3, 4\}$

   e $A \cap B = \{5, 6, 7\}$ **f** $A \cup B = \{2, 3, 4, 5, 6, 7, 8\}$

   g $A \cap B' = \{2, 3, 4\}$

8 **a** $P = \{9, 10, 11, 12, 13, 14, 15\}$

   b $P \cap Q = \{11, 12, 15\}$

   c $P \cup Q = \{2, 4, 5, 9, 10, 11, 12, 13, 14, 15\}$

   d $n(P) + n(Q) - n(P \cap Q) = 7 + 6 - 3 = 10$
   $= n(P \cup Q)$

9 **a** $P = \{1, 2, 4, 7, 14, 28\}$, $Q = \{1, 2, 4, 5, 8, 10, 20, 40\}$

   b $P \cap Q = \{1, 2, 4\}$

   c $P \cup Q = \{1, 2, 4, 5, 7, 8, 10, 14, 20, 28, 40\}$

   d $n(P) + n(Q) - n(P \cap Q) = 6 + 8 - 3 = 11$
   $= n(P \cup Q)$

10 a $M = \{32, 36, 40, 44, 48, 52, 56\}$, $N = \{36, 42, 48, 54\}$
   b $M \cap N = \{36, 48\}$
   c $M \cup N = \{32, 36, 40, 42, 44, 48, 52, 54, 56\}$
   d $n(M) + n(N) - n(M \cap N) = 7 + 4 - 2 = 9$
$$= n(M \cup N)$$

11 a $R = \{-2, -1, 0, 1, 2, 3, 4\}$, $S = \{0, 1, 2, 3, 4, 5, 6\}$
   b $R \cap S = \{0, 1, 2, 3, 4\}$
   c $R \cup S = \{-2, -1, 0, 1, 2, 3, 4, 5, 6\}$
   d $n(R) + n(S) - n(R \cap S) = 7 + 7 - 5 = 9$
$$= n(R \cup S)$$

12 a $C = \{-4, -3, -2, -1\}$,
   $D = \{-7, -6, -5, -4, -3, -2, -1\}$
   b $C \cap D = \{-4, -3, -2, -1\}$
   c $C \cup D = \{-7, -6, -5, -4, -3, -2, -1\}$
   d $n(C) + n(D) - n(C \cap D) = 4 + 7 - 4 = 7$
$$= n(C \cup D)$$

13 a $P = \{5, 6, 7, 8, 9, 10, 11, 12, 13, 14, 15, 16, 17\}$,
   $Q = \{10, 11, 12, 13, 14, 15, 16, 17, 18, 19, 20\}$,
   $R = \{15, 16, 17, 18, 19, 20, 21, 22, 23\}$
   b   **i** $P \cap Q = \{10, 11, 12, 13, 14, 15, 16, 17\}$
     ii $P \cap R = \{15, 16, 17\}$
     iii $Q \cap R = \{15, 16, 17, 18, 19, 20\}$
     iv $P \cup Q = \{5, 6, 7, 8, 9, 10, 11, 12, 13, 14, 15, 16, 17,$
         $18, 19, 20\}$
     v $P \cup R = \{5, 6, 7, 8, 9, 10, 11, 12, 13, 14, 15, 16, 17,$
         $18, 19, 20, 21, 22, 23\}$
     vi $Q \cup R = \{10, 11, 12, 13, 14, 15, 16, 17, 18, 19, 20,$
         $21, 22, 23\}$
   c   **i** $P \cap Q \cap R = \{15, 16, 17\}$
     ii $P \cup Q \cup R = \{5, 6, 7, 8, 9, 10, 11, 12, 13, 14, 15,$
         $16, 17, 18, 19, 20, 21, 22, 23\}$

14 a $A = \{4, 8, 12, 16, 20, 24, 28, 32, 36\}$,
   $B = \{6, 12, 18, 24, 30, 36\}$, $C = \{12, 24, 36\}$
   b   **i** $A \cap B = \{12, 24, 36\}$
     ii $B \cap C = \{12, 24, 36\}$
     iii $A \cap C = \{12, 24, 36\}$
     iv $A \cap B \cap C = \{12, 24, 36\}$
     v $A \cup B \cup C = \{4, 6, 8, 12, 16, 18, 20, 24, 28, 30,$
         $32, 36\}$
   c $n(A) + n(B) + n(C) - n(A \cap B) - n(B \cap C)$
     $\quad - n(A \cap C) + n(A \cap B \cap C)$
   $= 9 + 6 + 3 - 3 - 3 - 3 + 3$
   $= 12$
   $= n(A \cup B \cup C)$

15 a $A = \{6, 12, 18, 24, 30\}$, $B = \{1, 2, 3, 5, 6, 10, 15, 30\}$,
   $C = \{2, 3, 5, 7, 11, 13, 17, 19, 23, 29\}$
   b   **i** $A \cap B = \{6, 30\}$ **ii** $B \cap C = \{2, 3, 5\}$
     iii $A \cap C = \varnothing$ **iv** $A \cap B \cap C = \varnothing$
     v $A \cup B \cup C = \{1, 2, 3, 5, 6, 7, 10, 11, 12, 13, 15, 17,$
         $18, 19, 23, 24, 29, 30\}$
   c $n(A) + n(B) + n(C) - n(A \cap B) - n(B \cap C)$
     $\quad - n(A \cap C) + n(A \cap B \cap C)$
   $= 5 + 8 + 10 - 2 - 3 - 0 + 0$
   $= 18$
   $= n(A \cup B \cup C)$

EXERCISE 2F

1 a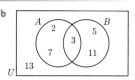

   c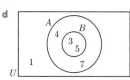

2 a $A = \{1, 3, 5, 7, 9\}$, $B = \{2, 3, 5, 7\}$
   b $A \cap B = \{3, 5, 7\}$, $A \cup B = \{1, 2, 3, 5, 7, 9\}$
   c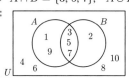

3 a $A = \{1, 2, 3, 6\}$, $B = \{1, 3, 9\}$
   b $A \cap B = \{1, 3\}$, $A \cup B = \{1, 2, 3, 6, 9\}$
   c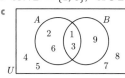

4 a $P = \{4, 8, 12, 16, 20, 24, 28\}$, $Q = \{6, 12, 18, 24\}$
   b $P \cap Q = \{12, 24\}$
   $P \cup Q = \{4, 6, 8, 12, 16, 18, 20, 24, 28\}$
   c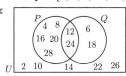

5 a $R = \{2, 3, 5, 7, 11, 13, 17, 19, 23, 29\}$,
   $S = \{4, 6, 8, 9, 10, 12, 14, 15, 16, 18, 20, 21, 22, 24, 25,$
   $26, 27, 28\}$
   b $R \cap S = \varnothing$
   $R \cup S = \{2, 3, 4, 5, 6, 7, 8, 9, 10, 11, 12, 13, 14, 15,$
   $16, 17, 18, 19, 20, 21, 22, 23, 24, 25, 26,$
   $27, 28, 29\}$
   c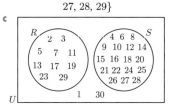

6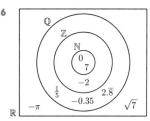

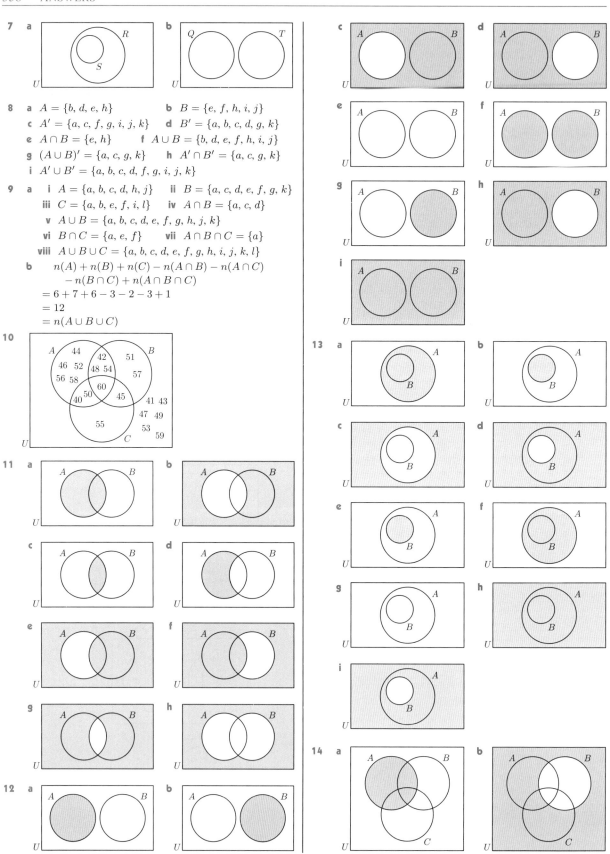

7 a ... **b** ...

8 a $A = \{b, d, e, h\}$ **b** $B = \{e, f, h, i, j\}$
c $A' = \{a, c, f, g, i, j, k\}$ **d** $B' = \{a, b, c, d, g, k\}$
e $A \cap B = \{e, h\}$ **f** $A \cup B = \{b, d, e, f, h, i, j\}$
g $(A \cup B)' = \{a, c, g, k\}$ **h** $A' \cap B' = \{a, c, g, k\}$
i $A' \cup B' = \{a, b, c, d, f, g, i, j, k\}$

9 a i $A = \{a, b, c, d, h, j\}$ **ii** $B = \{a, c, d, e, f, g, k\}$
iii $C = \{a, b, e, f, i, l\}$ **iv** $A \cap B = \{a, c, d\}$
v $A \cup B = \{a, b, c, d, e, f, g, h, j, k\}$
vi $B \cap C = \{a, e, f\}$ **vii** $A \cap B \cap C = \{a\}$
viii $A \cup B \cup C = \{a, b, c, d, e, f, g, h, i, j, k, l\}$
b $n(A) + n(B) + n(C) - n(A \cap B) - n(A \cap C)$
   $- n(B \cap C) + n(A \cap B \cap C)$
 $= 6 + 7 + 6 - 3 - 2 - 3 + 1$
 $= 12$
 $= n(A \cup B \cup C)$

10

11 a b c d e f g h

12 a b

13 a b c d e f g h i

14 a b

c

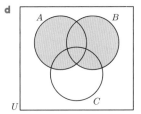

d

e

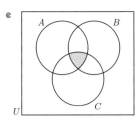

f

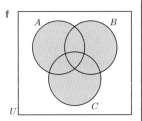

g

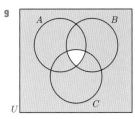

h

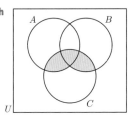

i

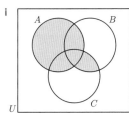

j

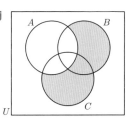

EXERCISE 2G

1 **a** 7 **b** 14 **c** 14 **d** 7 **e** 5 **f** 9

2 **a** 5 **b** 6 **c** 17 **d** 8 **e** 3 **f** 2

3 **a** $b+c$ **b** $c+d$ **c** b **d** $a+b+c$
  e $a+c+d$ **f** d

4 **a** **i** a **ii** $3a$ **iii** $2a+4$ **iv** $4a+4$
    v $3a-5$ **vi** $5a-1$
  b **i** $a=6$ **ii** $a=\frac{32}{5}=6.4$

  It is not possible to have a non-integer number of elements,
  as we have in **ii**.
  $\therefore$ $n(U)$ can be equal to 29, but not equal to 31.

5 **a** $n(A)+n(B)-n(A\cap B)=(a+b)+(b+c)-b$
$$=a+b+c$$
$$=n(A\cup B)$$
  b $n(A)-n(A\cap B)=(a+b)-b$
$$=a$$
$$=n(A\cap B')$$

6

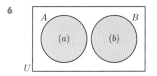

$n(A)+n(B)=a+b$
$$=n(A\cup B)$$

7 **a** 15 **b** 4 **8** **a** 18 **b** 6 **9** **a** 7 **b** 23

EXERCISE 2H

1 **a**

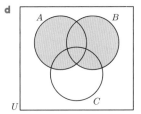

  b **i** 9 cavies
    ii 3 cavies
    iii 3 cavies

2 **a**

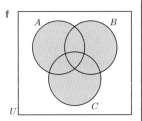

  b **i** 4 days
    ii 2 days

3 13 players **4** 20 people **5** **a** 4 stalls **b** 27 stalls

6 **a** 10 movies **b** 4 movies

7 **a**

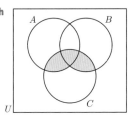

  b **i** 16 students
    ii 33 students
    iii 14 students
    iv 7 students

8 **a** 29 students **b** 6 students **c** 1 student
  d 11 students

9 **a**

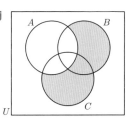

  b **i** 2 students
    ii 4 students
    iii 4 students
    iv 16 students

10 **a**

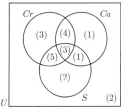

  b **i** 3 farms
    ii 4 farms
    iii 9 farms

11 **a**

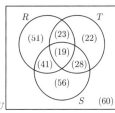

  b **i** 19 members
    ii 92 members

  c $\approx 30.7\%$

12 **a**

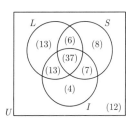

b Yes, $n(U) - n(L \cup S \cup I) = 100 - 88 = 12$ nations.

c **i** 8 nations   **ii** 30 nations   **iii** 7 nations

REVIEW SET 2A

1 **a** $A = \{V, E, N\}$, $B = \{D, I, A, G, R, M\}$

b $n(A) = 3$, $n(B) = 6$

c $A \cap B = \varnothing$,   'VENN' and 'DIAGRAM' have no letters in common.

d **i** false   **ii** true   **iii** true

2 $A' = \{12, 18, 24, 30, 42, 48, 54, 60\}$

3 **a** true   **b** false   **c** true   **d** false

4 **a**

b

c

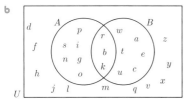

5 **a** **i** $P = \{1, 2, 3, 4, 6, 8, 12, 24\}$

ii $Q = \{1, 2, 3, 5, 6, 10, 15, 30\}$

iii $P \cap Q = \{1, 2, 3, 6\}$

iv $P \cup Q = \{1, 2, 3, 4, 5, 6, 8, 10, 12, 15, 24, 30\}$

b $n(P) + n(Q) - n(P \cap Q) = 8 + 8 - 4 = 12$
$$= n(P \cup Q)$$

6 **a** **i** $A \cup B = \{\text{the letters in "springbok" or "waterbuck"}\}$
$$= \{s, p, r, i, n, g, b, o, k, w, a, t, e, u, c\}$$

ii $A \cap B = \{\text{the letters common to both "springbok" and}$
$$\text{"waterbuck"}\}$$
$$= \{r, b, k\}$$

iii $A \cap B'$
$$= \{\text{the letters in "springbok" but not "waterbuck"}\}$$
$$= \{s, p, i, n, g, o\}$$

b

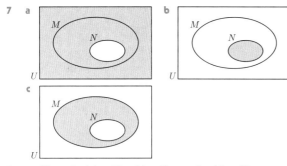

7 **a**

b

c

8 **a** C' **b** $(A \cap B) \cup (A \cap C)$ or $A \cap (B \cup C)$

9 **a** $P = \{1, 3, 5, 7, 9\}$, $Q = \{2, 4, 6, 8, 10\}$

b P and Q are disjoint.   **c**

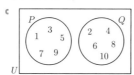

10 **a** 56 members   **c**

b **i** 8 members

ii 25 members

iii 5 members

d 11 members

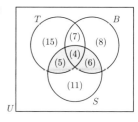

11 **a**

b **i** 72 students

ii 39 students

iii 268 students

12 8 dishes

13 **a** 9 students   **b** 7 students   **c** 17 students

REVIEW SET 2B

1 $\varnothing$, $\{1\}$, $\{3\}$, $\{5\}$, $\{1, 3\}$, $\{1, 5\}$, $\{3, 5\}$, $\{1, 3, 5\}$

2 **a** $S \cap T = \varnothing$ **b** $s + t$

3 **a** $\{x \in \mathbb{R} \mid 5 < x < 12\}$,   infinite

b $\{x \in \mathbb{Z} \mid -4 \leqslant x < 7\}$,   finite

c $\{x \in \mathbb{N} \mid x > 45\}$,   infinite

4 **a** $\{x \mid 2 < x \leqslant 5\}$ **b** $\{x \in \mathbb{Z} \mid 4 < x < 9\}$

c $\{x \mid x \leqslant -3\} \cup \{x \mid x \geqslant 1\}$

5 **a** $S = \{3, 4, 5, 6, 7\}$ **b**

c 5

6 **a** $A \subseteq B$ **b** $A \subseteq B$ **c** $A \nsubseteq B$ **d** $A \subseteq B$

7 **a** $X' = \{\text{orange, yellow, green, blue}\}$

b $X' = \{-5, -3, -2, 0, 1, 2, 5\}$

c $X' = \{x \in \mathbb{Q} \mid x \geqslant -8\}$

8 **a** **i** $A = \{2, 4, 6, 8\}$ **ii** $A \cap B = \{2, 4, 8\}$

iii $(A \cup B)' = \{3, 5, 7, 9\}$

b

9 **a** $A = \{1, 2, 4, 5, 8, 10, 20, 40\}$, $B = \{1, 2, 4, 5, 10, 20\}$

b $B \subset A$

c

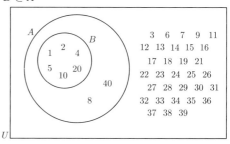

10 **a** $P = \{3, 4, 5, 6, 7, 8, 9\}$ **b** 7   **c** finite

d **i** 2 and 15 are in Q, but not in P

ii $R = \{3, 6, 9\}$, all these elements are in P, but $R \neq P$

e **i** $\{9\}$ **ii** $\{9\}$ **iii** $\{2, 3, 6, 9, 15\}$

11 a 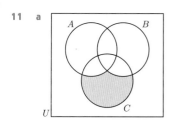 **b**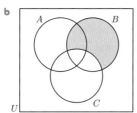

c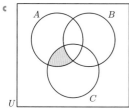

12 a

$$M \quad S$$
$$(8)\ (5)\ (10)$$
$$(4)$$
$$U$$

b i 27 members
ii 8 members
iii 14 members

13 4 students

14 a 1 delegate   **b** 7 delegates   **c** 15 delegates

EXERCISE 3A

1 a 11   **b** $\sqrt{15}$ **c** 3   **d** $\sqrt{30}$
e $\sqrt{12}$ **f** 4   **g** 12   **h** 42
i 45   **j** $\sqrt{90}$ **k** $-\sqrt{540}$ **l** $\sqrt{288}$

2 a $\sqrt{6}$ **b** $\sqrt{6}$ **c** 2   **d** $\frac{1}{2}$
e $\sqrt{\frac{1}{3}}$ **f** $\sqrt{5}$ **g** $\frac{1}{4}$ **h** $\frac{1}{4}$

3 a $2\sqrt{2}$ **b** $2\sqrt{3}$ **c** $2\sqrt{5}$ **d** $4\sqrt{2}$
e $3\sqrt{3}$ **f** $3\sqrt{5}$ **g** $4\sqrt{3}$ **h** $3\sqrt{6}$
i $5\sqrt{2}$ **j** $4\sqrt{5}$ **k** $4\sqrt{6}$ **l** $6\sqrt{3}$

4 a $\dfrac{\sqrt{125}}{\sqrt{5}} = \sqrt{\dfrac{125}{5}}$
$= \sqrt{25}$
$= 5$

b $\dfrac{\sqrt{125}}{\sqrt{5}} = \dfrac{\sqrt{25 \times 5}}{\sqrt{5}}$
$= \dfrac{\sqrt{25} \times \sqrt{5}}{\sqrt{5}}$
$= 5$

5 a $5\sqrt{2}$ **b** $-\sqrt{2}$ **c** $2\sqrt{5}$ **d** $8\sqrt{5}$
e $-2\sqrt{5}$ **f** $9\sqrt{3}$ **g** $-3\sqrt{6}$ **h** $3\sqrt{2}$

6 a $2\sqrt{3}$ **b** $8\sqrt{2}$ **c** $5\sqrt{6}$ **d** $10\sqrt{3}$
e $3\sqrt{3}$ **f** $-\sqrt{2}$

7 a $3\sqrt{2} - 2$ **b** $5 + \sqrt{5}$ **c** $3\sqrt{10} + 20$
d $21 - 4\sqrt{7}$ **e** $-5\sqrt{3} - 3$ **f** $12 - 14\sqrt{6}$
g $-8 + 5\sqrt{8}$ **h** $-12\sqrt{2} + 36$

8 a $22 + 9\sqrt{2}$ **b** $34 + 15\sqrt{3}$ **c** $22 + 14\sqrt{7}$
d $-7 - \sqrt{3}$ **e** $34 - 15\sqrt{8}$ **f** $30\sqrt{5} - 47$

9 a $11 + 6\sqrt{2}$ **b** $39 - 12\sqrt{3}$ **c** $6 + 2\sqrt{5}$
d $17 - 6\sqrt{8}$ **e** $28 + 16\sqrt{3}$ **f** $46 + 6\sqrt{5}$
g $89 - 28\sqrt{10}$ **h** $166 - 40\sqrt{6}$ **i** $12 - 8\sqrt{2}$

10 a 2   **b** -23 **c** 13   **d** 7   **e** -56 **f** 218

EXERCISE 3B

1 a $\frac{\sqrt{3}}{3}$ **b** $\sqrt{3}$ **c** $3\sqrt{3}$ **d** $\frac{11\sqrt{3}}{3}$ **e** $\frac{\sqrt{6}}{9}$
f $\sqrt{2}$ **g** $3\sqrt{2}$ **h** $6\sqrt{2}$ **i** $\frac{\sqrt{6}}{2}$ **j** $\frac{\sqrt{2}}{8}$
k $\sqrt{5}$ **l** $3\sqrt{5}$ **m** $-\frac{3\sqrt{5}}{5}$ **n** $40\sqrt{5}$ **o** $\frac{\sqrt{5}}{15}$
p $\sqrt{7}$ **q** $3\sqrt{7}$ **r** $\frac{2\sqrt{11}}{11}$ **s** $2\sqrt{13}$ **t** $\frac{\sqrt{3}}{9}$

2 a $\dfrac{3 - \sqrt{2}}{7}$ **b** $\dfrac{6 + 2\sqrt{2}}{7}$ **c** $-2 + \sqrt{5}$ **d** $\sqrt{2} + 1$
e $2\sqrt{6} + 2$ **f** $\dfrac{\sqrt{21} - 2\sqrt{3}}{3}$ **g** $-3 - 2\sqrt{2}$
h $\dfrac{4\sqrt{3} + 3}{13}$ **i** $2\sqrt{2} + 4$ **j** $-7 - 3\sqrt{5}$
k $\dfrac{5 + 3\sqrt{3}}{2}$ **l** $\dfrac{-38 + 11\sqrt{10}}{6}$ **m** $\dfrac{7 + \sqrt{5}}{11}$
n $\dfrac{28 + \sqrt{2}}{23}$ **o** $\dfrac{17 + 7\sqrt{7}}{3}$ **p** $\dfrac{\sqrt{11} - 1}{5}$

3 a $3 - 2\sqrt{2}$ **b** $11 + 6\sqrt{2}$ **c** $3 - 2\sqrt{2}$
d $\frac{14}{17} - \frac{1}{34}\sqrt{2}$ **e** $3 - 2\sqrt{2}$ **f** $\frac{11}{49} + \frac{6}{49}\sqrt{2}$
g $3 - 2\sqrt{2}$ **h** $-\frac{7}{41} - \frac{2}{41}\sqrt{2}$

EXERCISE 3C

1 a $2^1 = 2$, $2^2 = 4$, $2^3 = 8$, $2^4 = 16$, $2^5 = 32$, $2^6 = 64$
b $3^1 = 3$, $3^2 = 9$, $3^3 = 27$, $3^4 = 81$, $3^5 = 243$,
$3^6 = 729$
c $4^1 = 4$, $4^2 = 16$, $4^3 = 64$, $4^4 = 256$, $4^5 = 1024$,
$4^6 = 4096$

2 a $5^1 = 5$, $5^2 = 25$, $5^3 = 125$, $5^4 = 625$
b $6^1 = 6$, $6^2 = 36$, $6^3 = 216$, $6^4 = 1296$
c $7^1 = 7$, $7^2 = 49$, $7^3 = 343$, $7^4 = 2401$

3 a -1 **b** 1   **c** 1   **d** -1 **e** 1   **f** -1
g -1 **h** -32 **i** -32 **j** -64 **k** 625   **l** -625

4 a 16 384   **b** 2401   **c** -3125 **d** -3125
e 262 144   **f** 262 144   **g** $-262\,144$
h 902.436 039 6   **i** $-902.436\,039\,6$ **j** $-902.436\,039\,6$

5 a $0.\overline{1}$ **b** $0.02\overline{7}$ **c** $0.\overline{012\,345\,679}$ **d** 1

Notice that $a^{-n} = \dfrac{1}{a^n}$ and $a^0 = 1$.

6 3   **7** 7

8 a $21 + 23 + 25 + 27 + 29 = 125 = 5^3$
b $43 + 45 + 47 + 49 + 51 + 53 + 55 = 343 = 7^3$
c $133 + 135 + 137 + 139 + 141 + 143 + 145 + 147 + 149$
$+ 151 + 153 + 155 = 1728 = 12^3$

EXERCISE 3D

1 a k^6 **b** 5^8 **c** d^{10} **d** 11^{4+a}
e p^7 **f** 3^1 **g** c^{8+m} **h** x^{k+2}
i x^3 **j** 5^{-3} **k** r^{11} **l** 2^1

2 a 7^5 **b** b^2 **c** 5^3 **d** m^6
e 6^{-2} **f** $3^0 = 1$ **g** k^{12-a} **h** y^5
i t^{m-4} **j** x^{3a-2} **k** x^{-5} **l** a^4

3 a 5^6 **b** c^{12} **c** 3^{32} **d** v^{25}
e 7^{6d} **f** g^{8k} **g** m^{3t} **h** 11^{2xy}
i $3^0 = 1$ **j** 2^{-12} **k** x^{-8} **l** p^6

4 **a** b^{12} **b** t^7 **c** p^{18} **d** 7^{6-n}
  e x^{6s} **f** d^{k-3} **g** 3^{13} **h** j^{12x}
  i 11^7 **j** z^{7-4t} **k** 13^{5cd} **l** w^{7p-1}

5 **a** 2^2 **b** 2^{-2} **c** 2^3 **d** 2^{-3} **e** 2^5 **f** 2^{-5}
  g 2^1 **h** 2^{-1} **i** 2^6 **j** 2^{-6} **k** 2^7 **l** 2^{-7}

6 **a** 3^2 **b** 3^{-2} **c** 3^3 **d** 3^{-3} **e** 3^1 **f** 3^{-1}
  g 3^4 **h** 3^{-4} **i** 3^0 **j** 3^5 **k** 3^{-5}

7 **a** 2^{1+a} **b** 2^{2+b} **c** 2^{3+t} **d** 2^{2x+2} **e** 2^{n-1}
  f 2^{c-2} **g** 2^{2m} **h** 2^{1+n} **i** 2^1 **j** 2^{3x-1}

8 **a** 3^{2+p} **b** 3^{3a} **c** 3^{1+2n} **d** 3^{3+d} **e** 3^{2+3t}
  f 3^{y-1} **g** 3^{1-y} **h** 3^{2-3t} **i** 3^{3a-1} **j** 3^3

9 **a** 2^5 **b** 7^2 **c** 5^6 **d** 2^{10}
  e 2^{4p} **f** 3^{3t} **g** 5^{a+2} **h** 2^{5n}
  i 2^{3m-4n} **j** 5^{2p-4} **k** 2^3 **l** 3^{2t+4}
  m 2^{10-5r} **n** 3^{3-y} **o** 2^{2k} **p** 5^{4-3a}

10 **a** $4a^2$ **b** $9n^2$ **c** $125m^3$ **d** m^3n^3
  e $\dfrac{a^3}{8}$ **f** $\dfrac{9}{m^2}$ **g** $\dfrac{p^4}{q^4}$ **h** $\dfrac{t^2}{25}$

11 **a** 1 **b** $\frac{1}{3}$ **c** $\frac{1}{49}$ **d** 2 **e** $\frac{6}{5}$ (or $1\frac{1}{5}$)
  f 1 **g** $\frac{4}{7}$ **h** 6 **i** $\frac{9}{16}$ **j** $\frac{5}{2}$ (or $2\frac{1}{2}$)
  k $\frac{27}{125}$ **l** $\frac{151}{5}$ (or $30\frac{1}{5}$)

12 **a** 3^{-2} **b** 2^{-4} **c** 5^{-3} **d** $3^1 \times 5^{-1}$
  e $2^2 \times 3^{-3}$ **f** $2^{c-3} \times 3^{-2}$
  g $3^{2k} \times 2^{-1} \times 5^{-1}$ **h** $2^p \times 3^{p-1} \times 5^{-2}$

13 **a** $4a^2b^2$ **b** $4a^2$ **c** $36b^4$ **d** $-8a^3$
  e $-27m^6n^6$ **f** $16a^4b^{16}$ **g** 1 ($a \neq 0$, $b \neq 0$)
  h $\dfrac{m^4}{81n^4}$ **i** $\dfrac{x^3y^3}{8}$ **j** $\dfrac{-8a^6}{b^6}$ **k** $\dfrac{16a^6}{b^2}$ **l** $\dfrac{9p^4}{q^6}$

14 **a** $x^5 + x^3$ **b** $x^4 - 2x^3 + 3x^2$ **c** $x^5 - x$
  d $x^5 - x^4 + 2x^3 - 2x^2$ **e** $x^6 - 2x^4 + x^2$
  f $x^3 - 2x^2 + x$ **g** $x^2 + x - 1$
  h $x^4 + 2x + x^{-2}$ **i** $x^4 - x^{-2}$

15 **a** $4b^3$ **b** $6w^5$ **c** $4p^2$ **d** $30c^{11}$ **e** d^4 **f** $3ab^2$
  g $4n^3$ **h** t^7 **i** $20s^2t^4$ **j** k^{11} **k** $\dfrac{3xy^3}{2}$ **l** b^9

16 **a** $\dfrac{1}{x^3}$ **b** $\dfrac{2}{x^3}$ **c** $\dfrac{a}{b^2}$ **d** $\dfrac{1}{a^2b^2}$
  e $\dfrac{4a^2}{b^2}$ **f** $\dfrac{1}{25m^4}$ **g** $\dfrac{9b^2}{a^4}$ **h** $\dfrac{1}{27x^3y^{12}}$
  i $\dfrac{a^2}{bc^2}$ **j** $\dfrac{a^2c^2}{b}$ **k** a^3 **l** $\dfrac{b^3}{a^2}$
  m $\dfrac{2}{ad^2}$ **n** $12am^3$ **o** $\dfrac{a^2}{2}$ **p** $\dfrac{2}{x^4}$

17 **a** a^{-n} **b** $5a^{-m}$ **c** b^n **d** 2^{3-n}
  e 3^{n-2} **f** $3a^{m-4}$ **g** a^nb^m **h** a^{-2n-2}

18 **a** x^{-2} **b** $2x^{-1}$ **c** $x + x^{-1}$ **d** $x^2 - 2x^{-3}$
  e $x^{-1} + 3x^{-2}$ **f** $4x^{-1} - 5x^{-3}$
  g $7x - 4x^{-1} + 5x^{-2}$ **h** $3x^{-1} - 2x^{-2} + 5x^{-4}$

19 **a** $1 + 3x^{-1}$ **b** $3x^{-1} - 2$ **c** $5x^{-2} - x^{-1}$
  d $x^{-2} + 2x^{-3}$ **e** $x + 5x^{-1}$ **f** $x + 1 - 2x^{-1}$
  g $2x - 3 + 4x^{-1}$ **h** $x - 3x^{-1} + 5x^{-2}$
  i $5x^{-1} - 1 - x$ **j** $8x^{-1} + 5 - 2x^2$
  k $16x^{-2} - 3x^{-1} + x$ **l** $5x^2 - 3 + x^{-1} + 6x^{-2}$

20 **a** $4x + 2x^2$ **b** $5x^2 - 4x^3$ **c** $6x^3 + 3x^4$ **d** $x^3 + 3x$
  e $x^4 + x^3 - 4x^2$ **f** $x^6 - 3x^4 + 6x^3$ **g** $x^5 - 6x^3 + 10x^2$

EXERCISE 3E

1 **C** and **D**

2 **a** 2.59×10^2 **b** 2.59×10^5 **c** 2.59×10^9
  d 2.59×10^0 **e** 2.59×10^{-1} **f** 2.59×10^{-4}
  g 4.07×10^1 **h** 4.07×10^3 **i** 4.07×10^{-2}
  j 4.07×10^5 **k** 4.07×10^8 **l** 4.07×10^{-5}

3 **a** 4.745×10^7 kg **b** 3×10^{-3} m
  c 2.599×10^6 hands **d** 4.7×10^{-7} m

4 **a** 4000 **b** 500 **c** 2100 **d** $78\,000$
  e $380\,000$ **f** 86 **g** $43\,300\,000$ **h** $60\,000\,000$

5 **a** 0.004 **b** 0.05 **c** 0.0021
  d $0.000\,78$ **e** $0.000\,038$ **f** 0.86
  g $0.000\,000\,433$ **h** $0.000\,000\,6$

6 **a** $7\,400\,000\,000$ people **b** 0.0112 kg
  c $0.000\,000\,5$ m **d** $7\,300\,000$ kg

7 **a** $4.5 \times 10^7 = 45\,000\,000$ **b** $3.8 \times 10^{-4} = 0.000\,38$
  c $2.1 \times 10^5 = 210\,000$ **d** $4 \times 10^{-3} = 0.004$
  e $6.1 \times 10^3 = 6100$ **f** $1.6 \times 10^{-6} = 0.000\,001\,6$
  g $3.9 \times 10^4 = 39\,000$ **h** $6.7 \times 10^{-2} = 0.067$

8 **a** 4.964×10^{13} **b** 4×10^{-8} **c** 3.43×10^{-10}
  d 1.6416×10^{10} **e** $4.121\,64 \times 10^{-3}$ **f** $\approx 5.27 \times 10^{-18}$
  g $\approx 1.36 \times 10^2$ **h** $\approx 2.63 \times 10^{-6}$ **i** 1.728×10^9

9 7.5×10^7 peanuts **10** 2.61×10^{-6} m

11 **a** 1.15×10^{10} m
  b We have assumed that we will always be on the side of the planet that is closest to the next planet, at the time when the planets are closest. It could take a very long time for these ideal conditions to occur.

12 **a** **i** $\approx 1.80 \times 10^{10}$ m **ii** $\approx 2.59 \times 10^{13}$ m
  b $\approx 9.46 \times 10^{15}$ m **c** $\approx 3.99 \times 10^{16}$ m
  d **i** $\approx 9.27 \times 10^{21}$ m **ii** $\approx 5.46 \times 10^{22}$
  iii $\approx 9.46 \times 10^{12}$ hours (≈ 1.08 billion years)

13 **a** It allows us to write very small numbers without having to write and count lots of zeros.
  b **i** ≈ 1839 times **ii** ≈ 1836 times **iii** ≈ 1.001 times
  c 47 electrons, 60 neutrons **d** $\approx 2.18 \times 10^{21}$ electrons

REVIEW SET 3A

1 **a** $4\sqrt{5}$ **b** $-\sqrt{6}$ **c** $20\sqrt{3} - 15$
  d $4 + 3\sqrt{2}$ **e** $86 - 60\sqrt{2}$ **f** 4

2 **a** -1 **b** 27 **c** $\frac{2}{3}$

3 **a** x^6 **b** 2^{-7} (or $\frac{1}{128}$) **c** a^6b^{18}

4 **a** $\frac{1}{27}$ **b** $\dfrac{y}{x}$ **c** $\dfrac{b}{a}$ **5** **a** 3^3 **b** 3^{2t} **c** 2^{3-m}

6 **a** $\dfrac{5x}{y^2}$ **b** $\dfrac{1}{j^7}$ **c** $3g^3h^3$

7 **a** $\dfrac{t^3}{64s^3}$ **b** 1 ($m \neq 0$, $n \neq 0$) **c** $25p^6q^2$

8 **a** $x + 8x^{-1}$ **b** $4x^2 + x^3 + x^5$ **c** k^{-2x-6}

9 **a** a^6b^7 **b** $\dfrac{2}{3x}$ **c** $\dfrac{y^2}{5}$

10 **a** $460\,000\,000\,000$ **b** 1.9 **c** 0.0032

11 a 1.274×10^7 m   **b** 1.2×10^{-4} m

12 313 sheets   **13** 2.8×10^9 km

REVIEW SET 3B

1 a $-\sqrt{11}$ **b** $\sqrt{2}$ **c** $17 - 11\sqrt{3}$ **d** 28

2 a $\frac{2\sqrt{3}}{3}$ **b** $\frac{\sqrt{35}}{5}$ **c** $6 - 3\sqrt{3}$ **d** $\frac{4-\sqrt{7}}{9}$

3 a m^4 **b** 1 $(y \neq 0)$ **c** $\frac{w^2}{49z^2}$

4 a k^{x-2} **b** 11^{r-4} **c** 3^{2+b}

5 a 11^{-1} **b** ab^{-2} **c** jk^4l^{-a}

6 a 2^{-4} **b** 3^{k+4} **c** 5^{3a-b}

7 a $\frac{1}{8}$ **b** 1 **c** $\frac{10}{3}$ (or $3\frac{1}{3}$)

8 a $\frac{a^{18}}{64b^6}$ **b** $\frac{25}{d^8}$ **c** $2z^4$

9 a $\frac{1}{x^5}$ **b** $\frac{2}{a^2b^2}$ **c** $\frac{2a}{b^2}$

10 a 3^{3-2a} **b** 3^{6-8x}

11 a $143\,000$ km   **b** $0.000\,000\,082$ m

12 a $\approx 1.96 \times 10^{-5}$ s   **b** ≈ 0.0110 s   **13** 7500 sheets

EXERCISE 4A

1 a $x = \pm 2$ **b** $x = \pm 4$ **c** $x = \pm 1$ **d** $x = \pm\sqrt{7}$
  e no real solutions   **f** $x = 0$ **g** $x = \pm\sqrt{5}$
  h no real solutions   **i** $x = \pm\frac{3}{2}$

2 a $x = 7$ or -1 **b** $x = 2$ or -4 **c** no real solutions
  d $x = 2 \pm \sqrt{10}$ **e** $x = -4 \pm \sqrt{13}$ **f** $x = 7$
  g $x = 4$ or -1 **h** $x = \frac{-1 \pm \sqrt{14}}{3}$ **i** $x = 0$ or $2\sqrt{2}$
  j $x = -\sqrt{2} \pm 1$ **k** $x = \frac{\sqrt{3} \pm \sqrt{2}}{2}$ **l** $x = \frac{-1 \pm \sqrt{7}}{2}$

3 a $n > 0$ **b** $n = 0$ **c** $n < 0$

EXERCISE 4B

1 a $x = 3$ **b** $x = \pm 2$ **c** no real solutions
  d $x = \sqrt[5]{-13}$ **e** $x = -2$ **f** $x = \sqrt[3]{7}$
  g $x = \pm\sqrt[4]{6}$ **h** $x = \frac{2}{3}$ **i** $x = \pm\frac{1}{2}$
  j $x = \sqrt[5]{\frac{1}{3}}$ **k** $x = \sqrt[3]{-6}$ **l** $x = \pm 3$

2 a $x = 1 + \sqrt[3]{17}$ **b** $x = -4$ **c** $x = 2 \pm \sqrt[4]{20}$
  d no real solutions   **e** $x = -4 + \sqrt[5]{-12}$
  f $x = 3 \pm \sqrt[4]{5}$ **g** $x = 0$ or $\frac{2}{3}$
  h $x = \frac{3 \pm \sqrt[4]{15}}{2}$ **i** $x = -1$

3 a $x = 2$ **b** $x = 1 \pm \sqrt[4]{11}$ **c** $x = -2$

4 a $x = 6$ **b** $x = \pm 3$ **c** $x = -3$ **d** $x = \pm\frac{1}{7}$
  e $x = \pm 2$ **f** $x = -\frac{1}{4}$ **g** $x = \frac{14}{5}$ or $\frac{16}{5}$
  h no real solutions   **i** $x = \frac{5 + \sqrt[3]{5}}{2}$

EXERCISE 4C

1 a $x = 0$ **b** $a = 0$ **c** $y = 0$ **d** $a = 0$ or $b = 0$
  e $x = 0$ or $y = 0$ **f** $a = 0$
  g $x = 0$ or $y = 0$ or $z = 0$
  h $a = 0$ or $b = 0$ or $c = 0$

2 a $x = 0$ or 5 **b** $x = 0$ or -3 **c** $x = -1$ or 3
  d $x = 4$ or -7 **e** $x = 0$ or 7 **f** $x = 0$ or -1
  g $x = -6$ or $\frac{3}{2}$ **h** $x = -\frac{1}{2}$ or $\frac{1}{2}$ **i** $x = -2$ or 7
  j $x = 5$ or $-\frac{2}{3}$ **k** $x = 0$ or -5 **l** $x = 5$
  m $x = \frac{1}{3}$ **n** $x = 0, -1$, or 2
  o $x = 1, -2$, or 3 **p** $x = -2, -4$, or $\frac{1}{2}$

3 a $a = 0, \ b \neq 0$ **b** $x = 0$ or $y = 0, \ z \neq 0$
  c no solutions   **d** $x = 0, \ y \neq 0$

EXERCISE 4D.1

1 a $x = 0$ or $-\frac{7}{4}$ **b** $x = 0$ or $-\frac{1}{3}$ **c** $x = 0$ or $\frac{7}{3}$
  d $x = 0$ or $\frac{11}{2}$ **e** $x = 0$ or $\frac{8}{3}$ **f** $x = 0$ or $\frac{3}{2}$

2 a $x = 2$ or 3 **b** $x = 1$ **c** $x = -4$ or 2
  d $x = -3$ or -4 **e** $x = -2$ or 4 **f** $x = 3$ or 7
  g $x = 3$ **h** $x = -4$ or 3 **i** $x = -11$ or 3

3 a $x = \frac{2}{3}$ **b** $x = -\frac{1}{2}$ or 7 **c** $x = -\frac{2}{3}$ or 6
  d $x = \frac{1}{3}$ or -2 **e** $x = \frac{3}{2}$ or 1 **f** $x = -\frac{2}{3}$ or -2
  g $x = -\frac{2}{3}$ or 4 **h** $x = \frac{1}{2}$ or $-\frac{3}{2}$ **i** $x = -\frac{1}{4}$ or 3
  j $x = -\frac{3}{4}$ or $\frac{5}{3}$ **k** $x = \frac{1}{7}$ or -1 **l** $x = -2$ or $\frac{28}{15}$

4 a $x = 2$ or 5 **b** $x = -3$ or 2 **c** $x = 0$ or $-\frac{3}{2}$
  d $x = 1$ or 2 **e** $x = \frac{1}{2}$ or -1 **f** $x = 3$
  g $x = 1$ or -2 **h** $x = 6$ or -4 **i** $x = 7$ or -5
  j $x = 4$ or -2

EXERCISE 4D.2

1 a $x = 2 \pm \sqrt{3}$ **b** $x = -3 \pm \sqrt{7}$ **c** $x = 7 \pm \sqrt{3}$
  d $x = 2 \pm \sqrt{7}$ **e** $x = -3 \pm \sqrt{2}$ **f** $x = 1 \pm \sqrt{7}$
  g $x = -3 \pm \sqrt{11}$ **h** $x = 4 \pm \sqrt{6}$ **i** no real solutions

2 a $x = -1 \pm \frac{1}{\sqrt{2}}$ **b** $x = \frac{5}{2} \pm \frac{\sqrt{19}}{2}$ **c** $x = -2 \pm \sqrt{\frac{7}{3}}$
  d $x = 1 \pm \sqrt{\frac{7}{3}}$ **e** $x = \frac{3}{2} \pm \sqrt{\frac{37}{20}}$ **f** $x = -\frac{1}{2} \pm \frac{\sqrt{6}}{2}$

3 a $x = \frac{2}{3} \pm \frac{\sqrt{10}}{3}$ **b** $x = -\frac{1}{10} \pm \frac{\sqrt{21}}{10}$ **c** $x = -\frac{5}{6} \pm \frac{\sqrt{13}}{6}$

4 $x = \dfrac{-b \pm \sqrt{b^2 - 4ac}}{2a}$

EXERCISE 4D.3

1 a $x = 2 \pm \sqrt{7}$ **b** $x = -3 \pm \sqrt{2}$ **c** $x = 2 \pm \sqrt{3}$
  d $x = -2 \pm \sqrt{5}$ **e** $x = 2 \pm \sqrt{2}$ **f** $x = \frac{1 \pm \sqrt{7}}{2}$
  g $x = \frac{5 \pm \sqrt{37}}{6}$ **h** $x = 2 \pm \sqrt{10}$ **i** $x = \frac{7 \pm \sqrt{33}}{4}$

2 a $x = -2 \pm 2\sqrt{2}$ **b** $x = \frac{-5 \pm \sqrt{57}}{8}$ **c** $x = \frac{5 \pm \sqrt{13}}{2}$
  d $x = \frac{-4 \pm \sqrt{7}}{9}$ **e** $x = \frac{-7 \pm \sqrt{97}}{4}$ **f** $x = \frac{1 \pm \sqrt{145}}{8}$
  g $x = \frac{1 \pm \sqrt{7}}{2}$ **h** $x = \frac{1 \pm \sqrt{5}}{2}$ **i** $x = \frac{3 \pm \sqrt{17}}{4}$

EXERCISE 4D.4

1 a $\Delta = 13$ **b** 2 distinct irrational roots   **c** $x = \frac{7}{2} \pm \frac{\sqrt{13}}{2}$

2 a $\Delta = 0$ **b** 1 root (repeated)   **c** $x = \frac{1}{2}$

3 a $x^2 = -5, \ \therefore$ no real roots   **b** $\Delta = -20$

4 **a** 2 distinct irrational roots   **b** 2 distinct rational roots
   c 2 distinct rational roots   **d** 2 distinct irrational roots
   e no real roots   **f** a repeated root

5 **a**, **c**, **d**, and **f**

6 **a** $\Delta = 16 - 4m$

$$\xleftarrow{\quad + \quad | \quad - \quad}_{4} m$$

    i $m = 4$ **ii** $m < 4$ **iii** $m > 4$

   b $\Delta = 9 - 8m$

$$\xleftarrow{\quad + \quad | \quad - \quad}_{\frac{9}{8}} m$$

    i $m = \frac{9}{8}$ **ii** $m < \frac{9}{8},\ m \neq 0$ **iii** $m > \frac{9}{8}$

   c $\Delta = 9 - 4m$

$$\xleftarrow{\quad + \quad | \quad - \quad}_{\frac{9}{4}} m$$

    i $m = \frac{9}{4}$ **ii** $m < \frac{9}{4},\ m \neq 0$ **iii** $m > \frac{9}{4}$

EXERCISE 4E

1 **a** $x = 3$ or 2 **b** $x = -2$ or -7
   c $x = 4$ **d** no real solutions
   e $x = 0.25$ or -1.5 **f** $x \approx 1.29$ or -1.54
   g $x \approx 1.29$ or -1.09 **h** $x \approx 8.36$ or -0.359

2 **a** $x = 1$ or -7 **b** $x = 1.5$ or -2.5
   c $x = 3.5$ or 1.8 **d** $x \approx 1.18$ or 2.82
   e $x \approx -2.27$ or 1.77 **f** no real solutions
   g $x \approx 1.54$ or -0.869 **h** $x \approx 1.39$ or 0.360
   i $x \approx 4.18$ or -5.99

3 **a** $x = -3$ or -4 **b** $x = 1$ or -3
   c $x \approx 1.85$ or -4.85 **d** $x \approx 0.847$ or -1.18
   e $x = -0.5$ **f** no real solutions

4 **a** $x = -3, 0$, or 3 **b** $x \approx -1.13$ **c** $x = 3, 2$, or -4
   d $x = 1$ **e** $x = 0.5, \approx 0.618$, or -1.62
   f $x \approx 4.36, 0.406$, or -2.26

5 **a** no real solutions   **b** $x \approx 1.34$ or -3.17
   c $x = 1$ or -1 **d** no real solutions

6 **a** $x = 0, \approx 1.73$, or -1.73 **b** $x \approx -0.811$
   c $x = \pm 2$

EXERCISE 4F

1 **a** $x = -2$ or 3 **b** $x = -2$ or 3

2 **a** $x \approx 3.21$ **b** $x \approx 0.387$ or -1.72 **c** $x \approx 2.46$
   d $x \approx 5.17$ **e** $x \approx 1.52$ or 2.83 **f** $x \approx 3.56$ or -1.30

3 **a** $x \approx -1.59$ **b** $x \approx -0.861, 1.24$, or 16
   c $x \approx -2.62$ **d** $x \approx -0.572$ or 0.821
   e $x \approx -2.24$ or 2.34 **f** $x \approx -0.577$ or 0.577

4 **a** **i** $x = 1$ or 5 **ii** $x = 3$ **iii** no real solutions
   b **i** $k > -7$ **ii** $k = -7$ **iii** $k < -7$

REVIEW SET 4A

1 **a** $x = \pm\sqrt{19}$ **b** $x = -3$ or 7 **c** $x = 0$ or $2\sqrt{2}$

2 **a** no real solutions   **b** $x = \frac{1}{3}$ **c** $x = 1 + \sqrt[5]{2}$

3 **a** $x = 0$ or -2 **b** $x = -3$ or $\frac{7}{2}$ **c** $x = -5, -1$, or 6

4 **a** $x = 0$ or $\frac{5}{3}$ **b** $x = 5$ or -1 **c** $x = -3$

5 **a** $x = -5$ or 4 **b** $x = 2$ or 3 **c** $x = -\frac{5}{2}$ or 7
   d $x = 1$ or 3 **e** $x = \frac{1}{3}$ or -2 **f** $x = -6$ or 9

6 **a** $x = 3 \pm \sqrt{5}$ **b** $x = 1 \pm \sqrt{2}$ **c** $x = -2 \pm \frac{3}{\sqrt{2}}$

---

7 **a** $x = \dfrac{7 \pm \sqrt{41}}{2}$ **b** no real solutions

   c $x = \dfrac{-1 \pm \sqrt{37}}{6}$

8 **a** $x^2 - 9 = 0,\quad x - \pm 3$
   b $2x^2 + x - 3 = 0,\quad x = 1$ or $-\frac{3}{2}$
   c $3x^2 - x - 2 = 0,\quad x = 1$ or $-\frac{2}{3}$

9 **a** $\Delta = 49$, 2 distinct rational roots   **b** $x = -\frac{1}{2}$ or $\frac{2}{3}$

10 $\Delta = -7$ $\therefore$ no real roots

12 **a** $x = \frac{5}{2}, 1$, or -2 **b** $x = 2, \frac{1}{3}$, or 0
   c $x = 4, 3$, or -5 **d** $x \approx 1.84$ or -6.92

13 **a** $x \approx 2.81$ **b** $x \approx 1.73$ **c** $x \approx -1.84$

REVIEW SET 4B

1 **a** $x = 0$ **b** $x = -\frac{5}{2}$ **c** $x = \sqrt{3} \pm 4$

2 **a** $x = \pm\frac{3}{2}$ **b** $x = \sqrt[5]{-18}$ **c** $x = \frac{1}{2}$ or $\frac{3}{2}$

3 **a** $p = 0,\ q \neq 0$ **b** $x = 0$ or $z = 0,\ y \neq 0$
   c no solutions

4 **a** $x = 0$ or $\frac{5}{2}$ **b** $x = 0$ or 4 **c** $x = 1$ or 6
   d $x = -2$ **e** $x = -2$ or 6 **f** $x = -\frac{5}{3}$ or 2

5 **a** $x = 15$ or -4 **b** $x = \dfrac{-5 \pm \sqrt{5}}{2}$ **c** $x = 2$ or $-\frac{3}{4}$

6 We obtain $(x - 2)^2 = -1$ which has no solutions.

7 **a** $x = \dfrac{-5 \pm \sqrt{13}}{2}$ **b** $x = \dfrac{-11 \pm \sqrt{145}}{6}$

   c $x = \dfrac{-2 \pm \sqrt{14}}{5}$

8 **a** $\Delta = 0$, 1 root (repeated)
   b $\Delta = 41$, 2 distinct irrational roots
   c $\Delta = -11$, no real roots

9 **a** $m = \frac{9}{8}$ **b** $m < \frac{9}{8}$ **c** $m > \frac{9}{8}$

10 **a** **i** $x = \pm 6$
     ii

       $x = -6$ or 6

   c **i** $k > 0$ **ii** $k = 0$ **iii** $k < 0$

11 **a** $x \approx 2.77$ or -1.27 **b** $x \approx 3.70$ or -2.70
   c $x \approx -3.83$ or 1.83

12 **a** $x = 5, 0$, or -3 **b** $x \approx 4.93, 0.814$, or -1.74
   c $x \approx 2.39$ or 0.449

13 **a** $x \approx 2.81$ **b** $x \approx 1.85$ **c** $x \approx -2.15$ or 3.58

EXERCISE 5A

1 **a** $4, 13, 22, 31$ **b** $45, 39, 33, 27$ **c** $2, 6, 18, 54$
   d $96, 48, 24, 12$

2 **a** $u_2 = 3$ **b** $u_5 = 11$ **c** $u_{10} = 29$

3 **a** We start with 4 and add 3 each time.
   b $u_1 = 4,\ u_4 = 13$ **c** $u_8 = 25$

4 $u_1 = 7,\ u_2 = 9,\ u_3 = 11,\ u_4 = 13$

5 **a** $u_1 = 1$ **b** $u_5 = 13$ **c** $u_{27} = 79$

6 **a** **B** **b** $u_{20} = 390$

7 **a** The sequence starts at 8, and each term is 8 more than the previous term. The next two terms are 40 and 48.

b The sequence starts at 2, and each term is 3 more than the previous term. The next two terms are 14 and 17.

c The sequence starts at 36, and each term is 5 less than the previous term. The next two terms are 16 and 11.

d The sequence starts at 96, and each term is 7 less than the previous term. The next two terms are 68 and 61.

e The sequence starts at 1, and each term is 4 times the previous term. The next two terms are 256 and 1024.

f The sequence starts at 2, and each term is 3 times the previous term. The next two terms are 162 and 486.

g The sequence starts at 480, and each term is half the previous term. The next two terms are 30 and 15.

h The sequence starts at 243, and each term is one third of the previous term. The next two terms are 3 and 1.

i The sequence starts at 50 000, and each term is one fifth of the previous term. The next two terms are 80 and 16.

8 **a** Each term is the square of the term number; 25, 36, 49.

b Each term is the cube of the term number; 125, 216, 343.

c Each term is $n(n+1)$ where n is the term number; 30, 42, 56.

9 **a** 79, 75 **b** 1280, 5120 **c** 625, 1296

d 13, 17 **e** 16, 22 **f** 6, 12

10 **a** 2, 4, 6, 8, 10 **b** -1, 1, 3, 5, 7

c 13, 15, 17, 19, 21 **d** $-1, -5, -9, -13, -17$

e 3, 8, 15, 24, 35 **f** 2, 4, 8, 16, 32

g $3, \frac{3}{2}, \frac{3}{4}, \frac{3}{8}, \frac{3}{16}$ **h** $-2, 4, -8, 16, -32$

i 17, 11, 23, -1, 47

EXERCISE 5B.1

1 **a** arithmetic **b** not arithmetic **c** arithmetic

d not arithmetic

2 **a** $u_1 = 5$, $d = 4$ **b** $u_1 = -4$, $d = 7$

c $u_1 = 23$, $d = -5$ **d** $u_1 = -6$, $d = -9$

3 **a** **i** $u_1 = 19$, $d = 6$ **ii** $u_n = 6n + 13$

iii $u_{15} = 103$

b **i** $u_1 = 101$, $d = -4$ **ii** $u_n = 105 - 4n$

iii $u_{15} = 45$

c **i** $u_1 = 8$, $d = 1\frac{1}{2}$ **ii** $u_n = 1\frac{1}{2}n + 6\frac{1}{2}$

iii $u_{15} = 29$

d **i** $u_1 = 31$, $d = 5$ **ii** $u_n = 5n + 26$

iii $u_{15} = 101$

e **i** $u_1 = 5$, $d = -8$ **ii** $u_n = 13 - 8n$

iii $u_{15} = -107$

f **i** $u_1 = a$, $d = d$ **ii** $u_n = a + (n-1)d$

iii $u_{15} = a + 14d$

4 **a** $u_1 = 6$, $d = 11$ **b** $u_n = 11n - 5$

c $u_{50} = 545$ **d** yes, $u_{30} = 325$ **e** no

5 **a** $u_1 = 87$, $d = -4$ **b** $u_n = 91 - 4n$

c $u_{40} = -69$ **d** u_{97}

6 **b** $u_1 = 1$, $d = 3$ **c** $u_{57} = 169$ **d** $u_{150} = 448$

7 **b** $u_1 = 32$, $d = -\frac{7}{2}$ **c** $u_{75} = -227$ **d** $n \geqslant 68$

8 **a** $u_1 = 36$, $d = -\frac{2}{3}$ **b** u_{100} **9** $u_{7692} = 100\,006$

10 **b** $u_{200} = 1381$ **c** no

11 **a** u_1 and d are even **b** u_1 is odd and d is even

12 **a** $k = 17\frac{1}{2}$ **b** $k = 4$ **c** $k = 5$ **d** $k = \frac{3}{2}$

e $k = 7$ **f** $k = -4$ **g** $k = -2$ or 3 **h** $k = -1$ or 3

13 **a** $u_n = 6n - 1$ **b** $u_n = -\frac{3}{2}n + \frac{11}{2}$

c $u_n = -5n + 36$ **d** $u_n = -\frac{3}{2}n + \frac{1}{2}$

14 $5, 6\frac{1}{4}, 7\frac{1}{2}, 8\frac{3}{4}, 10$

15 $-1, 3\frac{5}{7}, 8\frac{3}{7}, 13\frac{1}{7}, 17\frac{6}{7}, 22\frac{4}{7}, 27\frac{2}{7}, 32$

16 **a** $50, 48\frac{1}{2}, 47, 45\frac{1}{2}, 44$ **b** $u_{35} = -1$

17 **a** Month 1: 5 cars Month 4: 44 cars

Month 2: 18 cars Month 5: 57 cars

Month 3: 31 cars Month 6: 70 cars

b The total number of cars made increases by 13 each month. So, the common difference $d = 13$.

c 148 cars **d** 20 months

18 **a** Week 1: 2817 L Week 3: 2451 L

Week 2: 2634 L Week 4: 2268 L

b The amount in the tank decreases by the same amount (183 L) each week.

c in the 17th week

EXERCISE 5B.2

1 **a** 140.75 g **b** $u_n = 140.75n$

2 **a** 59.25 g **b** $u_n = 32 + 59.25n$ **c** $0 \leqslant n \leqslant 12$

3 **a** $u_n = 580 - 16n$ **b** $u_n = 9850 - \frac{7880}{29}n$

4 **a** 5.75 online friends per week **b** $u_n = 28.25 + 5.75n$

c No, the model is only intended to *estimate* the number of online friends. We can simply round to the nearest whole number.

d $143.25 \approx 143$ online friends

5 **a** $u_n = 1950 + 100n$

b **i** Catering is €100 per guest.

ii The venue hire is €1950 (with 0 guests).

c €10 450

EXERCISE 5C

1 **a** $u_1 = 5$, $r = 3$ **b** $u_1 = 72$, $r = \frac{1}{2}$

c $u_1 = 2$, $r = -4$ **d** $u_1 = 6$, $r = -\frac{1}{3}$

2 **a** $b = 18$, $c = 54$ **b** $b = 2\frac{1}{2}$, $c = 1\frac{1}{4}$

c $b = 3$, $c = -1\frac{1}{2}$

3 **a** **i** $u_1 = 3$, $r = 2$ **ii** $u_n = 3 \times 2^{n-1}$ **iii** $u_9 = 768$

b **i** $u_1 = 2$, $r = 5$ **ii** $u_n = 2 \times 5^{n-1}$

iii $u_9 = 781\,250$

c **i** $u_1 = 512$, $r = \frac{1}{2}$ **ii** $u_n = 512 \times 2^{1-n}$

iii $u_9 = 2$

d **i** $u_1 = 1$, $r = 3$ **ii** $u_n = 3^{n-1}$ **iii** $u_9 = 6561$

e **i** $u_1 = 12$, $r = \frac{3}{2}$ **ii** $u_n = 12 \times (\frac{3}{2})^{n-1}$

iii $u_9 = \frac{3^9}{2^6}$

f **i** $u_1 = \frac{1}{16}$, $r = -2$ **ii** $u_n = \frac{1}{16}(-2)^{n-1}$

iii $u_9 = 16$

4 **a** $u_1 = 5$, $r = 2$ **b** $u_n = 5 \times 2^{n-1}$, $u_{15} = 81\,920$

5 **a** $u_1 = 12$, $r = -\frac{1}{2}$

b $u_n = 12 \times (-\frac{1}{2})^{n-1}$, $u_{13} = \frac{3}{1024}$

6 $u_1 = 8$, $r = -\frac{3}{4}$, $u_{10} \approx -0.601$

7 $u_1 = 8$, $r = \frac{1}{\sqrt{2}}$ **Hint:** $u_n - 2^3 \times (2^{-\frac{1}{2}})^{n-1}$

8 **a** $\dfrac{u_{n+1}}{u_n} = \dfrac{3 \times u_n}{u_n} = 3$, $\therefore\ r = 3$ **b** $u_{10} = 2916$

　　c 3 terms

9 **a** $k = 6$ **b** $k = \frac{125}{2}$ **c** $k = \pm 14$ **d** $k = \pm 2$

　　e $k = \pm 36$ **f** $k = \pm 8$ **g** $k = 2$ **h** $k = -2$ or 4

10 **a** $k = -3$ or 4   **b** For $k = -3$, next term is $\frac{27}{2}$.

　　　　　　　　　　　For $k = 4$, next term is 24.

11 **a** $u_n = 3 \times 2^{n-1}$ **b** $u_n = 32 \times (-\frac{1}{2})^{n-1}$

　　c $u_n = 3 \times (\sqrt{2})^{n-1}$ **d** $u_n = 10 \times (\sqrt{2})^{1-n}$

　　　or $u_n = 3 \times (-\sqrt{2})^{n-1}$ 　or $u_n = 10 \times (-\sqrt{2})^{1-n}$

12 **a** $u_9 = 13\,122$ **b** $u_{14} = 2916\sqrt{3} \approx 5050$

　　c $u_{18} = \frac{3}{32\,768} \approx 0.000\,091\,6$

EXERCISE 5D

1 **a** **i** 1553 ants   **ii** 4823 ants   **b** ≈ 12.2 weeks

2 **a** ≈ 278 **b** year 2057

3 **a** **i** ≈ 73 deer   **ii** ≈ 167 deer   **b** ≈ 30.5 years

4 **a** **i** ≈ 2860 **ii** $\approx 184\,000$ **b** ≈ 14.5 years

5 **a** ≈ 3.36 g   **b** ≈ 10.2 more years

6 **a** €39 712.41 p.a.   **b** €54 599.05 p.a.

EXERCISE 5E.1

1 £9367.58   **2** £3453.07   **3** **a** €2233.58   **b** €233.58

4 €3577.67   **5** $716.38

6 **a** $20 977.42   **b** $23 077.89

7 **a** €37 305.85   **b** €7305.85

8 $11 222.90   **9** Bank A   **10** £14 977

11 $11 478   **12** $22 054.85   **13** ¥3 000 340

EXERCISE 5E.2

1 **a** $8487.20   **b** $16 229.84   **c** $27 672.16

2 **a** $1218.99   **b** $1485.95   **c** $1811.36

3 $16 236.48

EXERCISE 5E.3

1 **a** $5567.55   **b** $5246.43

2 **a** €23 651.79   **b** €20 691.02

3 **a** $4782.47   **b** $782.47   **c** $3958.90

　　d The investment has not been effective. The real value of the investment after 6 years is less than what was originally invested.

EXERCISE 5E.4

1 €1280   **2** **a** €26 103.52   **b** €83 896.48

3 **a** ¥30 013   **b** ¥57 487   **4** 24.8%

EXERCISE 5E.5

1 74 614.60 pesos   **2** $6629.65   **3** €4079.77

4 **a** $9452.47   **b** $12 482.59

5 **a** €6705.48   **b** €1705.48   **6** £4159.08   **7** $1997.13

8 $80 000   **9** $108.69   **10** 2 years 9 months

11 13 years 3 months   **12** 15 years   **13** 14.5% p.a.

14 6.00% p.a.   **15** 5.15% p.a.   **16** 21.2% p.a.

EXERCISE 5F

1 **a** $S_3 = 18$ **b** $S_5 = 37$ **c** $S_{12} = 153$ **2** $u_5 = 7$

3 **a** $1, \frac{1}{2}, \frac{1}{3}, \frac{1}{4}, \frac{1}{5}$ **b** $S_4 = \frac{25}{12}$ **c** $n \geqslant 11$

4 **a** **i** $S_n = \displaystyle\sum_{k=1}^{n} (8k - 5)$ **ii** $S_5 = 95$

　　b **i** $S_n = \displaystyle\sum_{k=1}^{n} (47 - 5k)$ **ii** $S_5 = 160$

　　c **i** $S_n = \displaystyle\sum_{k=1}^{n} 12(\tfrac{1}{2})^{k-1}$ **ii** $S_5 = 23\frac{1}{4}$

　　d **i** $S_n = \displaystyle\sum_{k=1}^{n} 2(\tfrac{3}{2})^{k-1}$ **ii** $S_5 = 26\frac{3}{8}$

　　e **i** $S_n = \displaystyle\sum_{k=1}^{n} \dfrac{1}{2^{k-1}}$ **ii** $S_5 = 1\frac{15}{16}$

　　f **i** $S_n = \displaystyle\sum_{k=1}^{n} k^3$ **ii** $S_5 = 225$

5 **a** 24   **b** 27   **c** 10   **d** 25   **e** 168   **f** 310

6 $S_{20} = \displaystyle\sum_{k=1}^{20} (3k - 1) = 610$

8 **a** $1 + \quad 2 \quad + \quad 3 \quad + \dots + (n-1) + n$
　　　　$n + (n-1) + (n-2) + \dots + \quad 2 \quad + 1$

　　b $S_n = \dfrac{n(n+1)}{2}$ **c** $a = 16$, $b = 3$

9 $S_n = \displaystyle\sum_{k=1}^{n} (2k - 1)$

10 $\displaystyle\sum_{k=1}^{n} (k+1)(k+2) = \dfrac{n(n^2 + 6n + 11)}{3}$,

　　$\displaystyle\sum_{k=1}^{10} (k+1)(k+2) = 570$

EXERCISE 5G

1 **a, b, c** 128

2 **a** 160   **b** 820   **c** $3087\frac{1}{2}$ **d** -1460

　　e -150 **f** -740

3 **a** 1749   **b** 184   **c** 2115   **d** $1410\frac{1}{2}$

4 **a** $d = 6$ **b** $n = 12$ **c** $S_{12} = 504$

5 **a** 160   **b** -630 **c** 135   **6** 203   **7** $-115\frac{1}{2}$

8 18 layers

9 **a** **i** 38 laps   **ii** 78 laps   **b** 1470 laps

10 **a** $450   **b** $4125

11 **a** 65 seats   **b** 1914 seats   **c** 47 850 seats

12 **a** 14 025   **b** 71 071   **c** 3367

13 $u_1 = 56$, $u_2 = 49$ **14** 8 terms

15 **a** $d = 3$ **b** $n = 11$ **16** 15 terms

17 **a** $u_n = 2n - 1$

　　b $S_n = \dfrac{n}{2}(u_1 + u_n) = \dfrac{n}{2}(1 + 2n - 1) = n^2$

18 **Hint:** $S_n = \dfrac{n}{2}(2u_1 + (n-1)d)$

　　　　　$= \dfrac{n}{2}(2 \times 1 + (n-1) \times 1)$, and so on

19 $10, 4, -2$ or $-2, 4, 10$ **20** $u_8 = 32$

21 $2, 5, 8, 11, 14$ or $14, 11, 8, 5, 2$

22 **a** $u_1 = 7$, $u_2 = 10$ **b** $u_{20} = 64$ **23** $S_{80} = -80$

24 a

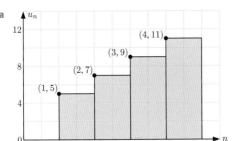

b S_n is the sum of the areas of the first n rectangles.

c i The left side of each rectangle increases in length by 2 units from the previous rectangle, $u_{n+1} = u_n + 2$.

ii The area of the $(n+1)$ th rectangle is u_{n+1}.
S_{n+1} is the sum of the areas of the first n rectangles and the $(n+1)$ th rectangle, $S_{n+1} = S_n + u_{n+1}$.

EXERCISE 5H

1 a, b 93

2 a 6560　　　**b** 5115　　　**c** $\frac{3069}{128} \approx 24.0$

d $\approx 189\,134$　　**e** $\frac{32\,769}{8192} \approx 4.00$　　**f** ≈ 0.585

3 a $S_n = \frac{3+\sqrt{3}}{2}\left((\sqrt{3})^n - 1\right)$　　**b** $S_n = 24\left(1 - (\frac{1}{2})^n\right)$

c $S_n = 1 - (0.1)^n$　　**d** $S_n = \frac{40}{3}\left(1 - (-\frac{1}{2})^n\right)$

4 a $u_1 = 3$　**b** $r = \frac{1}{3}$　**c** $u_5 = \frac{1}{27}$　**d** $S_5 = 4\frac{13}{27}$

5 a 3069　　**b** $\frac{4095}{1024} \approx 4.00$　　**c** $-134\,217\,732$

6 c $26\,361.59

7 a The number of grains of wheat starts at 1, and each square has double the number of grains of the previous square.

b $u_n = 2^{n-1}$

c $(2^{64} - 1) \approx 1.84 \times 10^{19}$ grains of wheat

8 a $5790　**b** $S_n = 100\,000((1.05)^n - 1)$　**c** $\approx \$40\,710$

9 a $S_1 = \frac{1}{2}$,　$S_2 = \frac{3}{4}$,　$S_3 = \frac{7}{8}$,　$S_4 = \frac{15}{16}$,　$S_5 = \frac{31}{32}$

b $S_n = \frac{2^n - 1}{2^n}$　　**c** $S_n = 1 - (\frac{1}{2})^n = \frac{2^n - 1}{2^n}$

d as $n \to \infty$, $S_n \to 1$

e As $n \to \infty$, the sum of the fractions approaches the area of a 1×1 unit square.

10 $u_4 = \frac{2}{3}$ or 54　　**11** $n = 5$　　**12** $n = 11$

13 a $u_8 = 1.25$　　**b** $S_8 = 318.75$　　**c** 12 terms

14 a In 3 years she will earn $183\,000 under *Option B*, compared with $126\,100 under *Option A*.

b i $A_n = 40\,000 \times (1.05)^{n-1}$　**ii** $B_n = 59\,000 + 1000n$

c ≈ 13.1 years

e i graph 1 represents T_A, graph 2 represents T_B

ii P(22.3, 1\,580\,000)　**iii** $0 \leqslant n \leqslant 22$

EXERCISE 5I

1 a It is geometric with $u_1 = \frac{3}{10}$ and $r = \frac{1}{10}$, and we are adding all the terms. Therefore it is an infinite geometric series.

b Using **a**,　$S = \dfrac{\frac{3}{10}}{1 - \frac{1}{10}} = \frac{3}{9} = \frac{1}{3}$　　$\therefore$　$0.\overline{3} = \frac{1}{3}$

2 a $0.\overline{4} = \frac{4}{9}$　　**b** $0.\overline{16} = \frac{16}{99}$　　**c** $0.\overline{312} = \frac{104}{333}$

4 a 54　　**b** 14.175

5 a 1　　**b** $4\frac{2}{7}$　　**6** $u_1 = 9$,　$r = \frac{2}{3}$

7 $u_1 = 8$,　$r = \frac{1}{5}$　and　$u_1 = 2$,　$r = \frac{4}{5}$

8 a $x = 4$ or -1

b When $x = 4$,　$r = \frac{1}{2}$　and　$|\frac{1}{2}| < 1$.

$\therefore$　the series converges with $S = 8$.
When $x = -1$,　$r = 3$　and　$|3| \not< 1$.

$\therefore$　the series is divergent so it does not converge.

9 b $S_n = 19 - 20(0.9)^n$　　**c** 19 seconds　　**10** 70 cm

11 a $0.\overline{9} = \frac{9}{10} + \frac{9}{100} + \frac{9}{1000} + ...$　which is geometric with $u_1 = \frac{9}{10}$ and $r = \frac{1}{10}$

$\therefore$　$0.\overline{9} = S = \dfrac{\frac{9}{10}}{1 - \frac{1}{10}} = 1$

c

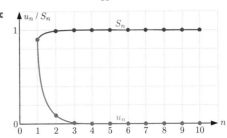

12 $x = \frac{1}{2}$

REVIEW SET 5A

1 a $u_2 = 9$　**b** $u_6 = 19$　**c** $S_4 = 37$

2 a arithmetic, $d = -8$　**b** geometric, $r = -\frac{1}{2}$　**c** neither

3 $k = -\frac{11}{2}$　　**4 b** $u_1 = 6$, $r = \frac{1}{2}$　**c** $u_{16} \approx 0.000\,183$

5 $u_n = \frac{1}{6} \times 2^{n-1}$　or　$-\frac{1}{6} \times (-2)^{n-1}$

6 23, 21, 19, 17, 15, 13, 11, 9　　**7** $S_9 = 234$

8 a ≈ 45.7 mL　**b** $u_n \approx 45.7n$　**c** ≈ 594 mL

9 a $10\frac{4}{5}$　**b** $16 + 8\sqrt{2}$　**10 a** 1272　**b** $302\frac{1}{2}$

11 a 2011: 630\,000 sheets,　2012: 567\,000 sheets

b $\approx 5\,630\,000$ sheets

12 a $u_n = 89 - 3n$　　**b** $u_n = \dfrac{2n+1}{n+3}$

c $u_n = 100(0.9)^{n-1}$

13 a $1 + 4 + 9 + 16 + 25 + 36 + 49 = 140$

b $\frac{4}{3} + \frac{5}{4} + \frac{6}{5} + \frac{7}{6} = \frac{99}{20}$

14 a $u_n = 3n + 1$　**15 a** £15\,425.20　**b** £15\,453.77

16 a €8180.46　　**b** €2180.46

17 $4800　　**18** 11 years 6 months

19 a €6622.87　　**b** €13\,313.28

20 a $24\,076.91　　**b** $22\,822.20

21 $u_n = 33 - 5n$,　$S_n = \dfrac{n}{2}(61 - 5n)$

22 a $u_8 = 61$　**b** $S_{10} = 435$　**c** $n = 15$

23 a $59\,900.22　　**b** $75\,099.78

24 a 17 terms　　**b** $\frac{131\,071}{512} \approx 255.998$

25 $u_1 = 54$, $r = \frac{2}{3}$　or　$u_1 = 150$, $r = -\frac{2}{5}$

$|r| < 1$ in both cases, so the series will converge.

For $u_1 = 54$, $r = \frac{2}{3}$, $S = 162$.

For $u_1 = 150$, $r = -\frac{2}{5}$, $S = 107\frac{1}{7}$.

26 **a** The number of cigarettes Tim smokes decreases by 5 each week, with 115 in the first week. The common difference $d = -5$.

b 24 weeks **c** 1380 cigarettes

27 **a** \$192 000

b **i** \$1000, \$1600, \$2200 **ii** \$189 600

c **i** \$500, \$600, \$720 **ii** \$196 242.12

d Option 3 **e** \$636.97

28 **a** $\frac{5}{2}\sqrt{2}$ **b** **i** $S_{10} = 310 + 155\sqrt{2}$ **ii** $320 + 160\sqrt{2}$

REVIEW SET 5B

1 **a** $\frac{1}{3}, \frac{1}{9}, \frac{1}{27}, \frac{1}{81}, \frac{1}{243}$ **b** 17, 22, 27, 32, 37

c $\frac{4}{3}, 1, \frac{4}{5}, \frac{2}{3}, \frac{4}{7}$

2 **b** $u_1 = 63$, $d = -5$ **c** $u_{37} = -117$

d $u_{54} = -202$

3 **a** $u_1 = 3$, $r = 4$ **b** $u_n = 3 \times 4^{n-1}$, $u_9 = 196\,608$

4 **a** $u_n = 73 - 6n$ **b** $u_{34} = -131$

5 **a** $u_{81} = -36$ **b** $u_{35} = -1\frac{1}{2}$ **c** $S_{40} = 375$

6 **a** $S_{12} = 432$ **b** $S_{12} = \frac{12\,285}{256} \approx 48.0$

7 **a** $a = 15$ **b** $a = 12$ or -12

8 **a** $u_n = \frac{25}{6}n - \frac{265}{6}$

b Stacy makes $\approx £4.17$ per customer. The setup fee for the stand $\approx £44.17$.

c $\approx £105.83$

9 $u_{12} = 10\,240$ **10** 27 metres **11** €9838.99

12 **a** \$8337.11 **b** \$8369.33 **c** \$8376.76

13 **a** $k = \pm\frac{2\sqrt{3}}{3}$ **b** When $k = \frac{2\sqrt{3}}{3}$, $r = \frac{\sqrt{3}}{6}$

When $k = -\frac{2\sqrt{3}}{3}$, $r = -\frac{\sqrt{3}}{6}$

14 **a** 35.5 km **b** 1183 km

15 **a** $\frac{1331}{2100} \approx 0.634$ **b** $\frac{98}{15} \approx 6.53$

16 $u_{11} = \frac{8}{19\,683} \approx 0.000\,406$ **17** 3.80% p.a.

18 182 months (15 years 2 months)

19 **a** \$10 069.82 **b** \$7887.74 **20** \$2174.63

21 **a** 70 **b** ≈ 241 **c** $\frac{64}{1875} \approx 0.0341$

22 **a** $u_n = \frac{3}{4} \times 2^{n-1}$ **b** $S_{15} = 24\,575\frac{1}{4}$

23 **a** 33 **b** The difference between terms is constant.

c 1328

24 after 3 years **25** **a** ≈ 3470 iguanas **b** year 2029

26 **a** $0 < x < 1$ (we require $|2x - 1| < 1$) **b** $35\frac{5}{7}$

27 **a** \$82 539.08

b

n (years)	0	1	2	3	4
V_n (\$)	100 000	106 000	112 360	119 101.60	126 247.70

c $V_n = 100\,000 \times (1.06)^n$ dollars

d $S_n = 6000n$ dollars

e

n (years)	0	1	2	3	4
T_n (\$)	100 000	112 000	124 360	137 101.60	150 247.70

f 19 years

EXERCISE 6A

1 **a** ≈ 5.24 cm **b** ≈ 12.4 cm

2 **a** ≈ 57.2 mm **b** ≈ 17.5 cm **c** ≈ 33.5 cm

d ≈ 10.2 cm **e** ≈ 40.5 m **f** ≈ 138 cm

3 ≈ 41.4 cm **4** ≈ 68.5 mm

5 **a** ≈ 133 cm^2 **b** ≈ 106 mm^2 **c** ≈ 9.62 m^2

d ≈ 58.5 cm^2 **e** ≈ 120 m^2 **f** ≈ 192 cm^2

6 ≈ 5.26 cm **7** ≈ 21.5 cm

8 **a** ≈ 191 m **b** ≈ 6.04 m s^{-1}

9 **a** $8\sqrt{2} \approx 11.3$ mm **b** $8\pi(1 + \sqrt{2}) \approx 60.7$ mm

c 128 mm^2

10 **c** $r = 0.98$ m, $\theta \approx 58.5$ **d** ≈ 1.29 m

EXERCISE 6B.1

1 **a** 413.34 cm^2 **b** 5.7802 m^2 **c** 78 mm^2

2 **a** ≈ 112 cm^2 **b** ≈ 14.9 cm^2 **c** ≈ 392 m^2

3 **a**

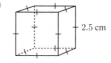

surface area = 37.5 cm^2

b

surface area = 356 cm^2

c

surface area ≈ 181 cm^2

4 **a** 1440 cm^2 **b** ≈ 51.6 cm^2 **c** ≈ 181 m^2

5 **a** 23 814 cm^2

b

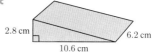

area = 2754 cm^2

area = 7446 cm^2

area = 2550 cm^2

area ≈ 5617 cm^2

c $\approx$ €540

6 \$239.10 **7** **a** 26 940 cm^2 **b** ≈ 407 m^2

8 ≈ 2310 cm^2

9 **a** $(10x^2 + 12x)$ cm^2 **b** $(1 + \sqrt{3})x^2$ cm^2

EXERCISE 6B.2

1 **a** ≈ 1005.3 cm^2 **b** ≈ 145.3 cm^2 **c** ≈ 188.5 cm^2

d ≈ 549.8 m^2 **e** ≈ 1068.1 cm^2 **f** ≈ 63.6 km^2

2 ≈ 84.8 cm^2

3 **a** ≈ 2210 cm^2 **b** ≈ 66.5 m^2 **c** $\approx 14\,800$ mm^2

d ≈ 12.1 cm^2

4 **a** ≈ 19.4 m^2 **b** $\approx \$883.38$ **c** $\approx \$21\,201$

5 **a** $s \approx 5.39$ **b** ≈ 46.4 m^2 **c** $\approx \$835.24$

6 **a** ≈ 50.3 m^2 **b** $\approx \$1166.16$ **c** ≈ 150.8 m^2
   d $\approx \$2789.73$ **e** $\approx \$3960$

7 **a** $SA = 4\pi r^2$ **b** ≈ 5.40 m

8 **a** $SA = 3\pi r^2$ **b** **i** ≈ 4.50 cm   **ii** ≈ 4.24 cm

9 **a** $SA = 6\pi x^2$ cm^2 **b** $SA = 3\pi r^2$ cm^2
   c $SA = \pi x^2(1 + \sqrt{5})$ cm^2

10 **a** 4 cm   **b** ≈ 25.1 cm   **c** ≈ 84.1 mm

11 **a** ≈ 34.7 m^2 **b** ≈ 285.4 m^2 **c** ≈ 62.8 cm^2

12 $\approx 24\,600$ km   **13** **a** $\dfrac{\theta \pi s}{180}$ **b** $\theta = \dfrac{360r}{s}$

EXERCISE 6C.1

1 **a** 96 m^3 **b** 25.116 cm^3 **c** 5.536 m^3
   d 373 cm^3 **e** 765.486 cm^3 **f** ≈ 2940 cm^3
   g ≈ 19.5 m^3 **h** ≈ 1.51 m^3 **i** 1440 cm^3

2 **a**

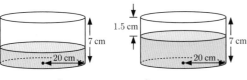

Uncooked cake   Cooked cake

   b **i** ≈ 2510 cm^3 **ii** ≈ 6910 cm^3 **c** 175%

3 **a** 648 000 000 mm^3 **b** ≈ 11.6 m^3 **c** 156 cm^3

4 **a** 0.5 m   **b** 0.45 m   **c** ≈ 0.373 m^3

5 **a** 7.176 m^3 **b** \$972

6 **a**

   b ≈ 40.8 m^2
   c ≈ 4.08 m^3

12 m
1 m

7 **a** ≈ 8.58 m^3
   c $\frac{1}{4\pi} \approx 0.0796$. The treefellers' formula gives a slightly
   lower volume, indicating that not all of the timber is usable.

8 ≈ 81.1 tonnes

9 **a** 2 trailer loads   **b** \$174.60
   c **i** 2 loads   **ii** \$95.90   **d** \$270.50

10 **a** 100 cm   **b** 1 500 000 cm^3 (or 1.5 m^3)   **c** 95 000 cm^2

11 **a** $\frac{8}{3} \approx 2.67$ cm   **b** ≈ 3.24 cm   **c** ≈ 1.74 cm

12 ≈ 12.7 cm

EXERCISE 6C.2

1 **a** ≈ 463 cm^3 **b** ≈ 4.60 cm^3 **c** ≈ 26.5 cm^3
   d ≈ 1870 m^3 **e** ≈ 155 m^3 **f** ≈ 226 cm^3

2 **a** $\approx 29\,000$ m^3 **b** 480 m^3 **c** ≈ 497 cm^3

3 **a** ≈ 11.9 m^3 **b** 5.8 m   **c** ≈ 1.36 m^3 more
   e The hemispherical design, as it holds more concrete and is
   shorter.

4 **a** ≈ 4.46 cm   **b** ≈ 2.60 m   **c** ≈ 5.60 cm

6 **a** **i** ≈ 67.0 cm^3 **ii** ≈ 113 m^3
   b $V = \frac{2}{3}\pi r^3$ This is half the volume of a sphere because
   when $h = r$, the cap is a hemisphere.

EXERCISE 6D

1 **a** 800 cm^3 **b** 12 000 cm^3 **c** 4.6 m^3 **d** 3200 cm^3

2 **a** 8.4 mL   **b** 1.8 L   **c** 1.8 kL   **d** 7154 kL

3 38.5 m^3

4 **a** 12.852 kL   **b** ≈ 61.2 kL   **c** ≈ 68.0 kL

5 **a** $\approx 12\,200$ cm^3 **b** ≈ 12.2 L   **6** 594 425 kL

7 **a** ≈ 954 mL   **b** 4.92 kL   **c** 5155 tins   **d** \$18 042.50

8 **a** 87 680 mm^2
   b The external surface area and internal surface area of a
   container may be different.
   c **i** 1 361 920 mm^3 **ii** 1361.92 mL   **iii** 327 680 mm^3

9 ≈ 0.553 m (or ≈ 55.3 cm)

10 **a** 1.32 m^3 **b** 1.32 kL   **c** ≈ 10.5 cm   **11** ≈ 7.8 cm

12 **a** ≈ 252 mL   **b** **i** ≈ 189 mL   **ii** 3.25 cm

13 35 truck loads

REVIEW SET 6A

1 **a** ≈ 18.3 cm   **b** ≈ 38.3 cm   **c** ≈ 91.6 cm^2

2 ≈ 10.4 cm

3 **a** ≈ 377.0 cm^2 **b** ≈ 339.8 cm^2 **c** ≈ 201.1 cm^2

4 **a** 71 m^2 **b** \$239.25   **5** ≈ 2670 m^2

6 **a** ≈ 4.99 m^3 **b** 853 cm^3 **c** ≈ 0.452 m^3

7 ≈ 3.22 m^3 **8** 16 333 spikes   **9** $\approx 82\,400$ cm^3

10 **a** 65 000 cm^3 **b** 0.065 m^3

11 **a** 734.44 mL   **b** ≈ 198 L   **12** ≈ 68.4 mm

13 **a** height $= 3.3$ m $- 1.8$ m $- 0.8$ m $= 0.7$ m $= 70$ cm
   b ≈ 1.06 m   **c** ≈ 15.7 m^2
   d **Hint:** Volume of silo
                $=$ volume of hemisphere $+$ volume of cylinder
                    $+$ volume of cone
   e ≈ 5.2 kL

REVIEW SET 6B

1 **a** $\theta° \approx 76.6°$ **b** ≈ 14.3 cm^2

2 **a** ≈ 29.1 cm   **b** ≈ 25.1 cm^2

3 **a** ≈ 84.7 cm^2 **b** ≈ 7110 mm^2 **c** ≈ 10.2 m^2

4 ≈ 23.5 m^2 **5** ≈ 434 cm^2

6 **a** ≈ 164 cm^3 **b** 120 m^3 **c** $\approx 10\,300$ mm^3

7 **a** 0.52 m^3 **b** 5.08 m^2 **8** ≈ 5.03 m^3 **9** ≈ 5680 L

10 **a** ≈ 133 cm^3 **b** 74 cones   **11** ≈ 1.03 m

12 **a** $\approx 6.08 \times 10^{18}$ m^2 **b** $\approx 1.41 \times 10^{27}$ m^3

13 **a** ≈ 56.5 cm^3 **b** 3 cm   **c** ≈ 96.5 cm^2

EXERCISE 7A

1 **a** **i** $\frac{4}{5}$ **ii** $\frac{3}{5}$ **iii** $\frac{4}{3}$
   b **i** $\frac{12}{13}$ **ii** $\frac{5}{13}$ **iii** $\frac{12}{5}$
   c **i** $\frac{8}{17}$ **ii** $\frac{15}{17}$ **iii** $\frac{8}{15}$
   d **i** $\frac{5}{8}$ **ii** $\frac{\sqrt{39}}{8}$ **iii** $\frac{5}{\sqrt{39}}$
   e **i** $\frac{\sqrt{33}}{7}$ **ii** $\frac{4}{7}$ **iii** $\frac{\sqrt{33}}{4}$
   f **i** $\frac{7}{\sqrt{65}}$ **ii** $\frac{4}{\sqrt{65}}$ **iii** $\frac{7}{4}$

2 **a** ≈ 0.342 **b** ≈ 0.970 **c** ≈ 0.891 **d** ≈ 0.731
   e ≈ 0.625 **f** ≈ 2.747

3 **a** $XY \approx 4.9$ cm, $XZ \approx 3.3$ cm, $YZ \approx 5.9$ cm
   b **i** ≈ 0.83 **ii** ≈ 0.56 **iii** ≈ 1.48

4 **a** [PQ]   **b** $\cos 23°$ **c** less than 1

5 **a** **Hint:** Base angles of an isosceles triangle are equal, and
                sum of all angles in a triangle is $180°$.
   b $AB = \sqrt{2} \approx 1.41$ m
   c **i** $\frac{1}{\sqrt{2}} \approx 0.707$ **ii** $\frac{1}{\sqrt{2}} \approx 0.707$ **iii** 1

6 The OPP and ADJ sides will always be smaller than the HYP. So, the sine and cosine ratios will always be less than or equal to 1.

7 a i $\dfrac{a}{c}$ **ii** $\dfrac{b}{c}$ **iii** $\dfrac{a}{b}$ **iv** $\dfrac{b}{c}$ **v** $\dfrac{a}{c}$ **vi** $\dfrac{b}{a}$

  b $A = 90° - B$

  c i $\sin\theta = \cos(90° - \theta)$ **ii** $\cos\theta = \sin(90° - \theta)$

   iii $\tan\theta = \dfrac{1}{\tan(90° - \theta)}$

EXERCISE 7B

1 a $\sin 21° = \dfrac{x}{k}$ **b** $\cos 50° = \dfrac{x}{m}$ **c** $\tan 38° = \dfrac{x}{t}$

  d $\cos 56° = \dfrac{a}{x}$ **e** $\tan 41° = \dfrac{p}{x}$ **f** $\sin 36° = \dfrac{x}{n}$

2 a ≈ 7.00 cm   **b** ≈ 7.50 m   **c** ≈ 7.82 cm
  d ≈ 4.82 cm   **e** ≈ 5.55 m   **f** ≈ 21.5 cm
  g ≈ 18.8 cm   **h** ≈ 5.17 m   **i** ≈ 6.38 m
  j ≈ 4.82 cm   **k** 7.22 cm   **l** ≈ 43.3 m

3 a $x \approx 3.98$ **b i** $y \approx 4.98$ **ii** $y \approx 4.98$

4 a $x \approx 2.87,\ y \approx 4.10$ **b** $x \approx 16.40,\ y \approx 18.25$
  c $x \approx 10.77,\ y \approx 14.50$

5 a perimeter ≈ 23.2 cm,   area ≈ 22.9 cm²
  b perimeter ≈ 17.0 cm,   area ≈ 10.9 cm²

6 a ≈ 5.83 cm   **b** ≈ 4.25 cm   **c** ≈ 16.2 cm
  d ≈ 16.0 cm²

EXERCISE 7C

1 a $\theta \approx 53.1°$ **b** $\theta \approx 45.6°$ **c** $\theta \approx 40.6°$
  d $\theta \approx 42.6°$ **e** $\theta \approx 13.7°$ **f** $\theta \approx 52.4°$
  g $\theta \approx 76.1°$ **h** $\theta = 60°$ **i** $\theta \approx 36.0°$

2 a $\theta \approx 56.3°$ **b i** $\phi \approx 33.7°$ **ii** $\phi \approx 33.7°$

3 a $\theta \approx 39.7°,\ \phi \approx 50.3°$ **b** $\alpha \approx 38.9°,\ \beta \approx 51.1°$
  c $\theta \approx 61.5°,\ \phi \approx 28.5°$

4 a The triangle cannot be drawn with the given dimensions.
  b The triangle cannot be drawn with the given dimensions.
  c The result is not a triangle, but a straight line of length 9.3 m.

5 a $x \approx 2.65,\ \theta \approx 37.1°$
  b $x \approx 6.16,\ \theta \approx 50.3°,\ y \approx 13.0$

EXERCISE 7D

1 a $x \approx 4.13$ **b** $\alpha \approx 75.5°$ **c** $\beta \approx 41.0°$
  d $x \approx 6.29$ **e** $\theta \approx 51.9°$ **f** $x \approx 12.6$

2 $\approx 22.4°$ **3** ≈ 11.8 cm

4 a ≈ 27.2 cm²   **b** ≈ 153 m²   **5** $\approx 119°$

6 ≈ 36.5 cm   **7** $\theta \approx 45.4°$

8 a $x \approx 3.44$ **b** $\alpha \approx 51.5°$

9 a ≈ 12.3 cm²   **b** ≈ 14.3 cm²

10 a   **b** ≈ 9.33 m
   c $\approx 71.3°$

11 a ≈ 2.59 cm   **b** ≈ 8.46 cm
12 a $\theta \approx 36.9°$ **b** $r \approx 11.3$ **c** $\alpha \approx 61.9°$
13 ≈ 7.99 cm   **14** $\approx 89.2°$ **15** $\approx 47.2°$

EXERCISE 7E

1 ≈ 18.3 m   **2 a** ≈ 46.4 m   **b** ≈ 259 m
3 ≈ 159 m   **4** $\approx 1.58°$ **5 a** $\approx 26.4°$ **b** $\approx 26.4°$

6 ≈ 142 m   **7** $\theta \approx 12.6°$ **8** ≈ 9.56 m   **9** ≈ 46.7 m
10 $\beta \approx 129°$ **11** ≈ 10.9 m   **12** ≈ 104 m   **13** ≈ 962 m
14 ≈ 3.17 km   **15** ≈ 30.8 m   **16** ≈ 13.9 cm
17 a ≈ 18.4 cm   **b** $\approx 35.3°$
18 a ≈ 10.8 cm   **b** $\approx 36.5°$ **c** ≈ 9.49 cm   **d** $\approx 40.1°$
19 a ≈ 82.4 cm   **b** ≈ 77.7 L
20 a i 2 m   **ii** ≈ 2.01 m   **b** $\approx 6.84°$
21 a ≈ 10.2 m   **b** no   **22 a** ≈ 73.4 m   **b** $\approx 16.2°$
23 $\approx 67.0°$
24 a ≈ 1.49 m³   **b** ≈ 0.331 m³   **c** ≈ 88.9 cm³
25 a Hint: Consider

  b ≈ 0.285 arc seconds

EXERCISE 7F

1 a 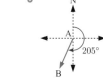   **b**

   c   **d**

2 a $126°$ **b** $245°$ **c** $060°$ **d** $311°$
  e $152°$ **f** $308°$

3 a $316°$ **b** $198°$ **c** $111°$ **d** $026°$

4 a $072°$ **b** $342°$ **c** $252°$ **d** $293°$

5 $\approx 125°$ **6 a** ≈ 224 m   **b** $\approx 333°$

7 a ≈ 38.4 km   **b** $\approx 051.3°$

8 a   **b** ≈ 1.20 km   **c** ≈ 0.903 km

9 ≈ 2.41 km   **10** ≈ 12.6 km
11 a ≈ 854 m   **b** $\approx 203°$
12 ≈ 73.3 km on the bearing $\approx 191°$
13 ≈ 17.8 km on the bearing $\approx 162°$

EXERCISE 7G

1 a i [EH]   **ii** [EF]   **iii** [EG]   **iv** [FH]
  b i [MR]   **ii** [MN]

2 a i $A\widehat{F}E$ **ii** $B\widehat{M}F$ **iii** $A\widehat{D}E$ **iv** $B\widehat{N}F$
  b i $B\widehat{A}M$ **ii** $B\widehat{N}M$ **iii** $E\widehat{A}N$

3 a i $\approx 36.9°$ **ii** $\approx 25.1°$ **iii** $\approx 56.3°$ **iv** $\approx 29.1°$
  b i $\approx 33.7°$ **ii** $\approx 33.7°$ **iii** $\approx 25.2°$ **iv** $\approx 30.8°$
  c i $\approx 59.0°$ **ii** $\approx 22.0°$ **iii** $\approx 22.6°$
  d i $\approx 64.9°$ **ii** $\approx 71.7°$

REVIEW SET 7A

1 a 10 cm   b $\frac{6}{10} = \frac{3}{5}$ c $\frac{8}{10} = \frac{4}{5}$ d $\frac{6}{8} = \frac{3}{4}$

2 a ≈ 0.515 b ≈ 0.139 c ≈ 4.011

3 a $x \approx 3.51$ b $x \approx 51.1$ c $x \approx 5.62$

4 a ≈ 200 cm   b ≈ 1500 cm^2

5 $\theta = 33°$, $x \approx 3.90$, $y \approx 7.15$ 6 $\theta \approx 8.19°$

7 a $x \approx 2.8$ b $x \approx 4.2$ c $x \approx 5.2$ 8 ≈ 13.5 m

9 a 118°   b 231°   c 329°

10 13 km on the bearing $\approx 203°$ from the helipad.

11 $\approx 8.74°$ 12 ≈ 0.607 L   13 a $\approx 53.1°$ b $\approx 62.1°$

REVIEW SET 7B

1 $\sin\theta = \frac{5}{\sqrt{146}}$, $\cos\theta = \frac{11}{\sqrt{146}}$, $\tan\theta = \frac{5}{11}$

2 a AB ≈ 4.5 cm, AC ≈ 2.2 cm, BC ≈ 5.0 cm

   b i ≈ 0.44 ii ≈ 0.90 iii ≈ 0.49

3 a $\theta \approx 34.8°$ b $\theta \approx 39.7°$ c $\theta \approx 36.0°$

4 AB ≈ 120 mm, AC ≈ 111 mm

5 $x \approx 25.7$, $\theta \approx 53.6°$, $\alpha \approx 36.4°$ 6 $\approx 124°$

7 ≈ 2.54 cm   8 ≈ 204 m   9 a 90°   b $\approx 33.9°$

10 ≈ 3.91 km on the bearing $\approx 253°$ from his starting point.

11 ≈ 485 m^3 12 a $\approx 14.4°$ b $\approx 18.9°$ c $\approx 21.8°$

13 a i ≈ 27.6 cm   ii ≈ 23.3 cm   b ≈ 6010 cm^3

EXERCISE 8A

1

θ	$\cos\theta$	$\sin\theta$	$\cos(180° - \theta)$	$\sin(180° - \theta)$
12°	0.9781	0.2079	-0.9781	0.2079
25°	0.9063	0.4226	-0.9063	0.4226
38°	0.7880	0.6157	-0.7880	0.6157
56°	0.5592	0.8290	-0.5592	0.8290
70°	0.3420	0.9397	-0.3420	0.9397
85°	0.0872	0.9962	-0.0872	0.9962

2 P(0.616, 0.788), Q(-0.766, 0.643)

3 a 135°   b 130°   c 162°   d 109°

4 a 77°   b 61°   c 54°   d 25°

5 a 177°   b 158°   c 133°   d 117°

6 a 85°   b 78°   c 34°   d 18°

EXERCISE 8B

1 a ≈ 28.9 cm^2 b ≈ 384 km^2 c 20 m^2

   d ≈ 18.7 cm^2 e ≈ 28.3 cm^2 f ≈ 52.0 m^2

2 $x \approx 19.0$ 3 a ≈ 166 cm^2 b ≈ 1410 cm^2

4 ≈ 18.9 cm^2 5 ≈ 137 cm^2

6 a ≈ 71.616 m^2 b ≈ 8.43 m

7 ≈ 374 cm^2 8 ≈ 7.49 cm   9 ≈ 11.9 m

10 a $\approx 48.6°$ or $\approx 131.4°$ b $\approx 42.1°$ or $\approx 137.9°$

11 $\frac{1}{4}$ is not covered

12 a ≈ 35.1 cm^2 b ≈ 61.8 cm^2 c ≈ 40.4 mm^2

13 ≈ 4.69 cm^2

EXERCISE 8C

1 a ≈ 3.84 cm   b ≈ 7.99 m   c ≈ 9.28 cm

   d ≈ 28.8 cm   e ≈ 3.38 km   f ≈ 14.2 m

2 a $\theta \approx 82.8°$ b $\theta \approx 54.8°$ c $\theta \approx 98.2°$

3 $B\widehat{A}C \approx 52.0°$, $A\widehat{B}C \approx 59.3°$, $A\widehat{C}B \approx 68.7°$

4 a $\approx 112°$ b ≈ 16.2 cm^2

5 a $\approx 40.3°$ b $\approx 107°$

6 a $\cos\theta = 0.65$ b $x \approx 3.81$

7 a $\theta \approx 75.2°$ b ≈ 6.30 m

8 a DB ≈ 4.09 m, BC ≈ 9.86 m

   b $A\widehat{B}E \approx 68.2°$, $D\widehat{B}C \approx 57.5°$ c ≈ 17.0 m^2

9 b $x = 3 + \sqrt{22}$

10 a $x \approx 10.8$ b $x \approx 2.77$ c $x \approx 2.89$

11 $x \approx 1.41$ or 7.78   12 BD ≈ 12.4 cm

13 $\theta \approx 71.6°$ 14 ≈ 6.40 cm

EXERCISE 8D.1

1 a $x \approx 28.4$ b $x \approx 13.4$ c $x \approx 3.79$

   d $x \approx 10.3$ e $x \approx 4.49$ f $x \approx 7.07$

2 a $a \approx 21.3$ cm   b $b \approx 76.9$ cm   c $c \approx 5.09$ cm

3 a $B\widehat{A}C = 74°$, AB ≈ 7.99 cm, BC ≈ 9.05 cm

   b $X\widehat{Z}Y = 108°$, XZ ≈ 13.5 cm, XY ≈ 26.5 cm

4 $x \approx 17.7$, $y \approx 33.1$ 5 $x = 11 + \frac{11}{2}\sqrt{2}$

EXERCISE 8D.2

1 a $x \approx 9.85$ b $x \approx 41.3$ c $x \approx 52.8$

2 a $B\widehat{A}C \approx 30.9°$ b $A\widehat{B}C \approx 28.7°$ c $A\widehat{C}B \approx 30.1°$

3 a We find that $\sin x \approx 1.04$ which has no solutions.
   b The triangle cannot be drawn with the given dimensions.

4 a i $A\widehat{C}B \approx 22.9°$ ii $B\widehat{A}C \approx 127°$ b ≈ 25.1 cm^2

EXERCISE 8E

1 ≈ 17.7 m   2 ≈ 207 m   3 $\approx 23.9°$

4 ≈ 10.1 km   5 ≈ 37.6 km

6 a ≈ 5.63 km   b on the bearing $\approx 115°$

   c i Esko   ii ≈ 7.37 min (≈ 7 min 22 s)   d $\approx 295°$

7 $\approx 9.38°$ 8 ≈ 69.1 m   9 a ≈ 38.0 m   b ≈ 94.0 m

10 a   b ≈ 2.98 km   c $\approx 179°$

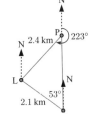

11 $\approx 65.6°$ 12 ≈ 9.12 km

13 a ≈ 74.9 km^2 b ≈ 7490 ha   14 ≈ 85.0 mm

15 $\approx 104.2°$

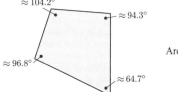

Area $\approx 13\,100$ m^2

16 ≈ 7400 m^2 17 ≈ 29.2 m

EXERCISE 8F

1 $C \approx 62.1°$ or $C \approx 117.9°$

2 a $\approx 46.6°$ b $\approx 55.5°$ or 124.5°

   c $\approx 25.4°$ or 154.6°

3   **a** $\approx 69.4°$ or $\approx 110.6°$

b

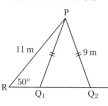

c For $P\widehat{Q}R \approx 69.4°$:
   i $\approx 60.6°$
   ii ≈ 43.1 m^2
   iii ≈ 30.2 m
For $P\widehat{Q}R \approx 110.6°$:
   i $\approx 19.4°$
   ii ≈ 16.5 m^2
   iii ≈ 23.9 m

REVIEW SET 8A

1   **a** $60°$ **b** $15°$ **2**   **a** $161°$ **b** $96°$

3   **a** ≈ 26.8 cm^2 **b** 14 km^2 **c** ≈ 33.0 m^2

4 ≈ 22.7 cm^2 **5**   **a** ≈ 10.5 cm   **b** ≈ 11.6 m

6   **a** $x \approx 9.24$ **b** $\theta \approx 59.2°$ **c** $x \approx 6.28$

7   If the unknown is an angle, use the cosine rule to avoid an ambiguous case.

8 ≈ 113 cm^2 **9** ≈ 51.6 cm^2

10   **a** $x = 3$ or 5 **b** Kady can draw 2 triangles:

11   **b** $x \approx 19.3$ **c** ≈ 43.3 cm   **12** ≈ 56.3 m

13 $x \approx 18.5$, $y \approx 13.8$ **14** 42 km

15   **a** $\approx 69.5°$ or $\approx 110.5°$
   b For $A\widehat{B}C \approx 69.5°$, area ≈ 16.3 cm^2.
   For $A\widehat{B}C \approx 110.5°$, area ≈ 8.09 cm^2.

REVIEW SET 8B

1   **a** $149°$ **b** $118°$ **2**   **a** $58°$ **b** $5°$

3   **a** $x \approx 34.1$ **b** $x \approx 18.9$ **4** $\approx 47.5°$ or $132.5°$

5   **a** $\theta \approx 29.9°$ **b** $\theta \approx 103°$

6   **a** AC ≈ 12.6 cm, $B\widehat{A}C \approx 48.6°$, $A\widehat{C}B \approx 57.4°$
   b $P\widehat{R}Q = 51°$,   PQ ≈ 7.83 cm,   QR ≈ 7.25 cm
   c $Y\widehat{X}Z \approx 78.3°$, $X\widehat{Y}Z \approx 55.5°$, $X\widehat{Z}Y \approx 46.2°$

7   **a** $x \approx 6.93$ **b** $x \approx 11.4$ **c** $x \approx 7.16$ **d** $x \approx 34.7$

8 ≈ 17.7 m   **9** ≈ 7.32 m

10   perimeter ≈ 578 m,   area $\approx 15\,000$ m^2

11 ≈ 560 m on the bearing $\approx 079.7°$

12 $B\widehat{A}D \approx 90.5°$, $B\widehat{C}D \approx 94.3°$, $A\widehat{D}C \approx 70.2°$

13 $Q \approx 39.7°$ **14**   **a** $\approx 10\,600$ m^2 **b** ≈ 1.06 ha

15   **a** The information given could give two triangles:
   b ≈ 2.23 m^3

16   **a** **i** ≈ 20.8 mm   **ii** ≈ 374 mm^2 **b** ≈ 2270 mm^3

EXERCISE 9A

1   **a**   **b**

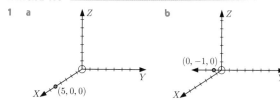

c

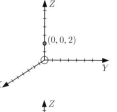

d

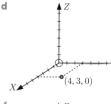

e

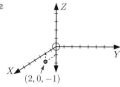

f

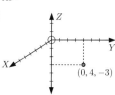

g

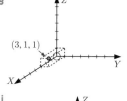

h

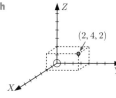

i

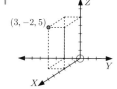

j

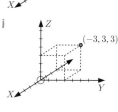

k

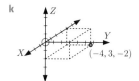

l

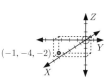

2   **a**   **i** $2\sqrt{14}$ units   **ii** $(3, -2, 1)$
   b   **i** $2\sqrt{5}$ units   **ii** $(2, 1, -1)$
   c   **i** $2\sqrt{6}$ units   **ii** $(3, -2, 1)$
   d   **i** $\sqrt{69}$ units   **ii** $(-4, \frac{7}{2}, 4)$
   e   **i** $5\sqrt{2}$ units   **ii** $(\frac{3}{2}, 3, \frac{1}{2})$
   f   **i** $\sqrt{83}$ units   **ii** $(-\frac{3}{2}, \frac{9}{2}, -\frac{1}{2})$

3   **a** isosceles with AB $=$ AC $= \sqrt{101}$ units   **b** scalene

4   AB $= \sqrt{342}$ units,   AC $= \sqrt{72}$ units,   BC $= \sqrt{414}$ units
   AB$^2 +$ AC$^2 = (\sqrt{342})^2 + (\sqrt{72})^2 = 414 =$ BC^2
   $\therefore$ triangle ABC is right angled.

5   **a** M$(\frac{7}{2}, -2, 3)$,   N$(\frac{1}{2}, -5, -1)$
   b PR $= 2\sqrt{34}$ units,   MN $= \sqrt{34}$ units $= \frac{1}{2}$ PR

6 $k = 2 \pm \sqrt{23}$

EXERCISE 9B

1   **a** 27 units^3 **b** 60 units^3 **c** 40 units^3

2   **a** D$(-7, 0, 3)$,   E$(-7, 4, 0)$ **b** 42 units^3
   c 5 units   **d** 96 units^2

3   **a** The centre of the base is $(3, 3, 0)$ which is directly below the apex.

b 108 units^3

c i M(6, 3, 0)   ii $3\sqrt{10}$ units   iii $36(1 + \sqrt{10})$ units^2

4 volume = 720 units^3, surface area = 564 units^2

5 a $\sqrt{41}$ units   b 82π units^3 c $\sqrt{77}$ units
   d ≈ 305 units^2

6 a $\sqrt{238}$ units   b $\approx 15\,400$ units^3

7 a $(-3, 4, -3)$ b $\sqrt{38}$ units
   c volume ≈ 981 units^3, surface area ≈ 478 units^2

8 a i A(10, 40, 0), B(50, 160, 0), C(110, 140, 0),
         D(70, 20, 0)
      ii (60, 90, 15)
   b 40 000 m^3 c ≈ 8540 m^2

EXERCISE 9C

1 a $\approx 50.2°$ b $\approx 48.1°$

2 a M(3, 3, 0)   b $\approx 25.4°$ c $\approx 50.2°$

3 a M(4, 6, 0)   b $\approx 66.5°$ c i $\approx 35.0°$ ii $\approx 44.1°$

4 a M(2, 4, 0)   b i $\approx 68.2°$ ii $\approx 60.5°$

5 a M$(-4, 3, 5)$ b i $\approx 30.3°$ ii $45°$ c $\approx 34.4°$

6 a M$(\frac{5}{2}, 3, 5)$ b i $\approx 40.3°$ ii $\approx 52.0°$

7 a Ayla is currently at (30, 20).
   b The bird is at (30, 20, 10).
   c i $10\sqrt{6}$ m ≈ 24.5 m   ii $\approx 24.1°$

8 a $(-3, 4, \frac{1}{2})$ b $\frac{\sqrt{101}}{2} \approx 5.02$ km   c $135°$
   d $\approx 5.05°$

REVIEW SET 9A

1 a   b

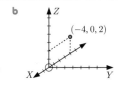

   c

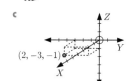

2 a i 6 units   ii $(-1, -4, 1)$
   b i $3\sqrt{10}$ units   ii $(-\frac{5}{2}, -3, \frac{7}{2})$

3 isosceles with AB = AC = $\sqrt{41}$ units

4 a $\sqrt{29}$ units
   b volume ≈ 327 units^3, surface area ≈ 273 units^2

5 a 128 units^3 b M(8, 4, 0)   c $2\sqrt{13}$ units
   d $32(2 + \sqrt{13})$ units$^2 \approx 179$ units^2 e $\approx 29.0°$

6 volume ≈ 628 units^3, surface area ≈ 408 units^2

7 a M(5, 4, 3)   b $\approx 64.9°$ c i $\approx 43.1°$ ii $\approx 25.1°$

8 a P(2, 7, -2.5), Q(8, 3, -2.9)   b ≈ 7.22 m
   c $\approx 3.17°$

REVIEW SET 9B

1 a i $\sqrt{41}$ units   ii $(-2, 3, \frac{9}{2})$
   b i $\sqrt{83}$ units   ii $(-\frac{9}{2}, \frac{5}{2}, \frac{5}{2})$

2 a PQ = $\sqrt{14}$ units, PR = $\sqrt{45}$ units, QR = $\sqrt{59}$ units
      PQ^2 + PR^2 = $(\sqrt{14})^2 + (\sqrt{45})^2 = 59 = $ QR^2
      $\therefore$ triangle PQR is right angled.
   b $\approx 60.8°$

3 $k = 1 \pm \sqrt{30}$

4 a 96 units^3 b $2\sqrt{13}$ units
   c $(104 + 16\sqrt{13}) \approx 162$ units^2

5 a $(-1, 0, -1)$ b $3\sqrt{5}$ units
   c volume ≈ 1260 units^3, surface area ≈ 565 units^2

6 a M(6, 9, 5)   b i $\approx 54.2°$ ii $\approx 36.7°$

7 a H(2, -4, $\frac{1}{5}$)   b ≈ 4.48 km
   c i M(-4, 1, $\frac{1}{2}$)   ii ≈ 7.82 km   iii $\approx 2.20°$

8 a ≈ 137 units^2 b $\approx 50.5°$

EXERCISE 10A

1 a ≈ 0.78 b ≈ 0.22

2 a ≈ 0.487 b ≈ 0.051 c ≈ 0.731

3 a 43 days   b i ≈ 0.0465 ii ≈ 0.186 iii ≈ 0.465

4 a ≈ 0.0895 b ≈ 0.126

5 a ≈ 0.265 b ≈ 0.861 c ≈ 0.222

6 a ≈ 0.146 b ≈ 0.435 c ≈ 0.565

7 a i ≈ 0.171 ii ≈ 0.613
   b ≈ 0.366 c ≈ 0.545

EXERCISE 10B

1 a 7510
   b i ≈ 0.325 ii ≈ 0.653 iii ≈ 0.243

2 a i $\frac{232}{447} \approx 0.519$ ii $\frac{197}{447} \approx 0.441$ iii $\frac{25}{447} \approx 0.0559$
      iv $\frac{250}{447} \approx 0.559$
   b $\frac{7}{25} \approx 0.28$

3 a

	Junior	Middle	Senior	Total
Sport	131	164	141	436
No sport	28	81	176	285
Total	159	245	317	721

   b i $\frac{436}{721} \approx 0.605$ ii $\frac{131}{721} \approx 0.182$ iii $\frac{257}{721} \approx 0.356$

4 a i $\frac{743}{1235} \approx 0.602$ ii $\frac{148}{1235} \approx 0.120$ iii $\frac{1085}{1235} \approx 0.879$
      iv $\frac{795}{1235} \approx 0.644$
   b $\frac{52}{492} \approx 0.106$ c $\frac{518}{862} \approx 0.601$

EXERCISE 10C

1 a {A, B, C, D}   b {1, 2, 3, 4, 5, 6, 7, 8}
   c {MM, MF, FM, FF}

2 a E' is the event that the captain's name will *not* contain the
      letter "e".
   b i U = {Peter, Quentin, Ronan, Sam, Thomas}
      ii E = {Peter, Quentin}
      iii E' = {Ronan, Sam, Thomas}
   c

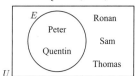

3 **a** $U = \{1, 2, 3, 4, 5, 6, 7, 8, 9, 10, 11, 12, 13, 14, 15, 16\}$
  b **i** $A = \{4, 8, 12, 16\}$ **c**
    ii $B = \{1, 4, 9, 16\}$

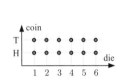

4 **a**

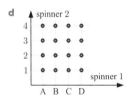

  b

  c spinner

  d spinner 2

5 **a** 5-cent   10-cent
  b coin   spinner
  c spinner 1   spinner 2
  d draw 1   draw 2

6

7 coin 1   coin 2   coin 3

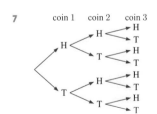

1 **a** $\frac{1}{5}$ **b** $\frac{1}{3}$ **c** $\frac{7}{15}$ **d** $\frac{4}{5}$ **e** $\frac{1}{5}$ **f** $\frac{8}{15}$

2 **a** 4   **b** **i** $\frac{2}{3}$ **ii** $\frac{1}{3}$

3 **a** $\frac{1}{4}$ **b** $\frac{1}{9}$ **c** $\frac{4}{9}$ **d** $\frac{1}{36}$ **e** $\frac{1}{18}$ **f** $\frac{1}{6}$
  g $\frac{1}{12}$ **h** $\frac{1}{3}$

4 **a** $\frac{1}{7}$ **b** $\frac{2}{7}$ **c** $\frac{124}{1461}$ **d** $\frac{237}{1461}$ {remember leap years}

5 **a** {AKN, ANK, KAN, KNA, NAK, NKA}
  b **i** $\frac{1}{3}$ **ii** $\frac{1}{3}$ **iii** $\frac{2}{3}$ **iv** $\frac{2}{3}$

6 **a** {GGG, GGB, GBG, BGG, GBB, BGB, BBG, BBB}
  b **i** $\frac{1}{8}$ **ii** $\frac{1}{8}$ **iii** $\frac{1}{8}$ **iv** $\frac{3}{8}$ **v** $\frac{1}{2}$ **vi** $\frac{7}{8}$

7 **a** {ABCD, ABDC, ACBD, ACDB, ADBC, ADCB,
    BACD, BADC, BCAD, BCDA, BDAC, BDCA,
    CABD, CADB, CBAD, CBDA, CDAB, CDBA,
    DABC, DACB, DBAC, DBCA, DCAB, DCBA}
  b **i** $\frac{1}{2}$ **ii** $\frac{1}{2}$ **iii** $\frac{1}{2}$ **iv** $\frac{1}{2}$

8 **a**
  b **i** $\frac{1}{4}$ **ii** $\frac{1}{4}$
    iii $\frac{1}{2}$ **iv** $\frac{3}{4}$

9 **a**
  b **i** $\frac{1}{10}$ **ii** $\frac{3}{10}$
    iii $\frac{2}{5}$ **iv** $\frac{3}{5}$

10 **a** $\frac{1}{36}$ **b** $\frac{1}{18}$ **c** $\frac{5}{9}$ **d** $\frac{11}{36}$ **e** $\frac{5}{18}$ **f** $\frac{25}{36}$

11 **a** Both grids show the sample space correctly, although **B** is more useful for calculating probabilities.
  b $\frac{1}{6}$

12 **a**

die 2					
6	7	8	9	10	11	12
5	6	7	8	9	10	11
4	5	6	7	8	9	10
3	4	5	6	7	8	9
2	3	4	5	6	7	8
1	2	3	4	5	6	7
	1	2	3	4	5	6
					die 1

  b **i** $\frac{2}{36} = \frac{1}{18}$
    ii $\frac{5}{36}$
    iii $\frac{9}{36} = \frac{1}{4}$
    iv $\frac{10}{36} = \frac{5}{18}$
    v $\frac{10}{36} = \frac{5}{18}$
    vi $\frac{26}{36} = \frac{13}{18}$

13 **a**

die 2					
6	5	4	3	2	1	0
5	4	3	2	1	0	1
4	3	2	1	0	1	2
3	2	1	0	1	2	3
2	1	0	1	2	3	4
1	0	1	2	3	4	5
	1	2	3	4	5	6
					die 1

  b **i** $\frac{6}{36} = \frac{1}{6}$
    ii $\frac{8}{36} = \frac{2}{9}$
    iii $\frac{18}{36} = \frac{1}{2}$
    iv $\frac{6}{36} = \frac{1}{6}$
    v $\frac{24}{36} = \frac{2}{3}$

14 **a**

spinner 1				
3	3	6	9	12	15
2	2	4	6	8	10
1	1	2	3	4	5
	1	2	3	4	5
			spinner 2

  b **i** $\frac{2}{15}$
    ii $\frac{7}{15}$
    iii $\frac{6}{15} = \frac{2}{5}$

15 **a** $\frac{3}{17}$ **b** $\frac{14}{17}$ **16** **a** $\frac{13}{62}$ **b** $\frac{49}{62}$

17 **a** $\frac{9}{65}$ **b** $\frac{4}{65}$ **c** $\frac{4}{5}$ **18** **a** $\frac{17}{29}$ **b** $\frac{26}{29}$ **c** $\frac{5}{29}$

19 a $\frac{9}{44}$ **b** $\frac{7}{44}$ **c** $\frac{17}{44}$ **20 a** $\frac{37}{50}$ **b** $\frac{2}{5}$ **c** $\frac{17}{50}$

21 a

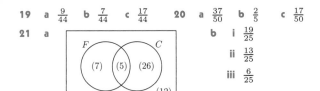

b i $\frac{19}{25}$

ii $\frac{13}{25}$

iii $\frac{6}{25}$

22 a $\frac{19}{40}$ **b** $\frac{1}{2}$ **c** $\frac{4}{5}$ **d** $\frac{5}{8}$ **e** $\frac{13}{40}$

23 a $\frac{7}{15}$ **b** $\frac{1}{15}$ **c** $\frac{2}{15}$

24 a $k = 5$

b i $\frac{7}{30}$ **ii** $\frac{11}{60}$ **iii** $\frac{7}{60}$ **iv** $\frac{53}{60}$ **v** $\frac{7}{60}$

vi $\frac{2}{15}$ **vii** $\frac{41}{60}$ **viii** $\frac{31}{60}$

25 a

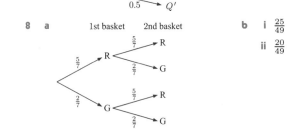

b i $\frac{27}{50}$

ii $\frac{3}{10}$

iii $\frac{8}{25}$

iv $\frac{1}{5}$

v $\frac{2}{25}$

26 a $a = 3$, $b = 3$

b i $\frac{3}{10}$ **ii** $\frac{1}{10}$ **iii** $\frac{7}{40}$ **iv** $\frac{3}{8}$ **v** $\frac{5}{8}$

EXERCISE 10E

1 $P(A \cup B) = 0.55$ **2** $P(B) = 0.6$ **3** $P(X \cap Y) = 0.2$

4 a $P(A \cap B) = 0$ **b** A and B are mutually exclusive.

5 $P(A) = 0.35$

6 a yes

b i $P(A) = \frac{4}{15}$ **ii** $P(B) = \frac{7}{15}$ **iii** $P(A \cup B) = \frac{11}{15}$

7 a $\frac{11}{25}$ **b** $\frac{12}{25}$ **c** $\frac{8}{25}$ **d** $\frac{7}{25}$ **e** $\frac{4}{25}$ **f** $\frac{23}{25}$

g not possible **h** $\frac{11}{25}$ **i** not possible **j** $\frac{12}{25}$

8 $P(A \cup B) = 1$

Hint: Show $P(A' \cup B') = 2 - P(A \cup B)$

EXERCISE 10F

1 a $\frac{1}{24}$ **b** $\frac{1}{6}$ **2 a** $\frac{1}{8}$ **b** $\frac{1}{8}$

3 a 0.0096 **b** 0.8096 **4 a** $\frac{1}{16}$ **b** $\frac{15}{16}$

5 a 0.56 **b** 0.06 **c** 0.14 **d** 0.24

6 a $\frac{8}{125}$ **b** $\frac{12}{125}$ **c** $\frac{27}{125}$

7 a

Rubbish bin   Recycling bin

P — 0.5 → Q
P — 0.5 → Q'
0.9 → P
0.1 → P'
P' — 0.5 → Q
P' — 0.5 → Q'

b i 0.45

ii 0.05

8 a

1st basket   2nd basket

R — $\frac{5}{7}$ → R
R — $\frac{2}{7}$ → G
$\frac{5}{7}$ → R
$\frac{2}{7}$ → G
G — $\frac{5}{7}$ → R
G — $\frac{2}{7}$ → G

b i $\frac{25}{49}$

ii $\frac{20}{49}$

9 a

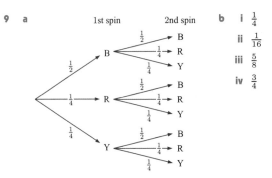

1st spin   2nd spin

b i $\frac{1}{4}$

ii $\frac{1}{16}$

iii $\frac{5}{8}$

iv $\frac{3}{4}$

10 a $\frac{7}{32}$ **b** $\frac{15}{64}$

11 a

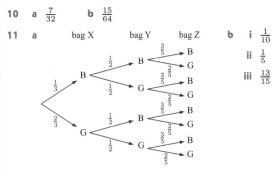

bag X   bag Y   bag Z

b i $\frac{1}{10}$

ii $\frac{1}{5}$

iii $\frac{13}{15}$

12 a $2p^2 - p^4$ **b** $p \approx 0.541$

13 Penny - Quentin - Penny

To win 2 matches in a row, Kane must win the middle match, so he should play against the weaker player in this match.

EXERCISE 10G

1 a $\frac{7}{15}$ **b** $\frac{7}{30}$ **2 a** $\frac{2}{15}$ **b** $\frac{4}{15}$

3 a $\frac{14}{55}$ **b** $\frac{1}{55}$

4 a $\frac{3}{100}$ **b** $\frac{3}{100} \times \frac{2}{99} \approx 0.000\,606$

c $\frac{3}{100} \times \frac{2}{99} \times \frac{1}{98} \approx 0.000\,006\,18$

d $\frac{97}{100} \times \frac{96}{99} \times \frac{95}{98} \approx 0.912$

5 a $\frac{4}{7}$ **b** $\frac{2}{7}$ **6 a** $\frac{10}{21}$ **b** $\frac{1}{21}$

7 a

F — 0.2 → violin
F — 0.8 → not violin
0.6 → F
0.4 → M
M — 0.3 → violin
M — 0.7 → not violin

b i 0.28

ii 0.24

8 a

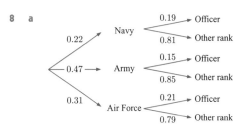

Navy — 0.19 → Officer
Navy — 0.81 → Other rank
0.22 → Navy
0.47 → Army
Army — 0.15 → Officer
Army — 0.85 → Other rank
0.31 → Air Force
Air Force — 0.21 → Officer
Air Force — 0.79 → Other rank

b i 0.1774 **ii** 0.9582 **iii** 0.8644

9 **a**

b $\frac{7}{50}$

10 0.032 **11** $\frac{17}{40}$ **12** $\frac{9}{38}$ **13** **a** $\frac{11}{30}$ **b** $\frac{19}{30}$

14 $\frac{187}{460} \approx 0.407$ **15** **a** $\frac{325}{833} \approx 0.390$ **b** $\frac{787}{833} \approx 0.945$

EXERCISE 10H

1 **a** $\frac{1}{4}$ **b** $\frac{1}{2}$ **c** 0 **2** $\frac{1}{2}$

3 **a**

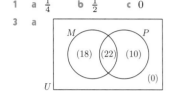

22 study both

b **i** $\frac{9}{25}$ **ii** $\frac{11}{20}$

4 **a**

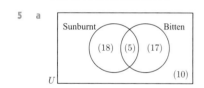

b **i** $\frac{3}{8}$

ii $\frac{15}{23}$

5 **a**

Sunburnt / Bitten

(18) (5) (17)

(10)

U

b **i** $\frac{14}{25}$ **ii** $\frac{4}{5}$ **iii** $\frac{5}{23}$ **iv** $\frac{9}{14}$

6 $\frac{7}{8}$

7 **a** $\frac{13}{20}$ **b** $\frac{7}{20}$ **c** $\frac{11}{50}$ **d** $\frac{7}{25}$ **e** $\frac{4}{7}$ **f** $\frac{1}{4}$

8 **a** $\frac{3}{5}$ **b** $\frac{2}{3}$ **9** **a** $\frac{23}{50}$ **b** $\frac{14}{23}$

10 **a** $\frac{31}{52}$ **b** $\frac{70}{163}$ **11** $\frac{2}{5}$

EXERCISE 10I

1 $P(R \cap S) = 0.4 + 0.5 - 0.7 = 0.2$ and $P(R) \times P(S) = 0.2$
$\therefore$ R and S are independent events.

2 **a** **i** $\frac{7}{30}$ **ii** $\frac{7}{12}$ **iii** $\frac{7}{10}$
b No, as $P(A \mid B) \neq P(A)$.

3 **a** 0.35 **b** 0.85 **c** 0.15 **d** 0.15 **e** 0.5

4 **Hint:** Show $P(A' \cap B') = P(A') P(B')$
using a Venn diagram and $P(A \cap B)$.

5 $P(B) = 0$ **6** 0.9

7 **a** $P(D) = \frac{89}{400}$ **b** No, as $P(D \mid C) \neq P(D)$.

8 $P(A \cup B) = 1$ or $P(A \cap B) = 0$

EXERCISE 10J

1 27 saves **2** ≈ 16 times **3** **a** $\frac{2}{3}$ **b** 2 times

4 **a** $\frac{1}{4}$ **b** 50 occasions **5** 15 days **6** 30 occasions

a **i** ≈ 0.55 **ii** ≈ 0.29 **iii** ≈ 0.16

b **i** ≈ 4125 people **ii** ≈ 2175 people
iii ≈ 1200 people

8 **a** ≈ 0.393 **b** 95 people

REVIEW SET 10A

1 **a** ≈ 0.13 **b** ≈ 0.53

2 **a** **i** $U = \{$A, B, C, D, E, F, G, H, I, J, K, L, M, N, O, P,
Q, R, S, T, U, V, W, X, Y, Z$\}$
ii $C = \{$C, E, H, S$\}$

b

c C' is the event that a letter randomly selected from the English alphabet is *not* in the word CHEESE.

d $P(C) = \frac{2}{13}$, $P(C') = \frac{11}{13}$

3 **a**

coin

T ∘ ∘ ∘ ∘
H ∘ ∘ ∘ ∘

A B C D → spinner

b **i** $\frac{3}{8}$ **ii** $\frac{1}{8}$ **iii** $\frac{5}{8}$

4 **a** Two events are independent if the occurrence of either event does not affect the probability that the other occurs. For A and B independent, $P(A \cap B) = P(A) \times P(B)$.

b Two events A and B are mutually exclusive if they have no common outcomes. $P(A \cup B) = P(A) + P(B)$

5 0.496

6 **a**

Rain   Wind
0.36 ⟶ W
0.25 ⟶ R
0.64 ⟶ W'
0.75 ⟶ R'
0.36 ⟶ W
0.64 ⟶ W'

b **i** 0.09
ii 0.52

c It is assumed that the events are independent.

7 **a** $P(A \cup B) = x + 0.57$ **b** $x = 0.16$

8 **a** 0 **b** 0.45 **c** 0.8

9 **a**

die 2

6 ∘ ∘ ∘ ∘ ∘ ∘
5 ∘ ∘ ∘ ∘ ∘ ∘
4 ∘ ∘ ∘ ∘ ∘ ∘
3 ∘ ∘ ∘ ∘ ∘ ∘
2 ∘ ∘ ∘ ∘ ∘ ∘
1 ∘ ∘ ∘ ∘ ∘ ∘ die 1
  1 2 3 4 5 6

b **i** $\frac{2}{9}$
ii $\frac{5}{12}$

10 **a**

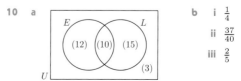

b **i** $\frac{1}{4}$
ii $\frac{37}{40}$
iii $\frac{2}{5}$

11 4350 seeds **12** **a** $\frac{25}{144}$ **b** $\frac{25}{72}$ **c** $\frac{7}{16}$ **d** $\frac{4}{9}$

13 a

	Female	Male	Total
Smoker	20	40	60
Non-smoker	70	70	140
Total	90	110	200

b i $\frac{7}{20}$ **ii** $\frac{1}{2}$ **c i** ≈ 0.121 **ii** ≈ 0.422

14 a $\frac{1}{5}$ **b** $P(B \mid A) \neq P(B)$ **c** $\frac{2}{3}$

REVIEW SET 10B

1 a

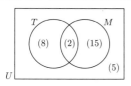

b i $\frac{1}{15}$

ii $\frac{2}{17}$

2 0.9975

3 a $P(A \cap B) = 0.28$ which is not equal to 0.
∴ A and B are not mutually exclusive.
b $P(A \cup B) = 0.82$

4 $\frac{5}{9}$

5 a

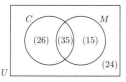

b $\frac{35}{61}$

6 a

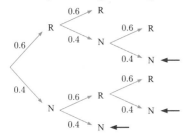

b P(N wins) = 0.352

7 a 0.93 **b** 0.8 **c** 0.2 **d** 0.65

8 a $\frac{4}{500} \times \frac{3}{499} \times \frac{2}{498} \approx 0.000\,000\,193$

b $1 - \frac{496}{500} \times \frac{495}{499} \times \frac{494}{498} \approx 0.0239$

9 a 0.2588 **b** ≈ 0.703

10 a $P(B) = \frac{1}{3}$ **b i** $\frac{16}{21}$ **ii** $\frac{13}{21}$

11 a $\frac{31}{70}$ **b** $\frac{21}{31}$ **12** $\frac{1}{2}$

13 a i 100 balloons **ii** 33 balloons

b i $\frac{19}{25}$ **ii** $\frac{37}{50}$

c i $\frac{17}{66}$ **ii** $\frac{2701}{4950}$ **iii** $\frac{25}{66}$ **iv** $\frac{29}{66}$

d i $\frac{1}{980}$ **ii** $\frac{17}{308}$

14 b ≈ 0.988 **c i** ≈ 0.547 **ii** ≈ 0.266 **d** females

e A 20 year old is expected to live much longer than 30 more years, so it is unlikely the insurance company will have to pay out the policy. A 50 year old however is expected to live for only another 26.45 years (males) or 31.59 years (females), so the insurance company may have to pay out the policy.

g For "third world" countries with poverty, lack of sanitation, and so on, the tables would show a significantly lower life expectancy.

EXERCISE 11A

1 This sample is too small to draw reliable conclusions from.

2 • The sample size is very small and may not be representative of the whole population.
• The sample was taken in a Toronto shopping mall. People living outside of the city are probably not represented.

3 a The sample is likely to under-represent full-time weekday working voters.
b The members of the golf club may not be representative of the whole electorate.
c Only people who catch the train in the morning such as full-time workers or students will be sampled.
d The voters in the street may not be representative of those in the whole electorate.

4 a The sample size is too small.
b With only 10 sheep being weighed, any errors in the measuring of weights will have more impact on the results.

5 a The journalist's question is worded in such a way as to lead the respondents to answer in a certain way.
b For example, "What are your views about the Government's proposed plan to move funding from education to health?".

6 a The whole population is being considered, not just a sample. There will be no sampling error as this is a census.
b measurement error

7 a Many of the workers may not return or even complete the survey.
b There may be more responses to the survey as many workers would feel that it is easier to complete a survey online rather than on paper and mailing it back. Responses would also be received more quickly however some workers may not have internet access and will therefore be unable to complete the survey.

8 a Yes; members with strong negative opinions regarding the management structure of the organisation are more likely to respond.
b No; the feedback from the survey is still valid. Although it might be biased, the feedback might bring certain issues to attention.

EXERCISE 11B

1 Note: Sample answers only - many answers are possible.
a 12, 6, 23, 10, 21, 25
b 11, 2, 10, 17, 24, 14, 25, 1, 21, 7
c 14, 24, 44, 34, 27, 1
d 166, 156, 129, 200, 452

2 a Select 5 random numbers between 1 and 365 inclusive. For example, 65, 276, 203, 165, and 20 represent 6th March, 3rd October, 22nd July, 14th June, and 20th January.
b Select a random number between 1 and 52 inclusive. Take the week starting on the Monday that lies in that week.
c Select a random number between 1 and 12 inclusive.
d Select 3 random numbers between 1 and 12 inclusive.
e Select a random number between 1 and 10 inclusive for the starting month.
f Select 4 random numbers between 1 and 52 inclusive. Choose the Wednesday that lies in that week.

3 a 17, 67, 117, 167, 217 **b** 1600 blocks of chocolate

4 a convenience sampling

b The people arriving first will spend more time at the show, and so are more likely to spend more than €20. Also, the sample size is relatively small.

c For example, systematic sample of every 10th person through the gate.

5 a systematic sampling   **b** 14 days

c Only visitors who use the library on Mondays will be counted. Mondays may not be representative of all of the days.

6 a 160 members

b 20 tennis members, 15 lawn bowls members, 5 croquet members

7 1 departmental manager, 3 supervisors, 9 senior sales staff, 13 junior sales staff, 4 shelf packers

8 a It is easier for Mona to survey her own home room class, so this is a convenience sample.

b Mona's sample will not be representative of all of the classes in the school. Mona's survey may be influenced by her friends in her class.

c For example, a stratified sample of students from every class.

9 a Not all students selected for the sample will be comfortable discussing the topic.

b quota sample

10 a All students in Years 11 and 12 were asked, not just a sample.

b 0.48

c **i** Sample too small to be representative.
  ii Sample too small to be representative.
  iii Valid but unnecessarily large sample size.
  iv Useful and valid technique.
  v Useful and valid technique.
  vi Useful and valid technique.

d **v** is simple random sampling, while **iii** and **iv** are systematic sampling, and **vi** is stratified or quota sampling.

EXERCISE 11C

1 a discrete; 0, 1, 2, 3, ...

b categorical; red, yellow, orange, green

c continuous; 0 - 15 minutes

d continuous; 0 - 25 m

e categorical; Ford, BMW, Renault   **f** discrete; 1, 2, 3, ...

g categorical; Australia, Hawaii, Dubai

h discrete; 0.0 - 10.0   **i** continuous; 0 - 4 L

j continuous; 0 - 80 hours   **k** continuous; $-20°C - 35°C$

l categorical; cereal, toast, fruit, rice, eggs

m discrete; 0, 1, 2, ...

2 *Name*: categorical, *Age*: continuous, *Height*: continuous, *Country*: categorical, *Wins*: discrete, *Speed*: continuous, *Ranking*: discrete, *Prize money*: discrete

EXERCISE 11D

1 a the number of goals scored in a game

b variable is counted, not measured

c

Goals scored	Tally	Frequency	Rel. Frequency
0	卌	5	≈ 0.208
1	卌 ||||	9	0.375
2	卌	5	≈ 0.208
3	|||	3	0.125
4			1	≈ 0.042
5		0	0
6			1	≈ 0.042
	Total	24	

d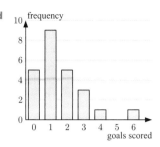

e 1 goal   **f** positively skewed, one outlier (6 goals)

g $\approx 20.8\%$

2 a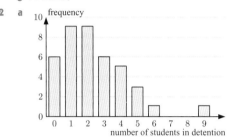

b 1 and 2   **c** positively skewed, one outlier, (9 students)

d $12\frac{1}{2}\%$

3 a

Number of previews	Tally	Frequency
1				2
2	卌	5
3	卌 卌	10
4	卌 ||||	9
5	卌	5
6					3
	Total	34

b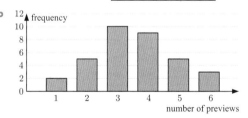

c 3 previews   **d** symmetrical, no outliers

e $\approx 79.4\%$

4 a 45 people **b** 1 time **c** 8 people **d** 20%

e positively skewed, no outliers

EXERCISE 11E

1 a

People waiting	Tally	Frequency	Rel. Freq.
0 - 9	||	2	≈ 0.067
10 - 19	卌	6	0.200
20 - 29	卌 卌		11	≈ 0.367
30 - 39	卌 ||	7	≈ 0.233
40 - 49	||||	4	≈ 0.133
	Total	30	

b 2 days **c** $\approx 36.7\%$ **e** 20 - 29 people

d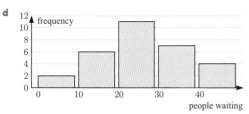

2 a 37 businesses   **b** 40 - 49 employees
c negatively skewed   **d** ≈ 37.8%
e No, only that it was in the interval 50 - 59 employees.

3 a

Number of houses	Tally	Frequency
0 - 9	ⅢⅡ	5
10 - 19	ⅢⅡ |||	8
20 - 29	ⅢⅡ |||	8
30 - 39	ⅢⅡ ⅢⅡ ||||	14
40 - 49	||||	4
50 - 59			1
	Total	40

b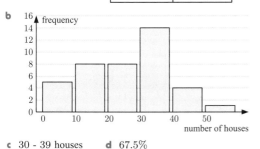

c 30 - 39 houses   **d** 67.5%

EXERCISE 11F

1 a Height is measured on a continuous scale.
b

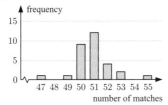

c $185 \leqslant H < 190$ cm. This is the class of values that appears most often.
d slightly positively skewed

2 a column graph

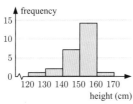

b frequency histogram

3 a continuous
b

Travel time (min)	Tally	Frequency
$0 \leqslant t < 10$	ⅢⅡ		6
$10 \leqslant t < 20$	ⅢⅡ ⅢⅡ ⅢⅡ ⅢⅡ ⅢⅡ		26
$20 \leqslant t < 30$	ⅢⅡ ⅢⅡ |||	13
$30 \leqslant t < 40$	ⅢⅡ ||||	9
$40 \leqslant t < 50$	ⅢⅡ		6
	Total	60

c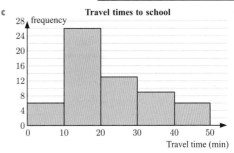

d positively skewed   **e** $10 \leqslant t < 20$ minutes

4 a, b

Distance (m)	Tally	Frequency
$0 \leqslant d < 10$	||	2
$10 \leqslant d < 20$	ⅢⅡ	5
$20 \leqslant d < 30$	ⅢⅡ ||||	9
$30 \leqslant d < 40$	ⅢⅡ		6
$40 \leqslant d < 50$	|||	3
	Total	25

c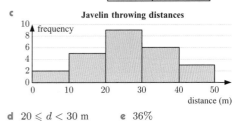

d $20 \leqslant d < 30$ m   **e** 36%

5 a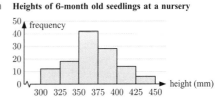

b 20 seedlings   **c** ≈ 58.3%
d i ≈ 1218 seedlings   **ii** ≈ 512 seedlings

6 a, b

Weight (g)	Tally	Frequency
$100 \leqslant w < 125$	ⅢⅡ	5
$125 \leqslant w < 150$	ⅢⅡ	5
$150 \leqslant w < 175$	ⅢⅡ ⅢⅡ		11
$175 \leqslant w < 200$	||||	4
$200 \leqslant w < 225$	ⅢⅡ	5
$225 \leqslant w < 250$	ⅢⅡ ||	7
$250 \leqslant w < 275$	ⅢⅡ ||||	9
$275 \leqslant w < 300$	||||	4
	Total	50

c

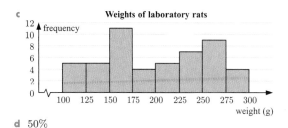

Weights of laboratory rats

d 50%

REVIEW SET 11A

1 a Students studying Italian may have an Italian background so surveying these students may produce a biased result.

   b For example, Andrew could survey a randomly selected group of students as they entered the school grounds one morning.

2 a It would be too time consuming and expensive.

   b

Age range	< 18	18 - 39	40 - 54	55 - 70	> 70
Sample size	50	82	123	69	26

3 a discrete   b continuous   c discrete

4 a convenience sampling

   b Yes, the sample will be biased as people are more likely to be drinking on a Saturday night. It is sensible for this sample to be biased since drink-driving is illegal.

5 a discrete   b 1 round   c positively skewed

6 a

Height (h cm)	Frequency	Relative frequency
$140 \leqslant h < 150$	1	≈ 0.0115
$150 \leqslant h < 160$	13	≈ 0.149
$160 \leqslant h < 170$	40	≈ 0.460
$170 \leqslant h < 180$	30	≈ 0.345
$180 \leqslant h < 190$	3	≈ 0.0345
Total	87	

   b $\approx 80.5\%$

   c

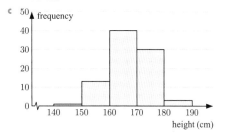

   d $160 \leqslant h < 170$ cm

   e slightly negatively skewed

7 a

Number of tickets	Tally	Frequency
0			1
1					3
2	⊥⊥⊥⊥	5
3	⊥⊥⊥⊥ ⊥⊥⊥⊥	10
4	⊥⊥⊥⊥	5
5					3
6			1

b

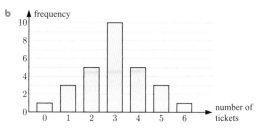

frequency

   c The data is symmetric with no outliers.

8 a continuous

   b

Diameter (d cm)	Tally	Frequency
$0 \leqslant d < 1$	|||	3
$1 \leqslant d < 2$	||||	4
$2 \leqslant d < 3$	⊥⊥⊥⊥		6
$3 \leqslant d < 4$	⊥⊥⊥⊥ ⊥⊥⊥⊥ ||	12
$4 \leqslant d < 5$	⊥⊥⊥⊥	5
	Total	30

   c

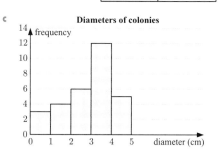

Diameters of colonies

   d $3 \leqslant d < 4$ cm

   e slightly negatively skewed

REVIEW SET 11B

1 a discrete   b continuous
   c categorical   d categorical
   e continuous   f continuous
   g discrete   h discrete

2 a systematic sampling

   b A house will be visited if the last digit in its number is equal to the random number chosen by the promoter, with the random number 10 corresponding to the digit 0. Each house therefore has a 1 in 10 chance of being visited.

   c Once the first house number has been chosen, the remaining houses chosen must all have the same second digit in their house number, that is, they are not randomly chosen. For example, it is impossible for two consecutively numbered houses to be selected for the sample.

3 a Petra's teacher colleagues are quite likely to ignore the emailed questionnaire as emails are easy to ignore.

   b It is likely that the teachers who have responded will have strong opinions either for or against the general student behaviour. These responses may therefore not be representative of all teachers' views.

4 a negatively skewed   b 47.5%   c 7.5%

5 a

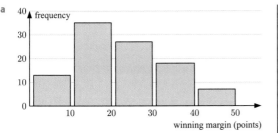

b i 48%   **ii** 25%

c No, only that it was in the interval 1 - 10.

6 a Mass is measured on a continuous scale.

b

Mass (*m* kg)	Frequency
$260 \leqslant m < 270$	1
$270 \leqslant m < 280$	2
$280 \leqslant m < 290$	3
$290 \leqslant m < 300$	3
$300 \leqslant m < 310$	4
$310 \leqslant m < 320$	3
$320 \leqslant m < 330$	3

c $300 \leqslant m < 310$ kg

d

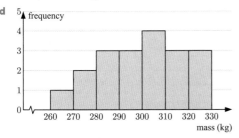

e slightly negatively skewed

7 a continuous

b

Length (*l* m)	Frequency
$10 \leqslant l < 12$	3
$12 \leqslant l < 14$	8
$14 \leqslant l < 16$	8
$16 \leqslant l < 18$	4
$18 \leqslant l < 20$	2
$20 \leqslant l < 22$	3
$22 \leqslant l < 24$	1
$24 \leqslant l < 26$	0
$26 \leqslant l < 28$	1

c

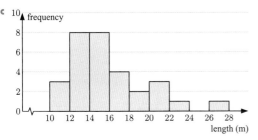

d positively skewed, one outlier (27.4 m)

8 a

Films watched	Frequency
0	7
1	6
2	3
3	3
4	5
5	2
6	1
8	1

b

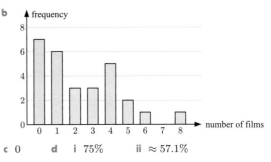

c 0   **d i** 75%   **ii** $\approx 57.1\%$

EXERCISE 12A

1 a 1 cup   **b** 2 cups   **c** 1.8 cups

2 a i ≈ 5.61 **ii** 6   **iii** 6

   b i ≈ 16.3 **ii** 17   **iii** 18

   c i ≈ 24.8 **ii** 24.9   **iii** 23.5

3 9   **4** Ruth

5 a data set A: ≈ 6.46, data set B: ≈ 6.85

   b data set A: 7, data set B: 7

   c Data sets A and B differ only by their last value. This affects the mean, but not the median.

6 a i motichoor ladoo: ≈ 67.1, malai jamun: ≈ 53.6

      ii motichoor ladoo: 69, malai jamun: 52

   b The mean and median were much higher for the motichoor ladoo, so the motichoor ladoo were more popular.

7 a Bus: mean = 39.7, median = 40.5
      Tram: mean ≈ 49.1, median = 49

   b The tram data has a higher mean and median, but since there are more bus trips per day and more people travel by bus in total, the bus is more popular.

8 a 44 points   **b** 44 points

   c i Decrease, since 25 is lower than the mean of 44 for the first four matches.

      ii 40.2 points

9 €185 604   **10** 3144 km   **11** 116

12 17.25 goals per game   **13** $x = 15$ **14** $a = 5$

15 37 marks   **16** ≈ 14.8 **17** 6 and 12

EXERCISE 12B

1 a mean = \$363 770, median = \$347 200
      The mean has been affected by the extreme values (the two values greater than \$400 000).

   b i the mean   **ii** the median

2 a mode = \$33 000, mean = \$39 300, median = \$33 500

   b The mode is the lowest value in the data set.

   c No, it is too close to the lower end of the distribution.

3 a mean ≈ 3.19 mm, median = 0 mm, mode = 0 mm

   b The median is not the most suitable measure of centre as the data is positively skewed.

   c The mode is the lowest value.

d 42 mm and 21 mm   **e** no

4 a mean ≈ 2.03,   median = 2,   mode = 1 and 2

  b Yes, as Esmé can then offer a "family package" to match the most common number of children per family.

  c 2 children, since this is one of the modes; it is also the median, and very close to the mean.

EXERCISE 12C

1 a 1 person   **b** 2 people   **c** ≈ 2.03 people

2 a **i** 2.96 phone calls   **ii** 2 phone calls   **iii** 2 phone calls

  b

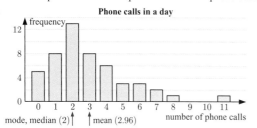

  Phone calls in a day

  mode, median (2)   mean (2.96)   number of phone calls

  c positively skewed

  d The mean takes into account the larger numbers of phone calls.

  e the mean

3 a **i** 49 matches   **ii** 49 matches   **iii** ≈ 49.0 matches

  b no

  c The sample of only 30 is not large enough. The company could have won its case by arguing that a larger sample would have found an average of 50 matches per box.

4 a **i** ≈ 2.61 children   **ii** 2 children   **iii** 2 children

  b This school has more children per family than the average British family.

  c positively skewed

  d The values at the higher end increase the mean more than the median and the mode.

5 a

Pocket money (€)	Frequency
1	4
2	9
3	2
4	6
5	8

  b 29 children

  c **i** ≈ €3.17
   ii €3
   iii €2

  d the mode

6 10.1 cm

7 a **i** \$63 000   **ii** \$56 000   **iii** \$66 600   **b** the mean

8 a $x = 5$ **b** 75%

EXERCISE 12D

1 a 40 phone calls   **b** ≈ 15 minutes   **2** ≈ 31.7

3 a 26 days   **b** 31 - 40 children   **c** ≈ 41.5 children

4 a 70 service stations   **b** ≈ 411 000 litres (≈ 411 kL)

  c ≈ 5870 L

  d $6000 < P \leqslant 7000$ L. This is the most frequently occurring amount of petrol sales at a service station in one day.

5 a

Runs scored	Tally	Frequency
0 - 9	ⅢⅢ ⅢⅢ Ⅰ	11
10 - 19	ⅢⅢ Ⅲ	8
20 - 29	ⅢⅢ Ⅲ	8
30 - 39	Ⅱ	2
	Total	29

  b ≈ 14.8 runs

  c ≈ 14.9 runs; the estimate in **b** was very accurate.

6 a $p = 24$ **b** ≈ 3.37 minutes   **c** ≈ 15.3%

7 a 125 people   **b** ≈ 119 marks   **c** $\frac{3}{25}$ **d** 28%

EXERCISE 12E

1 a **i** 13   **ii** $Q_1 = 9$, $Q_3 = 18$ **iii** 16   **iv** 9

  b **i** 18.5   **ii** $Q_1 = 13$, $Q_3 = 23$ **iii** 19   **iv** 10

  c **i** 26.5   **ii** $Q_1 = 20$, $Q_3 = 35$ **iii** 28   **iv** 15

  d **i** 37   **ii** $Q_1 = 28$, $Q_3 = 52$ **iii** 49   **iv** 24

2 a **i** range = 23 goals,   IQR = 17 goals
   ii range = 38 goals,   IQR = 24 goals

  b Natalie

3 a *Jane*:   mean = \$35.50,   median = \$35.50
   Ashley: mean = \$30.75,   median = \$26.00

  b *Jane*:   range = \$18,   IQR = \$9
   Ashley: range = \$40,   IQR = \$14

  c Jane   **d** Ashley

4 a range = 60,   IQR = 8.5   **b** '67' is an outlier.

  c range = 18,   IQR = 8   **d** the range

5 a *Derrick*:   range = 240 minutes,   IQR = 30 minutes
   Gareth: range = 170 minutes,   IQR = 120 minutes

  b **i** Gareth's   **ii** Derrick's

  c The IQR is most appropriate as it is less affected by outliers.

6 a g **b** **i** $m - a$ **ii** $\left(\dfrac{j+k}{2}\right) - \left(\dfrac{c+d}{2}\right)$

7

Measure	median	mode	range	interquartile range
a Value	11	9	13	6
b Value	18	14	26	12

EXERCISE 12F

1 a **i** 35 points   **ii** 78 points   **iii** 13 points
   iv 53 points   **v** 26 points

  b **i** 65 points   **ii** 27 points

2 a **i** 98, 25 marks   **ii** 70 marks   **iii** 85 marks
   iv 55, 85 marks

  b 73 marks   **c** 30 marks

3 a **i** min = 3, $Q_1 = 5$, med = 6, $Q_3 = 8$, max = 10

   ii

   iii 7
   iv 3

  b **i** min = 0, $Q_1 = 4$, med = 7, $Q_3 = 8$, max = 9

   ii

   iii 9
   iv 4

  c **i** min = 17, $Q_1 = 26$, med = 31, $Q_3 = 47$, max = 51

   ii

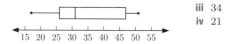

   iii 34
   iv 21

4 a median = 6, $Q_1 = 5$, $Q_3 = 8$ **b** IQR = 3

  c

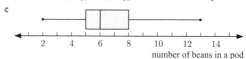

  number of beans in a pod

5 a min = 33, Q_1 = 35, med = 36, Q_3 = 37, max = 40

   b **i** range = 7   **ii** IQR = 2

   c

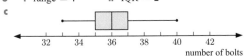

number of bolts

EXERCISE 12G

1 a 12   **b** lower = 13.5, upper = 61.5   **c** 13

   d

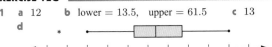

2 a median = 10, Q_1 = 8, Q_3 = 13   **b** IQR = 5

   c lower = 0.5, upper = 20.5, 22 is an outlier

   d

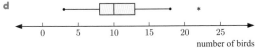

number of birds

3 a **A**   **b** **D**   **c** **C**   **d** **B**

4 a

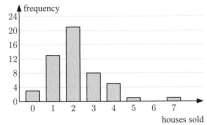

Houses sold by a real estate agent

houses sold

   b 7 houses appears to be an outlier.

   c lower boundary = −2, upper boundary = 6
     7 houses is an outlier

   d

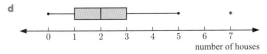

number of houses

EXERCISE 12H

1 a

Statistic	Year 9	Year 12
minimum	6	36
Q_1	30	60
median	45	84
Q_3	60	96
maximum	72	105

   b **i** Year 9: 66 min
      Year 12: 69 min

     ii Year 9: 30 min
       Year 12: 36 min

   c **i** cannot tell   **ii** true, since Year 9 Q_1 < Year 12 min

2 a Friday: min = €20, Q_1 = €50, med = €70,
         Q_3 = €100, max = €180

     Saturday: min = €40, Q_1 = €80, med = €100,
            Q_3 = €140, max = €200

   b **i** Friday: €160, Saturday: €160
     ii Friday: €50, Saturday: €60

3 a **i** class 1 (96%)   **ii** class 1 (37%)   **iii** class 1

   b 18%   **c** 55%   **d** **i** 25%   **ii** 50%

   e **i** slightly positively skewed   **ii** negatively skewed

   f .... class 2, ... class 1

4 a Kirsten: min = 0.8 min, Q_1 = 1.3 min, med = 2.3 min,
            Q_3 = 3.3 min, max = 6.9 min

     Erika: min = 0.2 min, Q_1 = 2.2 min, med = 3.7 min,
         Q_3 = 5.7 min, max = 11.5 min

b

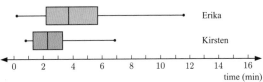

Phone call duration

time (min)

   c Both are positively skewed (Erika's more so than Kirsten's).
     Erika's phone calls were more varied in duration.

5 a discrete

   c

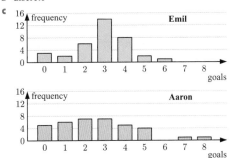

goals

   d Emil: approximately symmetrical
     Aaron: positively skewed

   e Emil: mean ≈ 2.89, median = 3, mode = 3
     Aaron: mean ≈ 2.67, median = 2.5, mode = 2, 3
     Emil's mean and median are slightly higher than Aaron's.
     Emil has a clear mode of 3, whereas Aaron has two modes
     (2 and 3).

   f Emil: range = 6, IQR = 2
     Aaron: range = 8, IQR = 3
     Emil's data set demonstrates less variability than Aaron's.

   g

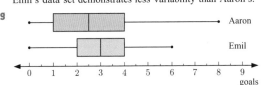

goals

   h Emil is more consistent with his scoring (in terms of goals)
     than Aaron.

6 a continuous (the data is measured)

   b Old type: mean = 107 hours, median = 110.5 hours,
             range = 56 hours, IQR = 19 hours

     New type: mean = 134 hours, median = 132 hours,
             range = 84 hours, IQR = 18.5 hours

     The "new" type of light globe has a higher mean and median
     than the "old" type.
     The IQR is relatively unchanged going from "old" to "new",
     however, the range of the "new" type is greater, suggesting
     greater variability.

   c

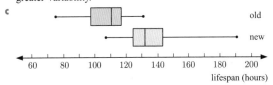

lifespan (hours)

   d Old type: negatively skewed
     New type: positively skewed

   e The "new" type of light globes do last longer than the "old"
     type. From **c**, both the mean and median for the "new" type
     are close to 20% greater than that of the "old" type. The
     manufacturer's claim appears to be valid.

EXERCISE 12I

1 a

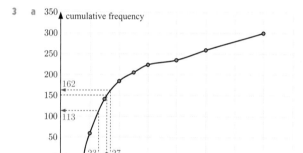

b ≈ 61 marks   **c** ≈ 92 students   **d** 76 students
e ≈ 23 students   **f** ≈ 75 marks

2 a ≈ 9 seedlings   **b** ≈ 28.3%   **c** ≈ 7.1 cm
d ≈ 2.4 cm
e 10 cm, which means that 90% of the seedlings are shorter than 10 cm.

3 a

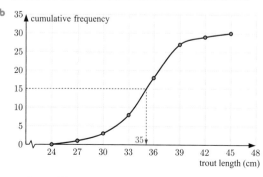

b ≈ 26 years   **c** ≈ 37.7%
d i ≈ 0.54   **ii** ≈ 0.04

4 a

Length (cm)	Frequency	Cumulative frequency
$24 \leqslant x < 27$	1	1
$27 \leqslant x < 30$	2	3
$30 \leqslant x < 33$	5	8
$33 \leqslant x < 36$	10	18
$36 \leqslant x < 39$	9	27
$39 \leqslant x < 42$	2	29
$42 \leqslant x < 45$	1	30

b

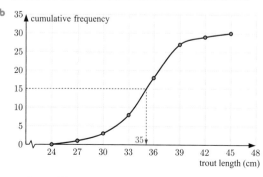

c median ≈ 35 cm

d median = 34.5 cm;   the median found from the graph is a good approximation.

5 a ≈ 27 min   **b** ≈ 29 min   **c** ≈ 31.3 min
d ≈ 4.3 min   **e** ≈ 28 min

f

Time (t min)	$21 \leqslant t < 24$	$24 \leqslant t < 27$	$27 \leqslant t < 30$
Number of competitors	5	15	30

Time (t min)	$30 \leqslant t < 33$	$33 \leqslant t < 36$
Number of competitors	20	10

6 a

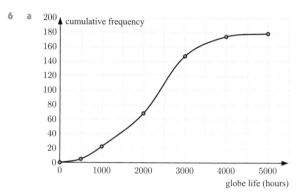

b ≈ 2280 hours   **c** ≈ 71%   **d** ≈ 67

7 a $19.5 \leqslant l < 20.5$ cm

b

Foot length (cm)	Frequency	Cumulative frequency
$19.5 \leqslant l < 20.5$	1	1
$20.5 \leqslant l < 21.5$	1	2
$21.5 \leqslant l < 22.5$	0	2
$22.5 \leqslant l < 23.5$	3	5
$23.5 \leqslant l < 24.5$	5	10
$24.5 \leqslant l < 25.5$	13	23
$25.5 \leqslant l < 26.5$	17	40
$26.5 \leqslant l < 27.5$	7	47
$27.5 \leqslant l < 28.5$	2	49
$28.5 \leqslant l < 29.5$	0	49
$29.5 \leqslant l < 30.5$	1	50

c

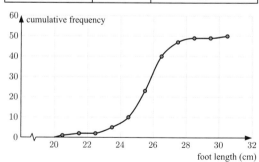

d i ≈ 25.2 cm   **ii** ≈ 18 people

EXERCISE 12J

1 a *Data set A*: mean $= \dfrac{10 + 7 + 5 + 8 + 10}{5} = 8$

Data set B: mean $= \dfrac{4 + 12 + 11 + 14 + 1 + 6}{6} = 8$

b Data set B appears to have a greater spread than data set A, as data set B has more values that are a long way from the mean, such as 1 and 14.

  c *Data set A:* $\sigma^2 = 3.6$, $\sigma \approx 1.90$
    Data set B: $\sigma^2 \approx 21.7$, $\sigma \approx 4.65$

2 **a** $\sigma \approx 1.59$ **b** $\sigma^2 \approx 2.54$

3 **a** $\mu = 24.25$, $\sigma \approx 3.07$ **b** $\mu = 28.25$, $\sigma \approx 3.07$
  c If each data value is increased or decreased by the same amount, then the mean will also be increased or decreased by that amount, however the population standard deviation will be unchanged.

4 $\sigma \approx 2.64$ **5** mean ≈ 30.0, $\sigma \approx 14.3$

6 **a** *Danny:* ≈ 3.21 hours; *Jennifer:* 2 hours
  b Danny
  c *Danny:* $\sigma \approx 0.700$ hours; *Jennifer:* $\sigma \approx 0.423$ hours
  d Jennifer

7 **a**

	Mean $\overline{x}$	Median	Standard deviation σ	Range
Boys	32.02	31.05	≈ 4.52	13.8
Girls	34.77	35.85	≈ 3.76	11.7

  b **i** boys   **ii** boys
  c Tyson could increase his sample size.

8 **a** *Rockets:* mean $= 5.7$, range $= 11$
    Bullets: mean $= 5.7$, range $= 11$
  b We suspect the Rockets, since they twice scored zero runs.
    Rockets: $\sigma = 3.9$ ← greater variability
    Bullets: $\sigma \approx 3.29$
  c standard deviation

9 **a** **i** *Museum:* ≈ 934 visitors; *Art gallery:* ≈ 1230 visitors
    ii *Museum:* ≈ 208 visitors; *Art gallery:* ≈ 84.6 visitors
  b the museum
  c **i** '0' is an outlier.
    ii This outlier corresponded to Christmas Day, so the museum was probably closed which meant there were no visitors on that day.
    iii Yes, although the outlier is not an error, it is not a true reflection of a visitor count for a particular day.
    iv *Museum:* mean ≈ 965 visitors, $\sigma \approx 121$ visitors
    v The outlier had greatly increased the population standard deviation.

10 $\sigma \approx 0.775$ **11** $\mu = 14.48$ years, $\sigma \approx 1.75$ years

12 **a** Data set A   **b** *Data set A:* 8, *Data set B:* 8
  c *Data set A:* 2, *Data set B:* ≈ 1.06
    Data set A does have a wider spread.
  d The standard deviation takes all of the data values into account, not just two.

13 **a** The female students' marks are in the range 16 to 20 whereas the male students' marks are in the range 12 to 19.
    i the females   **ii** the males
  b *Females:* $\mu \approx 17.5$, $\sigma \approx 1.02$
    Males: $\mu \approx 15.5$, $\sigma \approx 1.65$

14 The results for the mean will differ by 1, but the results for the standard deviation will be the same. Jess' question is worded so that the respondent will not include themselves.

15 **a** ≈ 48.3 cm   **b** ≈ 2.66 cm

16 **a** ≈ 17.45 **b** ≈ 7.87

17 **a** $\approx \$780.60$ **b** $\approx \$31.74$

18 **a** $\overline{x} = 40.35$ hours, $\sigma \approx 4.23$ hours
  b $\overline{x} = 40.6$ hours, $\sigma \approx 4.10$ hours
  The mean increases slightly; the standard deviation decreases slightly. These are good approximations.

REVIEW SET 12A

1 **a** **i** ≈ 4.67 **ii** 5   **b** **i** 3.99   **ii** 3.9

2 **a**

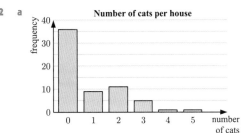

Number of cats per house

  b positively skewed
  c **i** 0 cats   **ii** ≈ 0.873 cats   **iii** 0 cats
  d The mean, as it suggests that some people have cats. (The mode and median are both 0.)

3 **a**

Distribution	Girls	Boys
median	36 s	34.5 s
mean	36 s	34.45 s
modal class	34.5 - 35.5 s	34.5 - 35.5 s

  b The girls' distribution is positively skewed and the boys' distribution is approximately symmetrical. The median and mean swim times for boys are both about 1.5 seconds lower than for girls. Despite this, the distributions have the same modal class because of the skewness in the girls' distribution. The analysis supports the conjecture that boys generally swim faster than girls with less spread of times.

4 $a = 8$, $b = 6$

5 **b** $k + 3$

6 **a** We do not know each individual data value, only the intervals they fall in, so we cannot calculate the mean winning margin exactly.
  b ≈ 22.6 points

7 **a** ≈ 70.9 g   **b** ≈ 210 g   **c** ≈ 139.1 g

8 **a** min $= 3$, $Q_1 = 12$, med $= 15$, $Q_3 = 19$, max $= 31$
  b range $= 28$, IQR $= 7$
  c

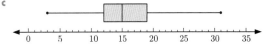

9 **a** 101.5   **b** 7.5   **c** 100.2   **d** ≈ 7.59

10 **a** A: min $= 11$ s, $Q_1 = 11.6$ s, med $= 12$ s,
        $Q_3 = 12.6$ s, max $= 13$ s
    B: min $= 11.2$ s, $Q_1 = 12$ s, med $= 12.6$ s,
        $Q_3 = 13.2$ s, max $= 13.8$ s
  b A: range $= 2.0$ s, IQR $= 1.0$ s
    B: range $= 2.6$ s, IQR $= 1.2$ s
  c **i** A, the median time is lower.
    ii B, the range and IQR are higher.

11 **a** ≈ 58.5 s   **b** ≈ 6 s   **c** ≈ 53 s

12 **a** ≈ 88 students   **b** $m \approx 24$

c

Time (t min)	Frequency
$5 \leqslant t < 10$	20
$10 \leqslant t < 15$	40
$15 \leqslant t < 20$	48
$20 \leqslant t < 25$	42
$25 \leqslant t < 30$	28
$30 \leqslant t < 35$	17
$35 \leqslant t < 40$	5

13 a $\sigma^2 \approx 63.0$, $\sigma \approx 7.94$ **b** $\sigma^2 \approx 0.969$, $\sigma \approx 0.984$

14 a ≈ 33.6 L   **b** ≈ 7.63 L

15 a No, extreme values have less effect on the standard deviation of a larger population.

b i mean   **ii** standard deviation

c A low standard deviation means that the weight of biscuits in each packet is, on average, close to 250 g.

REVIEW SET 12B

1 a

	mean (seconds)	median (seconds)
Week 1	≈ 16.0	16.3
Week 2	≈ 15.1	15.1
Week 3	≈ 14.4	14.3
Week 4	14.0	14.0

b Yes, Heike's mean and median times have gradually decreased each week which indicates that her speed has improved over the 4 week period.

2 a 5   **b** 3.52   **c** 3.5

3 a $x = 7$ **b** 6

4 $p = 7$, $q = 9$ (or $p = 9$, $q = 7$)

5 ≈ 414 patrons

6

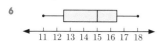

7 a $\sigma \approx 11.7$ **b** $Q_1 = 117$, $Q_3 = 130$ **c** yes, 93

d

8 a

	Brand X	Brand Y
min	871	891
Q_1	888	898
median	896.5	903.5
Q_3	904	910
max	916	928
IQR	16	12

b

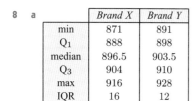

c i Brand Y, as the median is higher.

ii Brand Y, as the IQR is lower, so less variations.

⁷ days   **b** ≈ 12 days

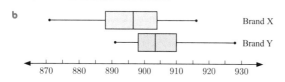

10 a

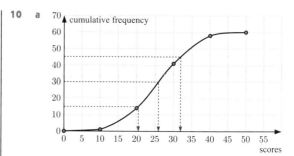

b i median ≈ 26.0 **ii** IQR ≈ 12

iii $\overline{x} \approx 26.0$ **iv** $\sigma \approx 8.31$

11 a $p = 12$, $m = 6$ **b**

Measure	Value
mode	9
median	9
range	4

c $\dfrac{254}{30} = \dfrac{127}{15}$

12 a 44 players   **b** $90 \leqslant t < 120$ min

c

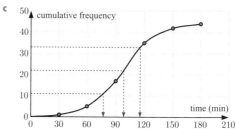

d i ≈ 98.6 min   **ii** 96.8 min   **iii** no

e ".... between 77.2 and 115.7 minutes."

13 a $\overline{x} \approx 49.6$ matches, $\sigma \approx 1.60$ matches

b The claim is not justified, but a larger sample is needed.

14 a $\approx €207.02$ **b** $\approx €38.80$

15 a Kevin: $\overline{x} = 41.2$ min; Felicity: $\overline{x} = 39.5$ min

b Kevin: $\sigma \approx 7.61$ min; Felicity: $\sigma \approx 9.22$ min

c Felicity   **d** Kevin

INDEX